SCRIBNER READING SERIES

FOLLOW THE WIND

Jack Cassidy

Doris Roettger   *Karen K. Wixson*

SCRIBNER **Laidlaw**

New York

ACKNOWLEDGMENTS

"The Speckled Band" by Sir Arthur Conan Doyle, dramatized by Michael and Mollie Hardwick. Reprinted by permission of the Conan Doyle Estate and London Management & Representation Ltd.

"Arthur's Last Battle" adapted from THE ROAD TO CAMLANN by Rosemary Sutcliff. Copyright © 1981 by Rosemary Sutcliff. Reprinted by permission of the publisher, E. P. Dutton, a division of New American Library and The Bodley Head, London.

"A Day in Megalopolis" from "T-Line to Nowhere" by Zenna Henderson published in *Fantasy and Science Fiction*, 1969. Copyright © 1969 by Zenna Henderson. Reprinted by permission of Curtis Brown, Ltd.

"Advice from an Innovator" adapted from PARTICULAR PASSIONS by Lynn Gilbert and Gaylen Moore. Text copyright © 1981 by Lynn Gilbert. Used by permission of Clarkson N. Potter, Inc.

"Amazing Allies" excerpted with permission from the May 1955 *Reader's Digest*. Copyright © 1955 by The Reader's Digest Assn., Inc.

"Battling the Grasshoppers" from LET THE HURRICANE ROAR, by Rose Wilder Lane. © 1932, 1933, 1960, 1961 Roger MacBride Productions, Inc. and Ed Friendly Productions, Inc. Used with permission.

"Beauty and the Beast" is the text only of pp. 112-119 from Beauty: A Retelling of the Story of Beauty and the Beast by Robin McKinley. Copyright © 1978 by Robin McKinley. Reprinted by permission of Harper & Row, Publishers, Inc. and Curtis Brown, Ltd.

"By the Light of the Earth" by Isaac Asimov from *American Way*, March 1980. Copyright 1980 by American Airlines. Reprinted by permission.

"Camelot" by Alan Jay Lerner & Frederick Loewe. Copyright © 1960 & 1961 by Alan Jay Lerner & Frederick Loewe. Chappell & Co., Inc., owner of publication and allied rights throughout the world. International Copyright Secured. ALL RIGHTS RESERVED. Used by permission.

"Charles" from THE LOTTERY by Shirley Jackson. Copyright 1948 by Shirley Jackson. Copyright renewed © 1976 by Laurence Hyman, Barry Hyman, Mrs. Sarah Webster and Mrs. Joanne Schnurer. Reprinted by permission of Farrar, Straus and Giroux, Inc. and Brandt & Brandt Literary Agents, Inc. "Cheryl Toussaint" is adapted from WOMEN WHO WIN by Francene Sabin. Copyright © 1975 by Francene Sabin. Adapted by permission of Random House, Inc. (Acknowledgments continued on page 604)

SCRIBNER LAIDLAW
866 Third Avenue
New York, New York 10022
Collier Macmillan Canada Inc.

Printed in the United States of America

ISBN 0-02-264870-4

9 8 7 6 5 4 3 2 1

FOLLOW
THE WIND

Contents

STRATEGIES
TO USE WHEN YOU MEET A NEW WORD

PRONOUNCE THE WORD

Is it a word you know?
Is it a word you have heard other people use?

EXAMINE THE WORD

Is it a compound word? Do you know the meanings of the smaller words?
Are any parts of the word like another word you know? Does it have a familiar base word? Does it have a familiar prefix or suffix?

EXAMINE THE SENTENCE IN WHICH THE WORD APPEARS

Are there any clues that help you understand the meaning of the new word?

If you are still not sure what the word means, look it up in the glossary or a dictionary to find out its meaning.

STRATEGIES
TO USE WHEN YOU WRITE

PREWRITING—Before you write,

- choose a topic.
- consider your purpose and audience.
- take notes and make an outline.

WRITING—When you write your first draft,

- use your notes.
- compose a topic sentence.
- compose detail sentences that support your topic.
- vary sentence length and structure for interest.

REVISING—When you revise,

- edit your first draft. Be sure you have kept to your topic, arranged your sentences in the best order, used vivid words, and achieved your purpose for writing.
- proofread. Be sure the punctuation, spelling, and grammar you have used are correct.

Use these marks when you edit and proofread.	¶	Start new paragraph
	∧	Add This
	ℒ	Delete this
⁄Lowercase		Make this lowercase
capital		Make this uppercase

- copy your revised draft neatly on a clean sheet of paper.

THE UNEXPECTED

How can something ordinary become extraordinary? When it turns up in unexpected places! The writers of the selections in this unit have prepared surprises—for their characters and for their readers.

It seems that every week Dad has a suggestion or an idea to try out on the Gilbreth children in this excerpt from the novel *Cheaper by the Dozen.* At first, the family usually complains about Dad's methods. But eventually they see that he has a knack for solving problems and inventing systems that work.

Why is the Family Council a good idea for such a large family? Why do the Gilbreth children decide that Dad's experiments are worthwhile?

THE GREAT EXPERIMENTER

by FRANK G. GILBRETH, JR. and ERNESTINE GILBRETH CAREY

Like most of Dad's and Mother's ideas, the Family Council was basically sound and, although it verged sometimes on the hysterical, brought results. Family purchasing committees, duly elected, bought the food, clothes, furniture, and athletic equipment. A utilities committee levied one-cent fines on wasters of water and electricity. A projects committee saw that work was completed as scheduled. Allowances were decided by the council, which also meted out rewards and punishment.

One purchasing committee found a large department store which gave us wholesale rates on everything from underwear to baseball gloves. Another bought canned goods directly from a manufacturer, in truckload lots.

It was the Council, too, which worked out the system of submitting bids for unusual jobs to be done.

When Lill was eight, she submitted a bid of forty-seven cents to paint a long, high fence in the backyard. Of course it was the lowest bid, and she got the job.

"She's too young to try to paint the fence all by herself," Mother told Dad. "Don't let her do it."

"Nonsense," said Dad. "She's got to learn the value of money and keep agreements. Let her alone."

Lill, who was saving for a pair of roller skates and wanted the money, kept insisting she could do it.

"If you start it, you'll finish it," said Dad.

"I'll finish it, Daddy. I know I can."

"You've got yourself a contract, then."

It took Lill ten days to finish the job, working every day after school and all day weekends. Her hands blistered, and some nights she was so tired she couldn't sleep. It worried Dad so that some nights he didn't sleep very well either. But he made her live up to her contract.

"You've got to let her stop," Mother kept telling him. "She'll have a breakdown or something—or else you will."

"No," said Dad. "She's learning the value of money and she's learning that when you start something it's necessary to finish it if you want to collect. She's got to finish. It's in her contract."

When Lill finally completed the job, she came to Dad in tears.

"It's done," she said. "I hope you're satisfied. Now can I have my forty-seven cents?"

Dad counted out the change.

"Don't cry, honey," he said. "No matter what you think of your old Daddy, he did it for your own good. If you go look under your pillow, you'll find that Daddy really loved you all the time."

The present was a pair of roller skates.

Fred headed the utilities committee and collected the fines. Once, just before he went to bed, he found that someone had left the faucet dripping and there was a bathtub full of hot water. Jack had been asleep for more than an hour, but Fred woke him up.

"Get in there and take a bath," he said.

"But I had a bath just before I went to bed."

"I know you did, and you left the faucet dripping," Fred told him. "Do you want to waste that perfectly good water?"

"Why don't you take a bath?" Jack asked.

"I take my baths in the morning. You know that. That's the schedule."

Jack had two baths that night.

At about that time Dad became a consultant to a typewriter company and, through motion study methods, helped develop the world's fastest typist.

He told us about it one night at dinner—how he had taken moving pictures and *time exposures* to see just what motions she employed and how those motions could be reduced.

"Anyone can learn to type fast," Dad concluded. "Why, I've got a system that will teach touch typing in two weeks. Absolutely guaranteed."

You could see the Great Experiment hatching in his mind.

"In two weeks," he repeated. "Why, I could even teach a child to type touch system in two weeks."

"Can you type touch system, Daddy?" Bill asked.

"In two weeks," said Dad, "I could teach a child. Anybody can do it if he will do just what I tell him to do."

The next day he brought home a new typewriter.

"Can I try the typewriter, Daddy?" asked Mart.

All of us wanted to use it, but Dad wouldn't let anyone touch it but himself.

"This is an optional experiment," he said. "I believe I can teach the touch system in two weeks. Anyone who wants to learn will be able to practice on the machine. The one who can type the fastest at the end of two weeks will receive the typewriter as a present."

Except for the two youngest, who still weren't talking, we all said we wanted to learn.

"Can I practice first, Daddy?" Lill asked.

"No one practices until I say 'practice.' Now, first I will show you how the typewriter works." Dad got a sheet of paper. "The paper goes in here. You turn this—so-oo. And you push the carriage over to the end of the line—like this."

And Dad, using two fingers, hesitatingly pecked out the first thing that came to his mind—his name.

"Is that the touch system, Daddy?" Bill asked.

"No," said Dad. "I'll show you the touch system in a little while."

"Do you know the touch system, Daddy?"

"Let's say I know how to teach it, Billy boy."

"But do you know it yourself, Daddy?"

"I know how to teach it," Dad shouted. "In just two weeks, I can teach it to a child. Do you hear me? I have just finished helping to develop the fastest typist in the world. Do you hear that? They tell me Caruso's* voice teacher can't sing a note. Does that answer your question?"

"I guess so," said Bill.

"Any other questions?"

There weren't. Dad then brought out some paper diagrams of a type-writer keyboard, and passed one to each of us.

"The first thing you have to do is to memorize that keyboard. QWER-TYUIOP. Those are the letters in the top line. Memorize them. Get to know them forward and backward. Get to know them so you can say them with your eyes closed. Like this."

Dad closed his right eye, but kept his left open just a slit so that he could still read the chart.

"QWERTYUIOP. See what I mean? Get to know them in your sleep. That's the first step."

We looked crestfallen.

"I know. You want to try out that white typewriter. Pretty, isn't it?"

He clicked a few keys.

"Runs as smoothly as a watch, doesn't it?"

We said it did.

"Well, tomorrow or the next day you'll be using it. First you have to memorize the keyboard. Then you've got to learn what fingers to use. Then you'll graduate to the big machine here. And one of you will win it."

Once we had memorized the key-board, our fingers were colored with chalk. The little fingers were colored blue, the index fingers red, and so forth. Corresponding colors were placed on the key zones of the dia-grams. For instance, the Q, A, and Z, all of which are hit with the finger of the left hand, were colored blue to match the blue little finger.

"All you have to do now is prac-tice until each finger has learned the right color habit," Dad said. "And once you've got that, we'll be ready to start."

In two days we were fairly adept at matching the colors on our fingers with the colors on the keyboard dia-grams. Ernestine was the fastest, and got the first chance to sit down at the typewriter. She hitched her chair up to it confidently, while we all gath-ered around.

"Hey, no fair, Daddy," she wailed. "You've put blank caps on all the keys. I can't see what I'm typing."

Blank caps are fairly common now, but Dad had thought up the idea and had had them made specif-ically by the typewriter company.

"You don't have to see," Dad said. "Just imagine that those keys

*the voice instructor of Enrico Caruso (1873–1921), a famous Italian opera singer.

are colored, and type just like you were typing on the diagram."

Ern started slowly, and then picked up speed, as her fingers jumped instinctively from key to key.

By the end of the two weeks, all children over six years old and Mother knew the touch system reasonably well. Dad said he knew it, too. We were a long way from being fast—because nothing but practice gives speed—but we were reasonably accurate.

Dad entered Ernestine's name in a national speed contest, as a sort of child prodigy, but Mother talked him out of it and Ern never actually competed.

"It's not that I want to show her off," he told Mother. "It's just that I want to do the people a favor—to show them what can be done with proper instructional methods and motion study."

"I don't think it would be too good an idea, dear," Mother said. "Ernestine is high-strung, and the children are conceited enough as it is."

Since Dad thought eating was a form of unavoidable delay, he utilized the dinner hour as an instruction period. His primary rule was that no one could talk unless the subject was of general interest.

19

Sometimes, the topic of conversation was a motion study project, such as clearing off the dishes from the table. Motion study was always of great general interest.

"Is it better to stack the dishes on the table, so that you can carry out a big pile?" Dad asked. "Or is it better to take a few of them at a time into the butler's pantry, where you can rinse them while you stack? After dinner we'll divide the table into two parts, and try one method on one part and the other method on the other. I'll time you."

Also of exceptional general interest was a series of tricks whereby Dad could multiply large numbers in his head, without using pencil and paper. The explanation of how the tricks worked is too complicated to explain in detail here, and two fairly elementary examples should suffice.

1. To multiply forty-six times forty-six, you figure how much greater forty-six is than twenty-five. The answer is twenty-one. Then you figure how much less forty-six is than fifty. The answer is four. You can square the four and get sixteen. You put the twenty-one and sixteen together, and the answer is twenty-one sixteen, or 2,116.

2. To multiply forty-four times forty-four, you figure how much greater forty-four is than twenty-five. The answer is nineteen. Then you figure how much less forty-four is than fifty. The answer is six. You square the six and get thirty-six. You put the nineteen and the thirty-six together, and the answer is nineteen thirty-six, or 1,936.

"I want to teach all of you how to multiply two-digit numbers in your head," Dad announced at dinner.

"Not of general interest," said Anne.

"Those who do not think it is of general interest may leave the table and go to their rooms," Dad said coldly, "and I understand there is apple pie for dessert."

Nobody left.

"Since everyone now appears to be interested," said Dad, "I will explain how it's done."

It was a complicated thing for children to understand, and it involved memorizing the squares of all numbers up to twenty-five. But Dad took it slowly, and within a couple of months the older children had learned all the tricks involved.

While we ate supper, Dad would shout out problems in mental arithmetic for us.

"Nineteen times seventeen."

"Three twenty-three."

"Right. Good boy, Bill."

"Fifty-two times fifty-two."

"Twenty-seven zero four."

"Right. Good girl, Martha."

Dan was five when this was going on, and Jack was three. One night at supper, Dad was firing questions at Dan on the squares of numbers up to twenty-five. This involved straight memory, and no mental arithmetic.

"Fifteen times fifteen," said Dad.

"Two twenty-five," said Dan.

"Sixteen times sixteen," said Dad.

Jack, sitting in his high chair next to Mother, gave the answer, "Two fifty-six."

At first Dad was irritated, because he thought one of the older children was butting in.

"I'm asking Dan," he said, "you older children stop showing off and . . ." Then he registered a double take.

"What did you say, Jackie boy?" Dad cooed.

"Two fifty-six."

Dad drew a nickel out of his pocket and grew very serious.

"Have you been memorizing the squares as I asked the questions to the older children, Jackie?"

Jack didn't know whether this was good or bad, but he nodded.

"If you can tell me what seventeen times seventeen is, Jackie boy, this nickel is yours."

"Sure, Daddy," said Jack. "Two eighty-nine."

Dad passed him the nickel and turned beaming to Mother.

"Lillie," he said, "we'd better keep that boy, too."

Martha, at eleven, became the fastest in the family at mental mathematics. Still feeling frustrated because he hadn't taken Ernestine to the speed typing contest, Dad insisted on taking Martha to an adding machine exhibition in New York.

"No, Lillie," he told Mother. "This one is not high-strung. She goes to New York with me."

Martha stood up on a platform at the adding machine show and answered the problems quicker than the calculators could operate. Dad, of course, stood alongside her. After the final applause, he told the assemblage modestly:

"There's really nothing to it. I've a boy named Jack at home who's almost as good as she is. I would have brought him here with me, but Mrs. Gilbreth said he's still too young. Maybe next year, when he's four . . ."

By this time, all of us had begun to suspect that Dad had his points as a teacher, and that he knew what he was talking about.

CHECK FOR UNDERSTANDING

1. What was the Family Council?
2. Why was the Family Council a good idea for such a large family?
3. What did Lill find under her pillow? Why did Dad give her that gift?
4. What was Dad's rule about table conversation? Did the rule apply to everyone? How do you know?
5. What did Dad's actions tell you about the kind of father he was?
6. Why did the Gilbreth children decide that Dad's experiments are worthwhile?

WRITE ABOUT *"The Great Experimenter"*

Choose one of the episodes in "The Great Experimenter." Rewrite it in play format.

Pride—genuine confidence in your own ability or strength—can be admirable. Too much pride, however, can lead people astray. M. C. Higgins is very proud of his swimming ability. What does he do to impress the girl he meets at the lake? What does the girl's pride in her own independence lead her to do?

INTO THE
TUNNEL

by VIRGINIA HAMILTON

When M. C. Higgins, his sister Macie, and his brothers Harper and Lennie Pool arrived at the lake for their morning swim, they found a stranger camping on the shore. The newcomer explained that she was traveling through the countryside. M. C. admired the girl, who seemed to be a few years older than he was, and he wanted to impress her.

"They call me M. C. Higgins, the Great," he told her. . . .

"M. C. the Great?" she said.

"Yea." He grinned.

"Why 'the Great'?" she asked him.

" 'Cause I can swim the best and everything." Now M. C. felt that he had to live up to his title.

In an instant M. C. plunged into the lake to begin a perfect backstroke. In water, all of the awkwardness of a youth standing on land left him. With his knowledge and skill in it, he made no unnecessary move. His powerful arms shot upward, then outward and rearward, as he cut through the lake like some bold sea creature. His back turned gold from the sun glistening on it.

Hemmed in by mountains, surrounded by tall pines, the dark surge of the lake was magical. Fascinated, the girl watched it and the way M. C. cut through it, until she could no longer resist. She backed away, turned, and disappeared into her tent. When she came out again, M. C. and the children were down at the far end of the lake.

She wore wrinkled, pink shorts and a faded man's shirt with sleeves cut away. She had tied the shirttails in a knot at her waist. M. C. thought she was about as nice-looking as she could be. But rather than strike out into the water from where she was, she came around the shore.

"Come on in," they shouted to her.

She preferred to walk down to the end of the beach. There she leaned on the rocks and plunged a foot in the water. "That's cold!" she said, looking pleased that they had invited her.

"Not underneath," Macie said.

"Just on the top. You get in, and it's real warm."

M. C. said something to his brothers, and then: "Don't let Macie . . . I'm going through."

Head first, he upended himself and vanished beneath the surface. The water grew still again as if he

25

had never been there. Macie rode on Harper's back until he grabbed the rocks and shook her off. Once he had climbed up on them, he gave Macie a hand. Lennie Pool followed.

The girl watched the water but it remained smooth and dark.

"What's your name?" Macie said, curious all of a sudden.

The girl smiled at Macie. But then her eyes flicked back to the lake where M. C. had gone under. She began to walk back and forth, her hands on her hips.

The children watched her.

"What's he doing down there?" she asked them.

They said nothing.

"I don't think he's coming up, you'd better do something."

Macie broke their silence with a giggle. "He's not even down there," she said, "just over and behind these rocks." She led the way around the edge of the rocks. Harper and Lennie went, too, and cautiously the girl followed.

On the other side lay a surprise. It was an opening in the rocks. No one who didn't know would suspect it was there. The rocks fell back in a small clearing where there was a silent pool with grassy banks.

The children stopped at the edge. Macie turned brightly to the girl and smiled.

M. C. surged up from the center of the pool in a great splash. He sucked in air as though he would never again get enough of it, as the girl covered her mouth to stifle a scream.

The kids laughed at her. "It's a water tunnel," Harper told her in his soft, urgent voice. He told how the tunnel went under the rocks beneath the water at the edge of the lake and ended at the pool.

"Only M. C. can travel it," Macie said. "We're not allowed. The kids from town don't even know there's a tunnel."

"You wouldn't know it, either, if you hadn't caught me doing it once," M. C. said. "Better keep the sense never to try it, too."

"How do you hold your breath so long?" The girl talked to M. C. as though he were older, showing respect for him now.

He pulled himself up on the grassy bank and wiped water out of his eyes. He had to smile. She kneeled next to him, her fear of him and the children gone.

Proud he'd done something she never expected he could do. And she had come from somewhere by herself in a car. But he could be by himself, too. He could travel through water like nobody. First he thought of lying, to tell her he could hold his breath longer than anyone. The kids would know.

Finally he said, "It's not so long. I came up before you all ever got here. Heard you coming, and I just went under and waited. Then I splashed up like I was out of breath."

She didn't seem to mind he had played a trick. "It's dark in the tunnel?" she asked him. Her face so close, he could see tiny bumps he hadn't noticed before.

Shyly, he looked at his feet hanging in the water. "It's gray light, kind of," he said. "This pool is at the end of the tunnel. Sunlight drifts in and gets faded, I guess. But I see, a little. It's ghosty, though, when fishes slide over your skin."

She cringed with the picture of it. Watching her, Macie shivered with delight.

His eyes on the pool, M. C. sensed the girl watching him. Felt himself reaching out for her, the way he often reached out when he sat next to his father. His skin itched and came alive with little things he seemed to know about her. She might travel alone, but every minute she was scared being by herself. The impression came to him, swift and certain.

Already he felt attuned to the girl, less self-conscious at having her so near.

He rubbed his arms and neck until the itching went away. Tiredness settled in the knot on his forehead in a dull ache that came and went. He wasn't feeling quite himself this morning. Yet he didn't want to go and leave her.

"What's your name?" he asked.

She shrugged. "No use of saying names."

"I told you our names," he said.

"I could tell you a name and you wouldn't know if it was really mine."

"Where do you come from, then?"

"Same thing," she said. "You wouldn't know if I came from where I said."

"Then why not tell?"

She said nothing. She looked at him and quickly away, as if she wanted to speak out, but couldn't.

Soon she was looking from the pool to the rocks and back to the pool.

She did this several times before it came to M. C. what was on her mind.

"A water tunnel won't be like a pool," he told her, "or even a lake."

She nodded, staring at the rocks.

"A pool or even a lake is simple. Water will lift you," he said.

She sat still, with just her head turning to look at him and then away.

"But the tunnel is a bottleneck. No place to take off the pressure; or maybe pressure's not the trouble. It's just a tight place without a top, and you can get sick to your stomach."

A long silence in which she said nothing.

"How long can you hold your breath?" M. C. asked her.

"What?"

"If you travel that tunnel," he said. "How long can you go with no breathing?"

Wide-eyed, she stared at him. "As long as anybody." All at once she breathed hugely, holding the air in.

Macie and the boys scrambled close to see. Everything was still. The girl's eyes began to pop and tear. She held out while none of them moved, until at last her breath burst through her teeth. She fell back, panting.

"That was long!" Harper said.

"Maybe forty-five seconds," M. C. said. "Not long enough."

The girl sat up again.

"Try it once more," M. C. said.

"You don't think I can do it," she said.

"I'm not thinking a thing. It just has to be longer," he said. "Long enough to reach the pool."

"Well, I don't know," she said, her voice edgy. She searched M. C.'s face.

"If you're worried, don't try it," he said.

Then she was smirking at him. "Sure think you're something, don't you?" she said.

Her anger shot through him. It hurt him and he didn't know what to say. He hadn't meant anything bad by what he said.

"The tunnel is fun," he said quietly, "but you have to have the lungs to hold out."

The girl sucked in her breath again. M. C. kept his eyes on the pool. He didn't want to be watching her if this time she failed. He tried just to feel when the time was long enough. But in spite of himself, he began counting in his head.

When he knew she would have to breathe, he turned to her. Still she held out. Tendons and veins stood

out on her neck. Her eyes were squeezed shut. Her cheeks and mouth were twisted in an awful face.

She exploded, bursting with air and squirming on the ground, trying to breathe again. Uncomfortably, M. C. turned his face away.

"You did it!" Macie yelled. Lennie Pool grinned and Harper clapped his hands.

"M. C., she did it!" Macie screeched. "Didn't she?"

He nodded at Macie to let all of them know. But he was wondering if he had forgotten something he should have remembered to ask.

Never taken someone through the tunnel, he thought. Maybe I shouldn't.

"Are you going to swim it right now?" Macie asked the girl.

But she couldn't answer. She seemed to be having that cold, sickening feeling that came from holding your breath too long. M. C. knew this. Drying sweat caused his skin to itch again.

"We maybe can swim it later on," he said. "Give you plenty of time . . ."

The girl shot up from the ground. Even though she looked weak, she stood with her hands firmly on her hips. "You think I can't do it." Her eyes snapped at him.

M. C. couldn't get himself loose from those eyes, they were so pretty. Slowly he got to his feet.

There grew a silence between them that separated them from the children. They stood close together, watching each other.

"You have to do just as I say," M. C. told her.

"Why?"

" 'Cause I know how to get through."

She thought a moment. "Okay," she said.

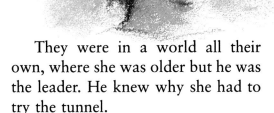

They were in a world all their own, where she was older but he was the leader. He knew why she had to try the tunnel.

Not because I've done it. 'Cause I'm the only one.

He turned and led the way over the rocks to the lake. The girl followed close on his heels.

The lake lay as serene and peaceful as when they had left it. Way down at the other end was the ridge. In between the ridge and the rocky end where now he and the girl crouched was the tent, like an intruder in the sun. All around them were pines, undergrowth, greens and browns closing in the magical shimmer of the lake.

He and the girl hung onto rocks just above the waterline. The children were clinging a foot above them.

"The tunnel's right down there," M. C. told her. "About eight to ten feet down. Maybe twelve feet long and that's a couple of body lengths." He paused, looking out over the lake. "Now I lead," he told her. "I lead and we hold together like this." With his right hand, he took hold of her left arm, forcing her to balance herself with her back against the rocks. "Hold on to my arm just above the wrist."

"Like this?" She grabbed his arm with fingers stronger than he'd expected. So close to her, he felt shy but calm.

"We jump here, we get more power," he told her. "We get down faster but it has to be done just right."

"How?" she said.

M. C. didn't know how. He was figuring it all out as he went along, working fast in his head the best way to jump and the quickest way to get through the tunnel.

"Best way is . . . if I jump backward and you jump frontward." He

spoke carefully. "See, I hit and go in facing the tunnel. I have your left arm and you are pulled over. You follow in just in back of me. Now. In the tunnel, you have your right arm free and I have my left." They would use their free arms to push them through if they had to, and they could kick with their feet.

"Tunnel sides are moss," he said. "Push off from them when you bump them. It'll feel slimy but it won't hurt."

"Okay," she said.

"Pay no mind to fishes," he went on. "Most times, they're but just a few. They get out of your way."

She nodded. M. C. could feel her tension through her arm.

"You all ready?" Macie asked from above them.

M. C. looked at the girl. "I'm ready," she said.

"You have to hold out for most of a minute."

"I can do it," she said.

"If you lose air, just stay calm," M. C. said. "I can get us out."

"I said I can do it!"

Her anger cut through him again, making him ashamed, he didn't know why.

"Macie, you count it off," he said grimly.

"She always gets to do something," Harper said.

"He told *me*, now shut," Macie said.

"Stay out of the water. Wait for us at the pool. Now," M. C. said.

"Ready!" Macie yelled. "Get yourself set . . ."

The girl grew rigid.

"You have to stay calm," M. C. told her. He held her arm as tightly as he could without hurting her. Her fingers dug into his wrist.

"Watch your nails!" he warned. They both sucked in air.

"Go, y'all!"

They leaped out and plunged. They hit water at the same time but M. C. went under first because he was heavier. The girl turned facing him before her head went under. That was good, but pulling her after him slowed M. C. It seemed to take forever to get down to the tunnel level. Water closed in on them. Sounds became muffled and then no sound at all. They were alone as never before. And there was nothing for M. C. to do but get it over with.

M. C. liked nothing better than being in the deep, with sunlight breaking into rays of green and gold. Water was a pressure of delicious weight as he passed through it, down and down. It was as if feeling no longer belonged to him. The water possessed it and touched along every inch of him.

He pulled out of his downward fall at the sight of the gaping tunnel opening. He no longer felt the girl next to him. He knew she was there with him by the impression she made on the deep. And he would remember her presence, her imprint, on this day for weeks.

Bending her wrist forward, he stretched her arm out straight as he kicked hard into the tunnel. Here the water was cooler and cast a gray shimmer that was ghostly. Pressure grew like a ball and chain hanging on his right shoulder. It was the girl like dead weight.

Kick with your feet!

With a powerful scissoring of his legs, he tried to swim midway between the ceiling and bottom of the tunnel.

Push off with your hand!

Her dead pressure dragged him down. His knees banged hard against the bottom. His back hit the tunnel side as he realized she was struggling to get away. Fractions of seconds

were lost as he tried twisting her arm to pull her body into line. Fishes slid over his skin, tickling and sending shivers to his toes. They must have touched the girl. For he had no moment to brace himself as she shot up on her back toward the ceiling.

Won't make it.

Horror, outrage stunned him. He had taken for granted the one thing he should have asked her. For the want of a question, the tunnel would be a grave for both of them.

She kicked futilely against the tunnel side and rose above him, twisting his arm straight up.

Yank, like Macie will pull down on a balloon.

If he could get the girl turned over, they might have a chance. But his breath seemed to be gone.

Not a grave, it's a tunnel.

In his lungs, emptiness was pain. But the will not to fail was there in his burning chest, in his free arm pushing hard against the deep. His legs were still loose and working. Then a sudden surge of strength, like a second wind.

Be M. C. Higgins, the Great.

He yanked the balloon down—he mustn't break the string. At the same time he propelled himself forward, knowing she would follow as she turned over.

An awful pounding in his head snapped his brain open. M. C. shot out of the tunnel like a cork from a jug of cider. And arching his back, he swung mightily with his right arm.

Dark balloon to the light above.

He hadn't the strength to hurl her to the surface. But he was right behind her. Before she could struggle down again, he was there, pulling at her. She opened her mouth in a pitiful attempt to breathe. He pounded her back, hoping to dislodge water. And held her close a split second to calm her. She was rigid.

Girl, don't drown.

Swiftly he caught her ankles and tossed her up over his head. She broke the surface. He was there, feeling sweet air just when he would have to open his mouth or have his lungs collapse.

M. C. fought against dizziness, aware he had his hand on her neck in a bruising clasp to hold her up. He had to let go or break it.

The girl was gagging, trying to breathe. He heard his own breath in a harsh, raw heaving. He was daydreaming, a distant cheering. Then he saw the children, feet jumping up and down on the grassy bank. A swirl of rocks before he realized the girl was sinking. He must have let her go. But he had the sense to catch her again around the waist.

Still M. C. Still the leader. He had taken her through the tunnel and they were back in the world together. Still, all the blame was his. But he could fix it. Could keep the children from knowing about her.

Moaning cry, coughing, she clung to him.

"No." He knocked her hands away. With just the pressure of his arm and shoulder on her back, he forced her flat out. As though she were dog-paddling, he glided her into the land. The feet jumping on the grassy bank fell back and were still.

Macie stood there on the bank, closest to M. C.'s head.

"She's weak," he said to Macie. "See if you can help pull her some . . . my wind is gone."

Macie clasped the girl's arms. M. C. had her by the waist. Halfway out of the water, she kicked M. C. away. She slithered and kneed her way over the bank. On the grass, she hunched into a ball and, struggling to breathe, closed her eyes.

Dark balloon.

M. C. climbed out and crawled a distance to collapse on his back. He was away from the girl, with the children behind them, but he kept his eye on her. They were close together in his mind, where a vision had started. Day after day, they swam the lake. Hour upon hour, they sunned themselves on the shore.

M. C.'s chest wouldn't stop its heave and fall. His mouth watered with stomach bile as the pounding ache spread out across his forehead.

None of them moved. For a long while neither Harper nor Macie asked a single question. Lennie Pool never did say much.

M. C. felt as if every muscle were trying to get out of his skin. He was sick with exhaustion. But light out of the sky bore into him, warming and relaxing him. It was a healing band on his eyelids. As the ache in his forehead moved off, tunnel and water filled his mind. His eyes shot open, blinding the awful memory.

Seeing that M. C. was awake, Macie came over to him. "You did it!" she said happily. "Were you scared?"

He knew he would vomit if he tried to talk. He swallowed hard.

"You sure took your time. Was it any trouble?" Macie went on.

"Just took it easy," he said finally.

The girl brought up pool water she had swallowed. Half an hour later, she sat up shakily on her knees. In a slow, mechanical sweep, she brushed grass and twigs from her drying clothes.

M. C. raised his head. "You all right?" he asked her.

When she stood, the children stood with her. M. C. was on his feet as well, as though he moved only when she moved.

Slowly she seemed to change. He watched her grow stronger, throwing her head back, thrusting out her chin.

"I went all the way through that tunnel," she said, smiling vaguely. "I could have drowned—I can't even swim a lick."

The children gaped at her. Shocked, they turned to M. C.

"And you took her down?" Macie gasped. "You took her clear through . . . you didn't even know!"

The kids began to giggle, jostling one another, with the girl looking solemnly on.

M. C. felt the heat of shame rising in his neck. Only this one secret between them, but the girl wouldn't have it. She made him stand there with the kids laughing at him. He stared at his hands, at the jagged nails which he bit down to the skin.

"I can't stand a lying kid," the girl said.

Worse than a slap in the face, but he said evenly, "I'm not any kid. And I didn't lie."

"You told your sister we took it easy," she said, smirking at him.

"*I* took it easy," he said. "If I hadn't, you wouldn't be here, girl."

The children stared at him soberly now. The girl looked uncertain.

"It's no joke not to tell somebody you can't swim," he said.

"Somebody didn't ask me," she said sullenly.

"Didn't need to ask—you should've told me!"

"I just wanted to see it. I didn't know it was going to be *so long*."

"So you want to see something and we almost drown?" He was shaking now with the memory of the tunnel. "Ever think of somebody but yourself?"

The girl shrank back. Uncomfortably, they watched her. M. C. hadn't meant to make her appear stupid. But she was quick to apologize.

"I'm sorry," she said simply. "You told me you were some M. C., the Great. . . ."

The look she gave him, as if she knew only he could have saved her, made him feel proud. He had to smile. "You have some good nerve. A lot of real good nerve," he said at last.

CHECK FOR UNDERSTANDING

1. What was so special about the tunnel?
2. What did M. C. do to impress the girl he met at the lake?
3. How did the girl prepare for the trip through the tunnel?
4. What did M. C. discover as he and the girl entered the tunnel?
5. What might have happened if M. C. had not remained calm?
6. What did the girl's pride in her independence lead her to do?
7. Do you think that the girl realized the danger she caused? Why or why not?

WRITE ABOUT *"Into the Tunnel"*

After his experience, would M. C. want to have the tunnel blocked up so that nobody could swim through it? Write a paragraph from M. C.'s point of view. State whether or not the tunnel should be closed. Then give your reasons.

PRIMER LESSON

by CARL SANDBURG

Look out how you use proud words.
When you let proud words go, it is
    not easy to call them back.
They wear long boots, hard boots;
    they walk off proud; they can't
    hear you calling—
Look out how you use proud words.

Predicting Outcomes

> "M. C., she did it!" Macie screeched. "Didn't she?"
>
> He nodded at Macie to let all of them know. But he was wondering if he had forgotten something he should have remembered to ask.

This was a fateful moment in "Into the Tunnel." M. C. never asked the all-important question.

Suppose that it had happened differently. Suppose that he *had* asked the question, and the girl had admitted that she could not swim. Would M. C. have taken the girl through the tunnel anyway, just to impress her?

There are ways to predict what will happen next in a story. In order to **predict outcomes**, you must use the information that the author provides for the reader. These clues are often contained in information the author gives you about the personality of a character. It is obvious that M. C. would not have taken the girl through the tunnel had he known that she could not swim, but how do you know this? What has the author revealed about M. C. that enables you to predict his behavior?

The author tells you that M. C. has kept the dangerous tunnel a closely guarded secret:

> "Only M. C. can travel it," Macie said. "We're not allowed. The kids from town don't even know there's a tunnel."

M. C. did not want others to risk their lives by trying to prove they were as good as he. M. C. would not agree to take the girl through the tunnel until he was satisfied that she could hold her breath long enough. Even then he was hesitant to bring her through:

> Never taken someone through the tunnel, he thought. Maybe I shouldn't.

M. C. is clearly a very responsible young man. It is easy to see that he would not have taken the girl through the tunnel if he had known her secret. This is evident by M. C.'s anger with the girl at the end of the story, after he has brought her to safety.

What would the girl's reaction have been if M. C. had discovered that she could not swim and then had refused to take her through the tunnel? Think about these lines:

> "If you're worried, don't try it," he said.
> Then she was smirking at him. "Sure think you're some-thing, don't you?" she said.
> Her anger shot through him. It hurt him and he didn't know what to say.

What do her words tell you about the girl? How does she react to a suggestion that she cannot do something? Her insecurity is demon-strated by anger and sarcasm. If M. C. had refused to take her through the tunnel, she would probably have become angry and abusive.

As you read the next selection, think about the personality of the main character. Is he brave or foolhardy? How does he react to unusual occurrences? How does he feel about the situation in which he finds himself? Such questions will help you predict what will happen next.

A pet dog or cat may respond to you in various ways—such as by wagging its tail or perking up its ears; but it certainly doesn't talk to you. Perhaps you have wished that an animal could actually tell you what it thinks and feels. You might be so curious to find out the results that you would forget it was not a natural occurrence. On the other hand, you might be so frightened by the unnaturalness that you would run away. In this story, a boy named Cody has an opportunity to speak to several animals that can talk. What is Cody's reaction when the first animal talks to him? Do you think that Cody really wants to meet Martin?

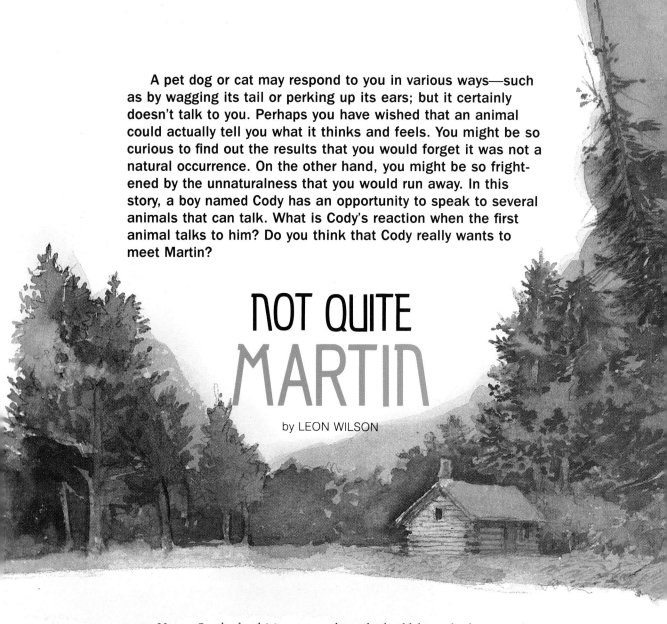

NOT QUITE
MARTIN

by LEON WILSON

Up on Cumberland Mountain, where the huckleberry bushes grow bigger than trees and faster than trouble, Cody set out one day for some scientific huckle harvesting. He did not let anyone come along to disturb his concentration, not his sister Omalia, not even his dog, Daybreak.

Cody got so busy picking and eating that he hardly noticed how dark it was getting or how far he'd strayed from home. It finally hit him that he wouldn't be making it back to his own bed that night, but Cody was not the kind of person who feared an adventure or two.

Now, if you were alone in the woods and it was pitch black dark, maybe you would be a little frightened. Cody wasn't, though. He knew all about the woods and being alone in the dark didn't worry him a bit. Of course he would have *preferred* being home with his father and mother and Omalia, but since this was out, he didn't intend to waste time wishing he were some place he couldn't be.

What he had to do was decide how and where to spend the night.

He wasn't sleepy yet because it wasn't bedtime, and he wasn't cold because it was midsummer, and he wasn't hungry because he was cram-jam full of his favorite food. All these things he wasn't. The main thing he *was* was tired of bumping into trees.

Now just as the last speck of daylight had vanished, Cody had sighted a little log cabin in which no one lived.

This is how he knew no one lived in it—

First thing: no light in the window.

Second thing: no smoke looping out of the chimney.

Third thing: no one moving around inside the cabin. Cody found *this* out by putting his ear to a crack in the logs and listening.

He couldn't hear a sound.

"Here's my home for tonight," says Cody to himself, mighty proud of his cleverness, and he climbs the steps to the door, and just to make absolutely *completely* sure no one is inside, he knocks loudly.

No answer.

(He would have been mighty surprised, of course, if there had been an answer!)

So he pushes the door open and takes a look inside. But you can bet he doesn't see much, for it's as dark in there as the inside of a cow.

He lights one of his matches and looks again. And sees—nothing. Or almost nothing. Just an old empty cabin. Not a chair or a table in it, not a lamp, a dish, or a bed. A few old sticks lying around on the floor to make a fire with, and that's all.

So in pops Cody, mighty pleased with himself, and shuts the door and scrammishes together some wood and makes himself a fire in the fireplace.

"Why," he says to himself, "this is almost as good as being home. The only thing I lack here that I would have at home (besides a dish of the huckleberry pie my mother was baking) is someone to talk to."

And now, listen:

The very minute he thinks about company, there comes a *tap-tap-tap* on the cabin door.

Very soft. So soft Cody hardly hears it. So soft Cody believes he has gone to sleep and he's dreaming that he heard it.

And now it comes again, a little louder this time. About like this: TAP-TAP-TAP.

This time Cody knows he's really hearing something. "Who in the world can be out there?" he asks himself. "Can't be anyone coming to see *me*, for who knows I'm here? Nobody!" He scratches his head to help himself think. "Maybe," he decides, "it's someone come to visit whoever it is that doesn't live here anymore."

And now on the door there comes a good loud TAP-TAP-TAPPETY-TAP.

(Whoever's out there, he's getting tired of waiting. He's wanting an answer.)

"Open the door and come in, sir," Cody says politely. "Whoever you are, come in and enjoy my good fire with me."

Cody hears the door begin to open. He turns his head and peeks over his shoulder. And sees—

Not a man—

Not a woman—

Not a boy—

And no, not a girl—

He sees a cat. A gray stripy cat with a long stripy tail.

The instant Cody sees it he knows it is no ordinary cat. For one thing, its yellow eyes are bigger and brighter and

yellower by a good deal than an ordinary cat's are. For another thing, this cat's whiskers are longer and its gray stripy tail is *much* longer than even Midnight's, and Midnight's is pretty long.

I haven't told you yet how surprised Cody is, but you can imagine!

He's so surprised, in fact, seeing a cat walk in when he expected to see a man, that he now says to the cat the very thing he had planned to say to the man.

"Good evening, sir," he says.

And the little cat switches its long stripy tail and looks Cody over with its big bright yellow eyes and replies as polite as you please:

"Good evening to *you*, sir."

Cody is *really* surprised this time! He has seen clever cats before—Midnight, for instance. If no one is around to help Midnight, she will push a door open when she wants in or pull it open when she wants out. But clever as Midnight is, she doesn't talk! Cody guesses mighty few cats are clever enough to talk, and he decides to keep an eye on this one and see what clever thing it will do next.

But the cat doesn't do much more. It pushes the door shut, but then that's no great feat for even an ordinary cat. Then it strolls to the hearthstone and plumps down where it's warm from the fire and tucks its paws under its chest, the way a cat will. And it curls its long stripy tail around itself, and that's all.

Or just about all. One thing more: it turns its big bright eyes on Cody and gives him one of those long-lasting looks cats are so good at.

Cody grins at the little critter, hoping it will feel at home and talk some more, but the cat says not another word. It yawns one of those gaping yawns cats go in for, and then it returns to watching Cody's fire. And this time, this is really all it does.

"Pretty nice fire, isn't it?" Cody remarks. He's out to make the little thing talk.

Does the cat reply? It does not! Does the cat even look at Cody again? It does not! It goes on watching the fire for all the world as if it hadn't heard Cody speak.

Cody shakes his head. "What a crying shame!" he says to himself. He's pretty sure he's never going to meet another cat clever enough to talk. Too bad this one won't open up so he can find out what cats think about.

And now on the cabin door there comes a *rap-rap-rap*. Not loud, but louder than the cat's *tap-tap-tap*. About like this: RAP-RAP-RAP.

"Well!" says Cody to himself. "Who is it this time? Someone looking for the man who doesn't live here anymore, or another cat?"

Cody thinks it would be dandy if another talking cat came in. Might be just what this fellow on the hearthstone needs to get him going. Then while the two cats discussed cat matters together, he could sit there and listen and learn.

RAPPETY-RAP-RAP-RAP! Good and loud this time—and Cody realizes that with all his wondering who it is, he's been keeping the rapper waiting. He pops his mouth open to say, "Come in, whoever you are," but before he has a chance to say it, the cat on the hearthstone cries out:

"You're wasting your time rapping—open and enter!"

Before Cody can get over his surprise at this, he has to peek over his shoulder again, for the door is opening.

A man this time?

No.

Another cat, then?

No, not another cat.

A big old smiling possum!

Chances are you've never seen a possum. If you haven't you've missed something. Possums' eyes are small, almost as small as apple seeds, and their mouths are famous for the very long thin white teeth in them. Possums are famous, too, for their tails, which are

not only long and thin but almost completely hairless.

And here's another thing: most any time you see a possum, it will seem to be smiling, only its smile isn't the kind you and I give out with when we're happy about something. It's a special, quite unhappy sort of smile and yet not altogether unhappy—about half and half, as if the possum had a bellyache but didn't mind it. Rather liked it, in fact. Possums seem to be saying with this special sickly smile of theirs, "Oh, I feel *so* sick, and I do hope *you* feel the same."

Cody has seen possums before this, of course, for there are lots of them on Cumberland Mountain, but in all his life he has never seen such a possumy-looking possum as this one coming in the door. Never has he seen such *very* long, sharp teeth or such a completely sickly smile.

And what does this most possumy-looking possum do? Nothing very much. It shuts the door and then comes creeping across the floor in that slow-going, take-it-easy way possums have, and slides in beside the cat. Then it looks up at Cody with its eyes that are like two shiny apple seeds, and of course it continues to smile its half-happy, half-unhappy bellyache smile. And now it turns to the cat and asks it in a take-it-easy possum sort of drawl:

"How soon?" And at the same time it jerks its head toward Cody so the cat will know what it's talking about.

The cat glances up at Cody with his bright golden eyes and says to the possum, as plain as you please, "We can't do anything until Martin comes."

Then it yawns another one of those tremendous cat yawns and goes back to watching Cody's fire.

This seems to satisfy the possum. Smiling its bellyache smile, it says not another word and commences watching the fire.

Cody politely waits for the cat and the possum to say something more, even though he has a question troubling him. "Excuse me, please," he says finally.

The cat and the possum look up to find out what's on Cody's mind.

"I heard you mention Martin," Cody says. "Who *is* Martin, and about how soon do you reckon he'll be coming along?"

The cat looks at the possum but says nothing. The possum looks at the cat and says nothing. They both look at Cody—silently. Then they look back at the fire.

So all Cody can do is wonder about Martin.

And as he wonders, he finds himself beginning to feel mighty regretful about something—what he said to Omalia. "The next time that girl asks to go somewhere with me," he says to himself, "I'm going to let her. Right now, company is something I'd like to have, and I don't mean this four-legged company."

And now, on the door:

Scrape-scrape-scrape.

This time Cody finds he isn't much interested in saying "Come in, whoever you are." Maybe it's Martin, and maybe he doesn't care to see Martin coming in, making himself at home. The more Cody thinks it may be Martin, the more he wants to think no one is outside at all, so he tries his level best to believe that the wind is blowing a tree branch against the door. Of course the scraping noise is a bit loud for a branch, especially when there isn't a breath of wind stirring—but Cody thinks there's no harm in trying.

Now here it comes again, much louder: SCRAPE-SCRAPE-SCRAPE. (It certainly isn't a tree branch!)

"Kick it open and join us!" the possum calls out in a loud voice, and the little cat cries out, "We're waiting for you!"

This time, as the door opens, Cody takes his time peeking around. He isn't by any means certain he wants to see who is coming in.

And who is? Another cat? Another possum? Martin, maybe?

Not quite.

When Cody gets his eyes around, he sees a sleek red fox with high pointed ears, a long pointed nose, shiny at the tip, and eyes as glittery as two polished black marbles. And a tail so bushy and long that it's almost the size of the fox.

And what does it do, this fox who is bigger than the possum, who in turn is bigger than the little cat? Well, it doesn't do anything, unless you want to call shutting the door something.

The fox steps quieter than a whisper across to the hearthstone and glides in beside the possum. Then it swings its rusty red head Cody's way and slowly winks one of its glittery black eyes, for all the world as if it and Cody were sharing some deep secret.

Then it turns to the possum and the cat and, in its super-sleek soft foxy voice, it asks:

"How soon?"

And the cat and the possum answer, "We can't do anything till Martin comes."

"Oh," says the fox, and once again it looks up at Cody and slyly winks one eye.

And while the fox winks, the possum smiles its bellyache smile, and the

little cat stares at Cody with its bright yellow eyes that every minute seem to grow a little bigger.

And all the time the animals are watching Cody, Cody is thinking. He's thinking so hard about something good to eat that he can almost taste it.

Strangely enough, it isn't huckleberries. It's an enormous plate of yellow cornbread fixed up with butter and bee honey. And just beyond sits a glass of ice-cold buttermilk at least ten inches tall.

What a slam-gorgeous supper, Cody thinks—my, if only I was home this minute with my ears pinned back, eating such a supper, I wouldn't be here in this crowded old cabin that's getting more crowded every minute. Boy, what I wouldn't give for a mess of cornbread!

Right in the middle of Cody's cornbread thinking: CRACKETY-BANG!

The door again, and this time it doesn't begin to sound like a branch scraping in the wind. All it sounds like is someone in a burning hurry to enter.

"Kick it open and roll in!" cries the fox.

"Waitin' for you!" cries the possum.

"Me, too!" cries the cat.

When Cody peeks over his shoulder this time, he sees a panther! Now, if you've never seen a panther, an easy way to imagine what this one looked like is to think how that little cat beyond the possum would look if it weren't little but gigantic.

What a whopper of a panther this one coming in the door is! Its ears are as big as baskets. His eyes are as bright as two flashlights. Its whiskers stick out like knitting needles. Its tail is so long Cody wonders if it's ever going to end. (The tail does end, finally, but not for a long time.)

And what does the panther do? Nothing much. It shuts the door, of course—but then they all shut the door—and stalks to the hearthstone and moves in beside the fox.

Then it turns its flashlight eyes on Cody and looks the boy up, looks him down, looks him back, looks him forth, and after the panther looks at Cody all these ways, he turns to the fox and the possum and the cat and, in a gigantic, panthery voice, he says just one word: "When?"

And the cat and the possum and the fox all reply at once. "We can't do anything till Martin comes."

Now, all the time this is going on, something else has been happening that I haven't had a chance to mention: Cody's fine fire has been burning lower and lower, the way any fire will when you fail to feed it. By now, the fire is so low and the cabin is so dark that when Cody looks at his four visitors, this is just about all he can see:

The stary yellow eyes of the little cat—

The shiny apple-seed eyes of the smiling possum—

The gilttery marble eyes of the fox (one of them slowly winking from time to time)—

And the flashlight eyes of the panther—

And all these eyes are looking straight at Cody!

So Cody scrammishes around in a hurry and builds up his fire. He wants to see more than just eyes. Yes, sir, as long as he has to sit here, he wants a good view of the folks he's sitting with.

And now at the door there is a new noise—not a *tap*, not a *rap*, not a SCRAPE, not a CRACKETY-BANG, but one tremendous—CRASH! as the door flies back and in springs the biggest old black bear Cody has ever seen. It's two sizes bigger than the biggest bear Cody has ever even *dreamed* of seeing, and it's three shades blacker, and its black shiny eyes look as big as doorknobs.

And what does it do, this bear of all bears? One thing it doesn't do: it doesn't shut the door, hasn't time—too big a hurry.

One spring and it's on the hearthstone beside the panther, and it's looking Cody over with its doorknob eyes, but not for long, because it has to find out something in a hurry—right now! It turns to quiz the panther, the fox, the possum, and the cat, but before the bear can say anything, they all reply at once:

"We can't do anything till Martin comes!"

"Thanks for telling me," says the bear in a booming, bear sort of voice, and it turns to look at Cody again.

But now, what's this? Where is Cody?

The animals look around the cabin quickly, thinking maybe he has run away.

But Cody hasn't gone anywhere—not yet. He's standing in the middle of the cabin looking down at his feet, and anyone can see that something about his feet is worrying him.

As the animals watch, Cody begins stamping, one foot and then the other. He makes quite a bit of noise with them.

The animals look at one another in amazement.

"What's the big idea?" they seem to be saying. "Why this stamping? Why isn't the boy Cody sitting here enjoying this good fire with us while we wait for Martin?"

And perhaps you are wondering. I'll tell you:

Back when the panther came stalking in, Cody began to feel an itchy sensation in his feet that wouldn't go away. In fact, the longer he sat on the hearthstone doing nothing to get rid of the sensation, the itchier it became. By the time the bear burst in, Cody's feet were itching so badly he couldn't sit still another second.

That's why he's stamping now in the middle of the cabin.

"Itch in my feet," he informs the bewildered animals. He can tell from the way they look at him that they don't believe a word of it. The yellow eyes of the little cat and the possum's apple seeds and the fox's glittery marbles and the panther's flashlights and the bear's doorknobs are all as full of disbelief as they can be.

"Young Mr. Cody seems not to care for our company," the animals appear to be saying.

Cody is sorry they don't believe him, but he doesn't see what he can do about it. After all, he's telling them the truth—it's their tough luck if they won't believe him.

"Stamping helps some," he goes on, "but not enough. I believe I've got to walk some. Walk fast. This little old cabin isn't half big enough for the walking I've got to do. I'd be hitting the walls six times a minute, trying to do my walking in here."

All the time Cody is explaining this, he's backing slowly to the door, and now he stands with one of his itchy feet already outside on the steps, waiting to go.

"Friends," he says—and his feet are so impatient he can hardly stand still long enough to say this one more thing he wants to say—"friends," he says quietly and politely, "when Martin gets here, tell him I was here, please, and tell him I waited for him as long as I could, but I couldn't wait one minute more."

And saying this, Cody commences his fast walk away from the cabin, and do you know?—the minute he looks back and sees that the cat and the possum and the fox and the panther and the bear aren't following him, his feet practically entirely stop itching!

Well, that's the adventure Cody had the day he ate more huckleberries than he had ever eaten before.

The sun was coming up as he started his swift departure from the cabin, so it wasn't a great time before he was home again, eating breakfast with his father and mother and Omalia. Between bites of pie (for Cody's breakfast was a piece of the huckle pie he had missed out on the night before), Cody told his story exactly as I have told it: how he met the cat, the possum, the fox, the panther, the bear, and almost, but not quite, Martin. The minute he finished, Omalia, who had been listening pop-eyed to every word, exclaimed, "Fiddle faddle! You made it up to give us a thrill."

"Made it up!" Cody said indignantly.

"Possums don't talk," Omalia said, "and neither do cats or panthers or foxes or bears."

"*This* possum talked," Cody said, "and so did the rest of them. They talked all kinds of stuff."

Omalia shook her head and looked exceedingly wise for a little girl of seven. "I suspect," she said sternly, "you went in that cabin and fell asleep and dreamed every bit of it."

"Dreamed it?" Cody cried. "You wouldn't have thought it was a dream if you'd been there!"

Omalia went right on as if she hadn't heard Cody. "In fact," she said, addressing her mother and father, "I've made up my mind it was a dream. Cody must have eaten some green huckleberries and they didn't sit right."

"Dream!" Cody muttered, spooning up the pie juice on his plate. "Green huckleberries!" Suddenly his face puckered up with thought.

"What's the matter, Cody?" his mother asked. She feared Cody might not be feeling well, having been up so late the night before.

"Nothing's the matter," Cody said. "I'm thinking."

"Thinking what?" his father asked, for he could see that Cody was pretty worried.

"He's thinking how glad he is we saved him this slab of pie," Omalia suggested.

"I'm thinking," Cody said slowly, "maybe my feet shouldn't have gotten itchy just when they did. The very *next* one might have been Martin himself. Now I'll always wonder who Martin was and never know."

"Dreams like that," Omalia said in her most grown-up tone, "always disappoint you when you wake up."

No sooner had she said this than there came a strange thumping noise at the front door. Omalia's heart almost jumped out of her mouth! Quickly she reached for the cream pitcher so Cody wouldn't see how startled she was.

But Cody was watching the door, not his sister. The door was opening, slowly, mysteriously. Cody felt the hair on the back of his neck begin to creep. He held his breath.

And Omalia forgot completely about the cream and held her breath!

And the door swung wide and in walked—

Yes, a cat—but this time the cat was a normal-looking, non-talking cat with regulation-size eyes. Just Midnight looking for breakfast.

Cody sighed in relief. Then he looked at his mother and father and Omalia. "Dream or not," he said, grinning, "that's exactly the way it started!"

CHECK FOR UNDERSTANDING

1. What was Cody's reaction when the first animal talked to him? Why did Cody have a different reaction to the other animals?
2. Why do you think Cody was bothered by the fact that the animals were waiting for Martin?
3. What reason did Cody give the animals for having to leave the cabin before Martin arrived? Did they believe him?
4. How did Cody's sister react when he told her what had happened?
5. Do you think Cody really wanted to meet Martin? Explain.

WRITE ABOUT *"Not Quite Martin"*

Recall the sequence in which the animals arrived at the cabin. Based on that sequence, can you imagine what Martin might have been like? What if Cody had waited for Martin? Write a paragraph describing Martin's arrival.

THE DOUBTFUL GUEST

written and illustrated
by EDWARD GOREY

When they answered the bell on that wild winter night,
There was no one expected — and no one in sight.

Then they saw something standing on top of an urn,
Whose peculiar appearance gave them quite a turn.

All at once it leapt down and ran into the hall,
Where it chose to remain with its nose to the wall.

It was seemingly deaf to whatever they said,
So at last they stopped screaming, and went off to bed.

It joined them at breakfast and presently ate
All the syrup and toast, and a part of a plate.

It wrenched off the horn from the new gramophone,
And could not be persuaded to leave it alone.

It betrayed a great liking for peering up flues,
And for peeling the soles of its white canvas shoes.

At times it would tear out whole chapters from books,
Or put roomfuls of pictures askew on their hooks.

Every Sunday it brooded and lay on the floor,
Inconveniently close to the drawing-room door.

Now and then it would vanish for hours from the scene,
But alas, be discovered inside a tureen.

It was subject to fits of bewildering wrath,
During which it would hide all the towels from the bath.

In the night through the house it would aimlessly creep,
In spite of the fact of its being asleep.

It would carry off objects of which it grew fond,
And protect them by dropping them into the pond.

It came seventeen years ago — and to this day
It has shown no intention of going away.

61

VOCABULARY • LANGUAGE

Prefixes and Suffixes

In "Not Quite Martin," Cody waited *politely* but *impatiently* for Martin to show up. Cody was *uncomfortable* because his feet were *itchy* and he was growing *restless*.

What do the above italicized words have in common? To answer this question, you must know something about the word parts from which many English words are formed: the base, the prefix, and the suffix.

The base is the part of the word that carries the basic meaning of the word. A **prefix** is added to the *beginning* of a base word. It changes or expands the meaning of the base word. Think of a prefix as being at the controls. It can tell you where a word is headed: before or after, in an opposite direction, beyond or apart. For example, what did you expect when you read the title of this unit? Was it (a) stories with endings that you could easily foresee, or (b) stories with endings that you could *not* easily foresee? In the unit title, the prefix *un-*, which means "not," has been added to the word *expected.* This forms a word that means "not expected" or "not easily foreseen." The word *unexpected* is an example of a word in which a prefix takes the base word—*expected*—in an opposite direction.

In contrast to a prefix, a **suffix** is added to the *end* of a word. And, unlike a prefix, a suffix does little to change the meaning of a base word. Most suffixes are used to help us form words that function as different parts of speech. In "Not Quite Martin," for example, you may have noticed how the author repeatedly uses the adjective-forming suffix *-y*, which means "like" or "full of." Do you remember

the gray *stripy* cat with *stary* eyes?
the *possumy*-looking possum with *shiny* eyes?
the fox with a *bushy* tail and *glittery* eyes?
the panther with a *panthery* voice?

Here, the writer has used his knowledge of word structure to create descriptions that combine real words and made-up words. Although *stary*, *possumy*, and *panthery* cannot be found in a dictionary, the suffix should tell you that each word is an adjective that conveys the meaning of the base word along with the idea of "like" or "full of."

Now let us go back to our original question. What do the words *politely*, *impatiently*, *uncomfortable*, *itchy*, and *restless* have in common? Each contains a base word and at least one prefix or suffix. Find the base in each word, and identify all the prefixes and suffixes.

In "The Doubtful Guest," you can find several words that contain a base and prefix or suffix. The word *doubtful* in the poem's title, for example, combines the suffix *-ful*, which means "full of," with the base word *doubt*. Why do you think that the guest in the poem is "doubtful"?

You discovered that the strange main character in the poem had a "peculiar appearance," was "seemingly deaf," and liked to rest "inconveniently close" to the drawing-room door. Identify the base words and the prefixes and suffixes in the expressions quoted above. What *other* base words and prefixes and suffixes can you find in the poem?

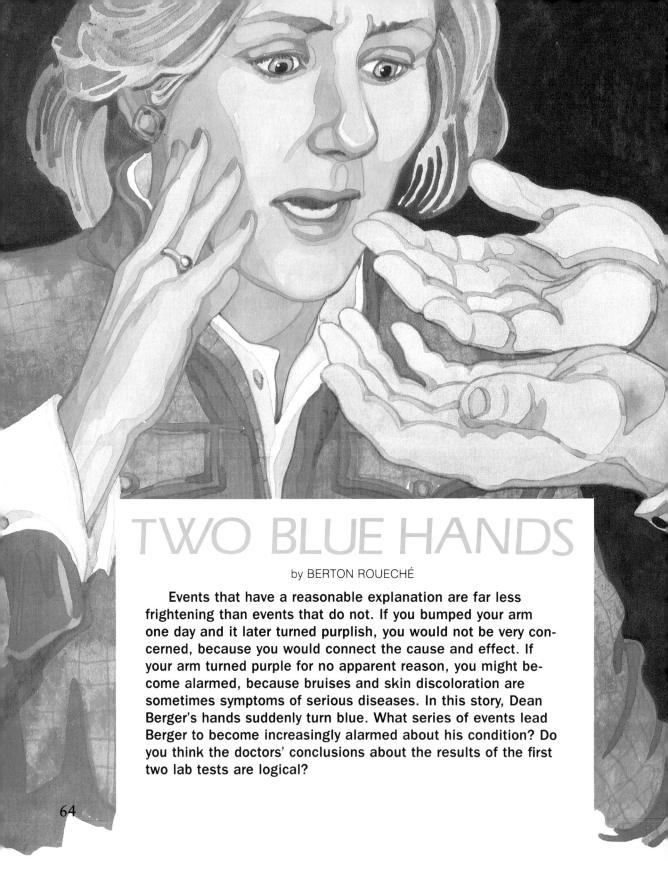

TWO BLUE HANDS

by BERTON ROUECHÉ

Events that have a reasonable explanation are far less frightening than events that do not. If you bumped your arm one day and it later turned purplish, you would not be very concerned, because you would connect the cause and effect. If your arm turned purple for no apparent reason, you might become alarmed, because bruises and skin discoloration are sometimes symptoms of serious diseases. In this story, Dean Berger's hands suddenly turn blue. What series of events lead Berger to become increasingly alarmed about his condition? Do you think the doctors' conclusions about the results of the first two lab tests are logical?

Dean M. Berger is a big, tall, smiling man, and on the night of January 10, 1974—a cold night with a light snow blowing, a night he still remembered with a shudder—he had just turned fifty-two. Berger is a paint chemist and lives in Reading, Pennsylvania. He loves to play bridge, and plays in the regular Thursday-night games of an American Contract Bridge League club. His usual partner at that time was his daughter, Mrs. Cheryl Crews. On his occasional bridge nights, Berger would dine with his daughter and her family at their home. January 10, 1974, was a Thursday, and it was such a night.

The event that evening was a tournament, and it was held in a private room at the Distelfink Restaurant, outside of Lancaster, Pennsylvania. Berger and his daughter arrived there in Berger's car at around 7:30 P.M. The meeting was well attended, with thirteen or fourteen tables in play, but the room was cold. Everybody complained about it, and Berger felt it in his hands, in his fingers. He was warmly dressed, in heavy socks and a flannel sports shirt, but his fingers were like ice.

Berger sat for a while with his hands tucked in his armpits, and then he tried keeping them warm in his trouser pockets. He went back to warming his hands under his arms. The room got colder. Finally, a little before eleven, the meeting broke up. Berger and his daughter placed second. They were sitting at their table recalling the better plays of the evening when Mrs. Crews gave a sudden gasp.

"Daddy!" she said. "Your hands! Look at your hands!"

Berger looked. He stared. His hands were blue—a gray, slaty blue.

Mrs. Crews said, "Are you all right?"

"I don't know," Berger said as he stared at his hands. They looked dead. "I feel a little woozy."

"I think we'd better go," Mrs. Crews said.

When they got out to the car, Berger gave his daughter the keys. He didn't feel like driving; he didn't feel he could trust his hands on the wheel. They drove in silence. Berger was too worried, too bewildered to talk, and Mrs. Crews was trying to decide what to do. "I'm taking you to Hershey Medical Center," she said. "I'm worried about you, Daddy, and I want a doctor to look at your hands."

Just before midnight, Berger, with Mrs. Crews at his side, walked into the emergency room of the Medical Center. He was received by a nurse, who took one look at his hands and

called the doctor on emergency duty that night, Dr. Robert Gordon. Dr. Gordon and the nurse both stood and stared at Berger's hands. They had never seen a case of cyanosis so deep in color.

Cyanosis (which takes its name from the Greek *kyanos,* meaning "blue") is a discoloration of the skin that shows there is not enough oxygen in the blood. The presence of oxygen is what gives normal blood its rich red color, and when for any reason the normal oxygen supply is reduced, the color fades and dulls. Cyanosis is an early symptom in a very large number of diseases, but Berger seemed to have none of these illnesses. After a thorough physical ex-

amination, Dr. Gordon could find no reason for Berger's blue hands. He decided to bring another doctor to look at Berger.

Berger sat huddled on the edge of the examining table and watched Dr. Gordon leave. Hershey Medical Center felt as cold as the Distelfink Restaurant. He tucked his cold blue hands in his armpits and sat alone and waited. "I was scared," Berger recalled later. "I mean I was getting really frightened. What was the matter with me? What was going on?"

Dr. John Field accompanied Dr. Gordon back to Berger's cubicle. He greeted Berger and looked at his hands—his bluish, cyanotic hands. He talked with Berger for a moment and reviewed Dr. Gordon's notes and findings. The various test results arrived from the laboratory, and certain aspects of these tests were not normal. They were in the category known as "blood gases."

When Dr. Field read the report on Berger's blood gases, he found it disturbing. On the basis of the laboratory findings, Berger seemed to be suffering from both low blood oxygen and acidity of his blood. That would seem to account for his cyanosis. But that would also mean that he was seriously ill, and he did not seem to be. Except for his hands, he showed no signs of illness.

"We have a rule here on admissions," explained Dr. Field later. "It requires that we either admit or discharge a patient after two hours. I didn't do either. I couldn't possibly discharge a man with that degree of cyanosis. But I wasn't quite ready to admit him to the hospital. I wanted some more information, and so I decided to keep him where he was for the time being. I wanted his blood pressure taken every hour, and at 6 A.M. I was going to run another check on his blood gases. Then I would know. At least, I hoped I would."

Berger was left alone again. Dr. Field and Dr. Gordon had gone. His daughter had been in to say good-

bye. The doctors had advised her to leave. She had talked to her mother and she would be back again in the morning; she knew everything was going to be all right. The nurse appeared and took the first of the hourly blood-pressure readings. Berger tried to make himself comfortable on the narrow examining table. The room was dimly lighted, and cold. He tried not to worry; he tried not to think. "I wanted to leave with Cher," he recalled. "They told me they couldn't let me. It would be against their better judgment. But they wouldn't tell me what was wrong. There was something wrong with my blood chemistry. They weren't sure what. I dozed off, then the nurse came in for another blood pressure. I don't think I slept at all after that."

But, of course, he did. He was asleep, hunched up on the table with his feet hanging over the end, when Dr. Gordon looked in a little after 6 A.M. Dr. Gordon awakened him gently and took a sample of blood from Berger's wrist. He arranged for a second blood-gases test. The results were ready by 7 A.M. Dr. Gordon and Dr. Field read them together. The second report showed even more abnormality than the first.

Berger lay awake after the doctors had gone. He got up and found his

way along the hall to the men's room. He straightened his clothes and combed his hair and washed his cold blue hands. As Berger recalled later: "Dr. Gordon came in while I was drying my hands. He watched me for a moment, and then he said he'd like to try something. He took me back to the sink and had me hold my right hand under the cold water. And was that water *cold!* It couldn't have been more than forty degrees. He kept it there for a full two minutes. And then my hand began to change. First it was blue, then it was red, and then it was blue again. There was something about it that really scared me. That's when I knew I was a goner."

Berger was admitted to the hospital and shown to a private room on the fourth floor. After a night on an examining table, he was more than ready for bed. "But first I had some telephone calls to make," he recalled. "I wanted to talk to Marilyn—my wife. She would have heard from Cher, by then, but that wasn't enough. I wanted her to hear the worst from me. I arranged for some clean clothes and all, and I called Cher. Then I undressed and got into bed.

At least I had things organized; that made me feel a little better. And I was warm and comfortable for once. I began to feel hungry, but nothing was said about breakfast. Around 9 A.M., a nurse came in, and the next thing I knew I had a tube up my nose and they were giving me oxygen. Then a doctor came in and took some more blood samples; I hardly felt a thing. Then I was left alone again, and I knew I wasn't going to get any breakfast, or any lunch, or anything. I was too far gone to waste food on."

By 9 A.M., the news of Berger and his strange case had spread through his floor and beyond. Dr. Graham H. Jeffries, the head of the medical department, heard the news as he stepped out on his regular morning rounds, and he at once added Berger to his list. He and eight other doctors arrived at Berger's bedside at a little past 9:30. Berger was asked to display his hands. Dr. Jeffries examined them with interest. He had never seen anything quite like them. Questions were asked and answered; opinions were given. Berger's work as a paint chemist was discussed. It was established that he was exposed almost daily to paint and solvent fumes. Dr. Jeffries ordered some new tests. He thanked Berger for his patience and help, and moved on.

Berger watched them go. "Nine doctors," he recalled. "Four head doctors and five of the brightest young doctors in a big institution like Hershey Medical Center—and there wasn't one of them could tell me what was my trouble. And it worried them. I could tell they were really worried."

Dr. Field did another blood-gases test on Berger. The results, this time, were very different from the earlier findings. Berger's blood gases were normal! "That shouldn't have been surprising," Dr. Field recalled. "It was exactly what we would expect after oxygen therapy. The oxygen balance in Berger's blood had been very nicely restored. But it was surprising. It didn't make sense. If Berger's blood gases were back to normal, why was he still cyanotic? Why were his hands still blue? I had seen them less than half an hour before. There was something wrong somewhere."

Dr. Field decided to end Berger's oxygen therapy. He wanted him breathing room air again. Then he would do another blood-gases study. He stopped in the corridor for a drink of water, and was joined by another doctor, James E. Meyer. Dr. Meyer had been with Dr. Jeffries on morning rounds. He said Berger's had been an interesting case. The look of Berger's hands had stuck in his mind. Those hands reminded him of something. And he had just realized what.

"What?" Dr. Field said.

"I don't know if I can explain it," Dr. Meyer said. "But you know how your hands look after you've been shoveling snow? I mean the way they look when you come in and take off your gloves. They have a certain look."

"Mmm," Dr. Field agreed. "Yes—I know what you mean."

But he didn't. As he and Dr. Meyer walked together down the corridor, he had no idea what Dr. Meyer meant. But the thought of gloves stayed with him—gloves and skin discoloration. It hung on in the back of his mind, and suddenly it came alive. He stopped.

He said, "Wait a minute."

He headed for the stockroom. He rummaged around and found a cotton swab soaked in acetone, a substance used as a solvent, to clean or dissolve other substances. He rejoined Dr. Meyer, who looked at the swab.

"What's that for?"

"I just had an idea," Dr. Field said. They came to Berger's room. Berger was alone and dozing. Dr. Field asked Berger to hold out a hand. He took the hand by the wrist and gave the back a vigorous rub with the swab. A pinkish pale streak appeared on the back of Berger's hand. The swab turned blue.

Berger had been almost half asleep, but now he was fully awake. He stared first at the swab, then at his striped hand. "I didn't understand it," he remembered later. "I just looked. My head was spinning. It was just too much too fast. Then I calmed down a little and saw something. The blue on the swab looked different from the blue on my hand. My hand looked dead, but the swab was simply blue, an attractive shade of blue. And blue is one of my favorite colors. I raised my head and looked across the room. My flannel shirt was hanging there on the back of a chair. It was exactly the same shade of blue. The shirt was new—Cher had given it to me. I looked at my shirt, and I didn't even have to think. I knew what had happened.

"I remembered sitting in the Distelfink and warming my hands in my

armpits—and later on, during the night in the examining room. It was as simple as that. The dye had come off on my hands. But how? That stopped me for a moment. But I'm a chemist, not just a paint chemist. The answer was that the dye was colorfast by ordinary standards. It hadn't come off when I washed my hands. But it was soluble in what Dr. Field was using—in acetone. And with sweat. Sweat isn't just water and a little salt. It also contains certain solvents and acids.

"Dr. Field was reaching for my other hand. I gave it to him. And while he was scrubbing it back to normal, I told him what I thought had happened."

Dr. Field believed him. "It was weird," he recalled. "The whole thing was staggering, but I knew it was true. It had to have happened that way.

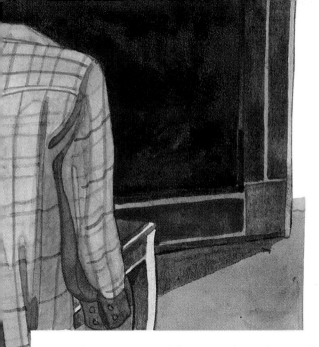

The only trouble was that that only explained his hands—his cyanosis. It didn't explain those blood gases. Was it possible that there actually was something wrong with his blood chemistry? Well, the way to make sure was to do what I had planned to do anyway. When Berger had been breathing room air for a time, I took a sample of blood and took it down to the lab.

"The blood-gases test doesn't take very long to complete, maybe ten or fifteen minutes. When we went over the results, we saw that they weren't precisely the same as the previous study, but the differences were small. Berger's blood gases were normal. That was the answer I wanted, of course, but still . . . what about last night? What about those two other studies? There isn't any absolute ex-

planation. My feeling—everybody's feeling—is that the lab had made a mistake." And that's the way it stands in the record.

Berger left the hospital at 5 P.M. that day. "I was ready to leave at noon," he recalled. "But that isn't the way they do things at Hershey. They wouldn't let me go until they had done a lung scan. It turned out to be normal. They expected it to be normal, but I guess they wanted to be absolutely certain. I didn't mind the wait too much. I was thankful just to be alive."

AUTHOR'S NOTE: Several readers of this article have found Mr. Berger's seeming cyanosis a more mysterious mystery than I intended it to be. The question these readers had was: "Weren't Mr. Berger's armpits also blue? And if not, why not?" Well, Mr. Berger's armpits were *not* blue, and the reason for this is simply explained. The sweat from the armpit was not the sweat that picked up the dye from Mr. Berger's shirt. The sweat that drew the dye from his shirt and stained his hands was sweat from his palms. These two secretions are made up differently. Dye—at least the dye of the sort contained in Mr. Berger's shirt—is fast to the sweat of the armpit. It yields, however, to sweat produced by the palms.

CHECK FOR UNDERSTANDING

1. What medical term did the doctors use to describe the color of Berger's hands? What definition was given?
2. What did the first two blood tests show about Berger's condition? Why were the results of these tests so puzzling? Why was the third blood test also puzzling?
3. What series of events led Berger to become increasingly alarmed about his condition?
4. Why did Berger find the color on the cotton swab less alarming than the same color on his hand?
5. Why wasn't Berger annoyed at having to stay in the hospital?
6. What were the doctor's conclusions about the results of the first two lab tests?

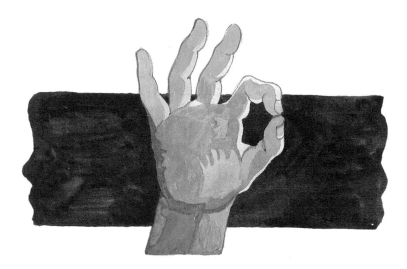

WRITE ABOUT *"Two Blue Hands"*

The factual information about Berger's experience is presented as if it were a mystery story. The cause of his two blue hands is not revealed until the end. The thoughts and reactions of Berger and some of the doctors are revealed. How would a doctor's report about the events be different? Retell the events in the story as if you were writing a medical report. Put the true cause, or diagnosis, of the blue hands first. Mention the tests that you ran on the patient.

Imagine that you have been transported to an alien planet and learn the aliens' language but that you later return home. Depending on your experience with the aliens, you might be either glad or fearful to meet them again. Why does the narrator of this story have reason to fear the invaders? Who are the invaders?

THE INVADERS

by JACK RITCHIE

None of them left the ship on the first day of its arrival, but I knew they would be watching carefully for signs of human life.

The skies were dark with scudding clouds, and the cold wind moved high in the trees. Thin snow drifted slowly to the ground.

From the cover of the forest, I now watched as a small, heavily armed group of them left the large craft. When they reached the edge of the woods, they hesitated for a few moments and then moved cautiously forward.

I had seen them before and I knew that in appearance, at least, they were not monsters. They looked very much like us. There were some differences, of course, but all in all, we were really quite similar to them.

I met them first when I was almost a boy and I had been without caution. I approached them and they seemed friendly, but then suddenly they seized me and carried me off in their strange ship.

It was a long journey to their land, and when our ship made a landing, I was shown about and exhibited as though I were some kind of animal.

I saw their cities, and I was shown plants and animals completely strange to me. I learned to wear their clothing and even to eat their food.

They taught me to communicate in their strange and difficult tongue until I could, at times, even think in their language.

I had almost given up the hope of ever seeing my home again, but they one day put me back on one of their ships and told me that they were returning me because they wished to establish friendly relations with my people. But by now, I knew enough of them to know that this was not true. However, I nodded and smiled and watched for my opportunity to escape.

When the ship landed, I went out with the first search party. It was near evening, and as the darkness gathered, I edged away from them and finally I fled into the blackness and safety of the forest.

They came after me, of course, but I was hidden deep in the woods where they could not find me.

Finally they gave up and I watched their ship become smaller and finally disappear, and I hoped fervently that they would never return.

But now they were back again.

I felt a coldness inside of me as I watched them moving slowly through the trees. They seemed somehow different from the others who had been here before. It was not so much in their appearance as in the air about them—the way they walked, the way they looked about with speculating eyes.

Slowly and instinctively, I realized that this time they were not here on just another raid for a captive or two.

This time they had come to stay.

What could we do now? Could we lure them deeper into the forest and kill them? Could we take their weapons and learn how to use them?

No, I thought despairingly. There were so many more of the invaders on the ship. And more weapons. They would come out and hunt us down like animals. They would hunt us down and kill us all.

I sighed. We must find out what it was that they wanted this time and whatever it might be, we must learn to adjust and to hope for the best.

But I still retreated silently before them, afraid to approach. I watched them search the ground ahead of them and knew they were looking for footprints, for some signs of life. But there was not yet enough snow on the ground to track us down.

Their strangely colored eyes glanced about warily. They were cautious, yes.

They could be cruel, I knew. I had seen with my own eyes how they treated their animals and even their own kind.

I sighed again. Yes, we could be cruel, too. In this respect we could not claim to be superior to the invaders.

They paused now in a clearing, their eyes gleaming beneath their helmets.

It was time for me to approach them.

I took a deep breath and stepped into the open.

Their weapons quickly pointed at me.

"Welcome," I said.

They stared at me, and then one of them turned to their bearded leader. "It appears that this savage can speak some English, Captain Standish."*

"Welcome," I said again. But I wondered what they would do to my land and my people now.

*Miles Standish (1584–1656), an English colonist who helped to establish the Plymouth colony in America.

CHECK FOR UNDERSTANDING

1. Why did the narrator have reason to fear the aliens?
2. In what way did the new group of aliens seem different from the aliens who had been there before?
3. Why did the man greet the new aliens with the word "Welcome"?
4. Who were the invaders?
5. How did the story's presentation affect your view of the events?

WRITE ABOUT *"The Invaders"*

How would one of the invaders tell this story? Imagine that you are a member of the ship's crew. Write a journal entry describing the landing.

The World's
Simplest Quiz

by DENNIS BERSON

This quiz is called "simple" because the answers appear to be part of the questions.

1. How long did the Hundred Years' War last?
2. In which country were Panama hats made originally?
3. From which animal do we get catgut?
4. Where do Chinese gooseberries come from?
5. What kind of creatures were the Canary Islands named after?
6. What was King George VI's first name?
7. What color is a purple finch?
8. In what season of the year does William Shakespeare's "A Midsummer Night's Dream" take place?
9. What is a camel's hair brush made of?
10. How long did the Thirty Years' War last?

ANSWERS

1. 116 years, from 1337 to 1453
2. Ecuador
3. the sheep
4. They're fruits grown in New Zealand.
5. A breed of large dogs. The Latin name was Canariae insulae, meaning "Island of Dogs." The Latin word canaria means "dog." The word canine is derived from the same root.
6. Albert. When he came to the throne, he respected the wish of Queen Victoria that no future king of Great Britain should be called Albert.
7. The distinctively colored parts are crimson.
8. It takes place in the spring, from April 29 to May 1.
9. It is usually made of squirrel's hair.
10. 30 years, of course—1618 to 1648

Adjusting Reading Rate

What would it be like if every time you wanted to look up a telephone number, you started at the beginning of the phone book and read every entry until you found the one you wanted? What would it be like if, on the other hand, you gave just a quick glance at the recipe when you were making a new, complicated dish for the first time? Would you end up wasting time and making mistakes?

It would be foolish to read a telephone book the same way you read a recipe, or a recipe the same way you read a telephone book. The two kinds of reading material are very different, and your purpose in reading each is different. Even when the reading material is the same, your purpose affects the way you read. For example, you would read the recipe one way to find out whether you wanted to make the dish and another way to actually make the dish.

There are a variety of ways to read. The one you choose depends on what you are reading and why.

When you want to get a general idea of what a paragraph, a chapter, or a book is about, you **skim** the text. In skimming, you read quickly, checking just the headings (if there are any) and key words and sentences. Skim the paragraph below. Determine what the paragraph is about by reading the first and last sentence, and looking quickly for key words.

> Since it was first explored, the American West has been a popular subject for artists. Some have concentrated on the landscape, drawn by the imposing spaces, mountains, and sky. Others have been attracted by the history of the West and have depicted important events in its expansion and settlement. Whatever their outlook, they have ranged stylistically from the representational to the abstract.

By reading the first and last sentences, you can tell that the topic of the paragraph is artists' interests in the American West. Key words in the rest of the text include *landscape* and *history*.

When you are looking for a specific piece of information, you **scan** the text. Your eyes move quickly, looking for the word that answers your question or for the fact you need to know. Scan the guide below to find out how long the news program on Channel 2 is, whether there is a movie on, and what program is on Channel 11.

Friday, December 6   **TV TODAY**

Evening _____

7:00   (2)   **Evening News**

       (4)   **Weekly Magazine**
            News and entertainment

       (5)   **The Big Question**
            Quiz show

       (7)   **Early Movie**
            "Coconuts" with the Marx
            Brothers. Comedy. (1½ hrs.)

       (11) **Arts Alive**
            Interview with ballet dancer
            Alice Drummond

7:30   (2)   **Wildlife on Parade**

       (5)   **Scientific Review**
            Report on the use of
            laserbeams in medicine

When you **read for information**, the material is usually nonfiction. It often contains long, complex words and sentences, difficult ideas, and an abundance of names, dates, facts, and explanations. If the material has been assigned for school, you need to read slowly and carefully.

Sometimes nonfiction can be read more quickly. "Two Blue Hands," for example, uses narrative and dialogue very much the way a story does. It can be read for entertainment as well as for information. Decide what your purpose in reading the selection below should be. What made you choose this purpose? How will you adjust your reading rate?

> Women won the right to vote in the United States in 1920, when the 19th Amendment to the Constitution was ratified. The struggle that led to this victory, however, began much earlier. One early struggle, for example, was equal education. The result was the establishment of a number of schools—from the Troy Female Seminary in 1821 to Oberlin College in 1833 to Mount Holyoke College in 1837. These institutions offered women the same "difficult" subjects commonly taught to men.

When you **read for pleasure**, the material, whether it is fiction or nonfiction, is not usually as difficult as material you read for information. Read the selection below. In what ways does it differ from the selection you read above? How does your reading rate differ?

> Laura and Alison had enjoyed exploring the old house at first. They had poked into dusty corners, admired the old furniture, and tried to imagine what life had been like for the people who lived here fifty years before. Then, suddenly, Alison stopped and stared.
>
> "What do you suppose this was for?" she asked in a strange voice.
>
> She was standing in front of a tiny door, just visible in the brick surface of the wall.

Using What You Have Learned

Turn to the reading selection entitled "Katherine Stinson." Skim the first five paragraphs to find out what kind of selection this is and what it is about. How difficult is "Katherine Stinson"? Which of the selections you have already read is it most like? Decide what your purpose in reading this selection will be. Are you going to read strictly for information, just to be entertained, or a combination of the two? Write a statement of your purpose and a description of how you plan to read the selection.

Expanding Your Skills

- Find an informational article or chapter and explain to the class when it would be appropriate to skim a selection like this.
- Find a timetable, television guide, or index and make up five questions that can be answered by scanning it. Swap with a classmate and try to answer each other's questions.
- Find a nonfiction article or chapter that you would probably read just for information and a nonfiction article that can be read for entertainment as well as for information. Write a comparison of the two.

KATHERINE STINSON

by MARY BETH ROGERS and JANELLE D. SCOTT

How would you react if one of your friends announced that he or she was going to be a space pilot. Katherine Stinson faces much greater opposition than a modern would-be astronaut when she announces that she wants to fly.

What aviation records does Katherine Stinson set? What qualities make her a successful pilot?

She had no plans to become a world-famous pilot.

Originally, all Katherine Stinson wanted was to go to Europe to study music and then to come back to America to be a great piano teacher. However, because her family was not wealthy, Katherine had to earn money to pay for her trip to Europe. How was a nineteen-year-old girl going to earn that much money in 1910?

Young Katherine read a newspaper article about the pilots who put on air shows—exhibitions that showed off the newest in airplanes. Pioneer pilots flew daring stunts over vacant fields on the outskirts of towns and cities all over America. They tested their own courage and ability, as well as the endurance of newly developed flying machines.

Katherine had an idea. Perhaps this was the way she could earn a lot of money in a very short time. Besides, it looked like fun.

"If other people can do it, so can I," Katherine thought.

First, she had to persuade her parents.

Katherine already knew how to drive a car, something most young women did not do in 1910. Her mother had given her permission to learn, then had served as a contented passenger while Katherine drove around the countryside.

"When I began to talk about flying, she already had confidence in me," Katherine said about her mother.

Convincing her father was more difficult.

"My father didn't approve in the *least*. He was like the hen with an unmanageable duckling in its brood. But I finally gained the consent of both my parents, and ... I set out to be an aviator—as a means to becoming a music teacher," Katherine said.

Katherine had never flown before. Neither had most Americans. Very few people knew what flying was like. Many were too afraid to try it—but not Katherine.

When she took a hot-air balloon ride with friends in Kansas City in 1911, Katherine found out that riding in the sky was exhilarating. She had a wonderful feeling as she floated peacefully in the air, high above the trees and houses below. What was there to fear?

Now Katherine wanted to ride in one of those new airplanes she had been reading about.

Her friends told her that airplanes were different. After all, hot-air balloons had been around for years. But airplanes! They were noisy and dangerous. Made of muslin stretched over a thin frame of wood and wire, the early planes were flimsy and precarious. The Wright brothers had only just completed their first successful flight in 1903. Some people thought that airplanes were still a joke, a silly idea that would never catch on.

But Katherine was fascinated by these new machines, the money she might earn, and the chance to fly with the birds. Nothing could discourage her.

She got her first chance to ride in an airplane in January 1912.

"People had filled my ears with all sorts of stories of how I would feel—of the fright, the dizziness, the airsickness, and all sorts of things," Katherine said. But none of them happened.

Katherine's twenty minute flight excited her so much that she hated to land. She was determined to become a pilot.

Who would teach Katherine? There were fewer than two hundred licensed pilots in the whole world at the time. Only three of them were women. But Katherine was determined to learn how to fly, and she sought out one of the most famous early aviators, Max Lillie of Chicago. She asked him to teach her.

He took one look at Katherine and said, "No!"

Katherine stood only a little over five feet tall and weighed only 101 pounds. She looked like she might be twelve years old, instead of twenty-one, and Lillie just didn't think this "little girl" was strong enough to manage his two-handled "pusher" airplane.

He patiently explained to her that the pilot had to handle two shoulder-high sticks to control the height and angle of the wings of the airplane. The propeller was at the rear of the plane, and the pilot's seat was on the front edge of the lower wing. The cockpit was like a giant swing with wings attached to each side, and the propeller in back pushed the pilot and the whole machine up into the air. Nothing separated the pilot from the vast sky. And the pilot had to guide the clumsy machine with those two big sticks. Max Lillie thought it was too much for most men to handle—but it would be impossible for this curly haired girl!

He underestimated Katherine. She finally persuaded Lillie to take her up in one of his planes to prove to him that size, strength, and gender had nothing to do with being a pilot. What was required was clear thinking, calmness, dexterity, and determination. And Katherine had those qualities in abundance.

After only four hours of flight time with Max Lillie, Katherine flew alone. She loved it. And on July 12, 1912, she passed the test to earn her pilot's license. She became the fourth woman pilot in America.

Katherine tucked her long curls under a helmet, put on a coat and knee-high boots like the famous aviators wore, and began to fly the air show circuit. She loved to take her flying machine into the sky, turn it sideways, fly it upside down, and fling it into head-spinning circles.

And people loved to watch her. There was something exciting about watching this pretty young woman undertake daring stunts in those strange flying machines. Farm families and small-town residents who had only seen pictures of the new air planes flocked to county fairs to see this "Flying Schoolgirl" soar above them among the puffy white clouds.

Katherine loved the sensation of flying.

"When you are flying toward a cloud, it does not seem as if you, yourself, are moving. The cloud seems to be rushing at you. And when you enter it, you are in the thickest fog you ever imagined. You can't see the wings of your plane. I have been in clouds so dense that I couldn't even see my own hands operating the controls."

Flying in the open-air cockpits didn't always create such pleasant sensations, however. Katherine compared flying in the rain without a windshield to being "peppered with buckshot. The raindrops sting your face like sleet driven by a gale."

Katherine flew her aircraft into a thunderstorm once.

"Lightning would streak right through the wings of my machine. It is a very curious thing to see it so close to you," she said.

Katherine wasn't frightened at the time, but when she learned that some airplanes had been struck by lightning while being flown in thunderstorms, she decided not to take any more chances. She tried to limit her flights to good weather.

Katherine flew in air shows at county and state fairs in Ohio, Georgia, Arkansas, Texas, Louisiana, and hundreds of other places. She and other stunt pilots introduced flying to thousands of Americans. People began to believe there might be more to this new adventure than a few tricks and thrills in the air.

Katherine's family decided that her love for flying might provide a new business opportunity for them. In 1913, Katherine's mother, Emma Stinson, joined Katherine in founding the Stinson Aviation Company in Hot Springs, Arkansas, the family's current home. They began to build, sell, and rent aircraft. Katherine's love of flying not only made her forget her dreams of a music career, but it opened up a whole new way of life for her entire family. Katherine's younger sister, Marjorie, and her younger brothers, Jack and Eddie, also fell in love with flying. So did people all over the United States.

Katherine's instructor, Max Lillie, went to San Antonio, Texas, in 1912. The winters were mild there and pilots could fly almost every day without worrying about bad weather. Steady winds and flat terrain created ideal conditions for flying.

Lillie had persuaded the United States Army to let him use the parade grounds of Fort Sam Houston as a flying field. Military officers were interested in watching the progress of the new aviation business to see if airplanes might be useful in warfare.

Max Lillie encouraged Katherine to move to San Antonio in 1913 to continue her flying. She decided to give it a try. She, too, was delighted with the ideal flying conditions. And she persuaded her family to move there with her. They eventually leased city land to establish the Stinson School of Flying.

Katherine practiced her stunts over the military parade grounds, and her Wright Model-B plane became a familiar sight to the people of San Antonio. However, some of Katherine's stunts caused alarm.

The San Antonio Light newspaper noted that "Miss Katherine Stinson, the girl aviator who is making daily flights in her aeroplane at Fort Sam Houston, must not attempt to loop-the-loop in the air or execute other aeronautical stunts that are dangerous to her life."

Everyone considered the loop-the-loop stunt particularly dangerous. To perform the stunt, the pilot headed the plane almost straight up into the air. At the top of the loop, the plane and its pilot were almost upside down. Then the pilot headed toward the ground to complete the circle, or loop, in the air. The danger was that the small airplane engine frequently stalled at the high point of the loop. A stalled plane fell freely, without any power or control, until the pilot could restart the engine. If the pilot was knowledgeable and experienced, he or she could usually go high enough to gain time to start a stalled engine. But some pilots failed, and crowds always feared the pilot would crash during a loop-the-loop stunt. When the pilot succeeded, the crowd went wild with cheering applause.

Katherine taught herself to loop-the-loop and became the first woman to complete the stunt. In only six months Katherine had looped 500 times without an accident.

Katherine was a daring pilot, but she was not foolish. Most of her stunts were carefully planned and precisely executed. She took particularly good care of her aircraft and was one of the first pilots on the air show circuit to clean her plane before each performance. Some of the male pilots teased her because she went over every inch of her plane, scrubbing and polishing the wires and cleaning the joints. Katherine wrote in *The American Magazine* in 1917:

The men thought I was a regular old maid about it. They said I would ruin the cloth with my scrubbing, and that the oil didn't hurt the wires and joints, anyway ... But I wanted to see the condition of things under all that dirt. And I really did find that a good many wires needed to be replaced. It's all right if your automobile goes wrong while you are driving it. But if your airplane breaks down, you can't sit on a convenient cloud and tinker with that!

Katherine was not only a good pilot, she was also a good mechanic. Like many early pilots, she had to understand engines and have some mechanical ability. She knew how to take apart her whole plane and put it back together. In fact, each time Katherine traveled by train to the air show she carried her plane on the train, disassembling it for the trip and reassembling it at her destination. She studied and learned the principles of aerodynamics and understood that a pilot could be only as good as the aircraft.

"The important thing is to be as careful as you possibly can to have every part of your engine and of your airplane in perfect condition," Katherine said. She believed that most accidents occurred because of some failure of the machine, not from the pilot's lack of ability. She made sure her planes were safe and in good working condition *before* she undertook her daring stunts.

When she knew that her plane was in good working order, she would try anything. She added a snap roll on the top of her loop. She performed night exhibition flying and dazzled crowds when she used fireworks on the tips of her wings.

Katherine became world famous; she was called the "world's greatest woman pilot." Whenever she flew, thousands of people went to see her. Newspapers and magazines carried articles about her. Spectators and fellow aviators respected her flying abilities.

Katherine was now 26 years old and had been flying for five years. Military flying was out, so she decided she would try for a major aviation record. Her friend and fellow aviator Ruth Law had set a long-distance record of 512 miles in 1916, and Katherine was determined to better it.

Katherine ordered a special plane, one with a maximum air speed of 85 miles per hour and the capability of traveling 700 miles before refueling.

Katherine decided to set her record by flying the San Diego to San Francisco route, over the treacherous mountains of Southern California.

At 7:31 A.M. on December 11, 1917, her small open-air plane sped off a dirt runway in San Diego into the foggy Southern California sky. Its destination, San Francisco, lay 610 miles away—farther than any pilot had ever flown without stopping.

Katherine completed the first leg to Los Angeles with relative ease. But past Los Angeles, she began to lift the plane higher and higher, over the jagged Tehachapi Mountains and through the treacherous winds.

The cold head wind sliced into her plane, cut her lips, and chilled her to the bone. She coaxed the plane to 9,000 feet, higher than she had ever flown before.

Time moved slowly. Katherine had forgotten to pack a lunch, and she was hungry. If she could just make it over the mountains, she would be fine. The Santa Fe Railroad tracks served as her guide through the mountains. Suddenly they disappeared. Was she lost? Had she let the plane drift off course? Would she ever find her way out of the mountains?

A less experienced pilot would have panicked, but Katherine remained calm and waited, staying firmly on course. Her patience was rewarded when the railroad tracks reappeared below her. They had been hidden from her view as they ran into a long mountain tunnel. Katherine breathed a sigh of relief as she pulled her plane out of the mountains.

"Beyond Tehachapi, the sky cleared. The beautiful California landscape spread under me like a huge painting as I sped along at the rate of 62 miles per hour," she recounted.

"Occasionally I shifted my map mounted on rollers, so I could handle a great length of it. It was easy to tell where I was all the time ... towns, cities, farms, hills, and mountains passed rapidly ... I never had any fear."

She described her historic landing: "I circled around the Golden

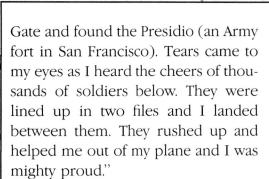

Gate and found the Presidio (an Army fort in San Francisco). Tears came to my eyes as I heard the cheers of thousands of soldiers below. They were lined up in two files and I landed between them. They rushed up and helped me out of my plane and I was mighty proud."

On the San Francisco waterfront, ships and vessels of all types blew horns to give her a noisy welcome. It was 4:41 P.M. Katherine had flown 610 miles in nine hours and ten minutes. She had just two gallons of fuel left in her tank. She had flown longer and covered more miles than any aviator in the world, man or woman. Katherine had set a record; her place in the history of aviation was assured. When she proved that she was the world's greatest long-distance flyer that December day in 1917, she became an international star.

She worked briefly for the U.S. air mail. And she set another aviation record doing so.

One day in May 1918, she set out to fly the mail nonstop from Chicago to New York, a record distance. But she ran into trouble. She hit heavy head winds and ran out of fuel 150 miles short of New York City. She landed on a hillside near Binghamton, New York, and her plane nosed over in the mud. But the shortened flight of 783 miles broke her own long-distance record. Later, she wrote about that flight, revealing a lot about her sheer determination.

"I had been sick in bed for five days before I made that flight . . . I was pretty weak and shaky and had a high temperature, but I had set my heart on making that flight. After all, you have to choose which is going to rule, your mind or your body . . . If you determine that it shall be your mind, your body will surprise you by the way it bucks up and behaves itself.

"At 4:30 in the morning, I went to the hangar, gave the machine another minute examination, and at six-thirty I was off. If the wind had been favorable, I should have made the flight to New York without stops. As it was, I broke both the distance and the endurance record in this country. That seems to me more worthwhile than staying in bed with nothing to show for it but doctor's bills."

Katherine lived to be eighty-six years old. She never gave in to the fear that prevents people from trying to do something they believe is important.

"Fear, as I understand it, is simply due to lack of confidence or lack of knowledge—which is the same thing," Katherine said. "You are afraid of what you don't understand, of the things you cannot account for. You are afraid to attempt something you believe you cannot do."

Katherine was not afraid. She believed in herself, her abilities, and her dreams. She believed that "we can fly." And she did.

CHECK FOR UNDERSTANDING
1. Why did Katherine Stinson decide to become a pilot?
2. Do you think that Katherine's mother wanted her to be an aviator? Explain.
3. What aviation records did Katherine Stinson set?
4. What qualities made Katherine Stinson a successful aviator? Support your answer with details from the text.
5. Katherine Stinson flew from Chicago to New York when she was sick with a high fever. Do you think that this was foolish or brave? Give reasons for your answer.

WRITE ABOUT *"Katherine Stinson"*
Imagine that, during the early days of aviation, you needed to hire a pilot. What sort of person would you want to hire? Look through the story to find appropriate adjectives. Then write a Help Wanted ad, beginning with:
HELP WANTED. Aviator. He or she must be…

Plot

The sequence of events in a story is called the **plot.** The plot is made up of a problem, the climax, and the resolution. The problem is also known as a **conflict.** We want to know how the conflict will be solved. When the plot builds to the highest point of interest and excitement, that point is called the **climax.** After the climax, we discover how the conflict is settled and how the story ends. The final outcome is called the **resolution.**

For example, in a mystery story, a detective may be looking for a murderer. The problem, or conflict, is to find the murderer before another murder occurs. The plot builds until the detective comes face to face with the murderer, who holds a knife. This is the climax of the story, the highest point of excitement. The detective manages to disarm the murderer and capture him. In the resolution, we learn that the detective hands the murderer over to the police, who arrest him.

An author writes a story with a specific outcome in mind. Often we can use the author's clues to predict what will happen. But in some stories, the plot is organized in such a way that there is an unexpected, or surprise ending. Reversal is the term used to describe the unexpected change or surprise for a main character in the outcome of the story. Plot reversal usually comes very late in the story and can mean a happy or an unhappy ending.

The next selection, "Hunting Monkeys in the Ozarks," is another example of plot reversal. Jay Berry Lee is about to lure and trap the thirty monkeys which had escaped from a circus train. The circus owners are offering two dollars each for the smaller monkeys and one hundred dollars for the largest one if they are returned safely. Jay is confident that he will be able to outsmart a few monkeys, especially with the special traps that his grandfather had prepared for him.

As you read this story, try to identify the various elements of the plot.

What are some of the events that cause us to become more and more interested in Jay's predicament?

When does the climax occur?

What is the plot reversal of the story? When does it begin to take place?

Are you as surprised as Jay at the way the monkeys behaved?

How would you react if you saw giraffes or lions roaming freely in your neighborhood? Jay Berry Lee sees an equally unexpected and amazing sight. He plans to turn his discovery to his advantage.

Why are there monkeys roaming free in the foothills of the Ozarks? What surprises Jay Berry about their behavior?

HUNTING MONKEYS in the *OZARKS*

Jay Berry Lee had been sure that the jungle was the only place to find wild monkeys—until his own dog treed a monkey near his home in the Ozarks. Jay Berry's grandfather had the explanation. About thirty monkeys had escaped from a circus train. The owners of the circus were offering a reward for the safe return of the animals. They would pay two dollars for each of the smaller monkeys and the huge sum of one hundred dollars for the largest one.

Jay Berry was the happiest boy in the Ozark hills when he heard about the reward. If he could catch all of the animals, he could get what he longed to own: a paint pony. Equipped with the special, padded traps that his grandfather had prepared for him, Jay Berry and his dog Rowdy set off for the river bottom where the monkeys roamed.

Side by side, and walking as quietly as cats on the prowl, we moved on into monkey country. It was so still in the bottoms I could hear my heart thumping. Every nerve in my body was as tight as the iron bands around a rain barrel.

I went right back to the bur oak tree where Rowdy had treed the monkey and started looking it over. I looked on every limb, and in each dark shadow. Not being able to see anything that even looked like a monkey, I was beginning to get a little discouraged when all at once, from somewhere close by, something let out a cry that rang through the bottoms like a blacksmith's anvil. The cry didn't sound scary. It was more like a warning cry.

Not being able to identify what had made the racket scared me a little. My old heart started flopping around. It seemed like every time I got scared a little, my old heart was the first one to know about it. I never could understand why it acted that way. To make things worse, Old Rowdy growled way down deep, and started walking around stiff-legged, like when he was getting ready for a fight.

In a quavering voice, I whispered to Rowdy, "What in the world was that? It couldn't have been a monkey. Monkeys are little bitty things. Whatever made that racket must have been as big as a barn."

That one loud cry was all I heard, and again the silence closed in around us. I sent Rowdy to do a little sniffing around. This was an old game to me, and one I never grew tired of playing. I could follow every movement my old dog made by ear.

Over on my left a twig snapped, and there was a padding of soft feet. Then ahead of me a small bush wavered as his ghostly shadow passed beneath. He moved on to my right, and I heard the scratching of his claws on bark as he walked a log. Ending up behind me, I heard his loud snuffings and a rustling in the leaves.

Old Rowdy had made a complete circle around me, and I knew that if the tracks of anything dangerous had crossed the line of that circle, he would have let me know about it.

Rowdy was gone for about five minutes. When he came back, he didn't act like he had seen anything more than a grasshopper. As if he didn't have a worry in the world, he sat down on his rear and started digging at a flea that wasn't even there.

Feeling much better, I started setting my traps like Grandpa had told me. All around the bur oak, about three feet out from the trunk, I dug six small holes in the soft soil. Then, one by one, I mashed the trap springs down with my foot and set the triggers. Very carefully I placed a trap in each hole and covered it with leaves. I didn't tie the trap chains to anything because I didn't figure that a little old monkey could do much climbing with a trap on his foot.

Then I took six apples and punched a nail down deep in each one. Tying short pieces of string to the heads of the nails, I hung an apple to the underbrush about each trap. When I was finished I had a complete circle of traps about the trunk of the bur oak tree.

Backing off to one side, I took a good look at my trap setting. It looked like a pretty good job to me. In fact, at that moment I felt sure that Daniel

Boone* would have been proud of me. The traps were completely hidden. All I could see was those big red apples hanging there. They looked so good I kind of wanted to take a bite out of one myself.

I was still standing there admiring my work when, from the corner of my eye, I thought I saw a movement in the branches of a sycamore tree. It was just a flash and I didn't see it again, but I was pretty sure that I had seen something.

Picking up my gunny sack, I whispered to Rowdy, "I'm not sure, boy, but I think I saw something. It could have been a monkey. Come on, let's hide and see what happens."

About thirty-five yards away, but still in view of my traps, I found a small opening in a thick stand of elders. It was a dandy hiding place, and I proceeded to make myself comfortable. Taking my lunch and apples from the gunny sack, I laid them to one side and sat down on the empty sack.

Now, I never did like to wait for anything. It seemed that half of my life had been wasted away waiting for things. I had to wait for Christmas, and Thanksgiving. Then there was a long spell of waiting for spring and fishing time. Now I was waiting for a monkey.

*the famous hunter and trapper

The longer I sat there, the more uncomfortable I became. First I got hungry, then I got thirsty. The sack I was sitting on got hard as a rock, and my tail bone started hurting. I got hot and began to sweat. Deer flies and mosquitoes came and started gnawing on me. Just about the time that I had convinced myself that there wasn't a living thing within a hundred miles of me, up popped a monkey, and out popped my eyes.

I never did know where the monkey came from. One instant there wasn't as much as a jaybird around my traps; then there was a monkey. I could have sworn that he just popped up out of the ground. Anyhow, there he was, standing on his spindly legs, staring at those big red apples.

I held my breath, watched, and waited.

For several seconds, the monkey just stood there, staring at the apples and twisting his head, as if he were trying to make up his mind about something. Then he started jumping around and squealing, and making all kinds of noises.

The next thing that happened all but caused me to have a jerking spell. It started raining monkeys. They seemed to come from everywhere; down from the branches of the bur oak tree, from out of the underbrush,

and everywhere else. There were big monkeys and little monkeys, fat monkeys and skinny monkeys.

I was paralyzed. It looked like ten jillion monkeys, leaping and squealing. They bunched up about ten feet from my traps and started chattering as if they were talking something over.

Before the monkeys showed up, Rowdy had been lying at my side. Growling and showing his teeth, he started getting to his feet. He was getting ready to tie into those monkeys and I knew it. I laid my hand on his back and I could feel his rock-hard muscles knotting and quivering.

"Rowdy," I whispered, "for heaven's sake, don't do anything now.

Those monkeys are worth more money than we'll ever see the rest of our lives. If you make any noise and scare them away, I'll tie you in the corn crib for a year, and I won't even give you a drink of water."

Of course, I didn't mean that, but Rowdy thought I did. He lay down again and kept his mouth shut.

One little monkey, bolder than the others, left the bunch and started over toward my traps. I reached for my gunny sack and got ready.

Just when I thought for sure that the monkey was going to walk right into my trap, that same loud cry that I had heard before rang out through the bottoms. As if the cry were some kind of signal, the monkeys stopped chattering and stood still. The one that I had thought was going to get in my trap hurried back to the bunch.

I could tell that whatever had made the cry was much closer now than it had been before, and I didn't feel too good about it.

"Rowdy," I whispered, "you keep your eyes open and whatever it is that's squalling like that, don't let it get too close to us."

The way Old Rowdy was sniffing and looking, I couldn't tell whether he was mad or scared. This didn't help me at all. I put a lot of confidence in

Old Rowdy; and if he was scared, then it was time for me to be getting away from there.

I was trying to make up my mind what to do, when I heard the cry again. This time it was so close it made my eardrums ring. My hair flew straight up and felt as if it was pushing the top out of my old straw hat.

The noise was coming from above me. I started looking around in the treetops. On the limb of a big sycamore, I saw something. At first I thought it was a boy. It looked just like a small boy, standing there on a limb. I wondered what he was doing up in a tree, screaming his head off. Maybe he had climbed the tree and couldn't get down. I had done that several times and Papa had had to come and help me down.

I forgot about being scared and got kind of mad.

"Rowdy," I whispered, "I don't know if that's a boy or not, but if it is, he's sure messing things up for us. If he keeps on screaming like that, and scares the monkeys away, I'm going to wear him out."

Just then the thing moved out on the limb into some sunlight and I got a better look at it. I could see then that it wasn't a boy but was some kind of black, hairy animal. It had short stubby legs, and long arms that hung down almost to the limb it was standing on. When I discovered that it didn't have a tail, I didn't know what to think. I had never seen an animal that didn't have a tail of some kind.

It was too far away to tell what color its eyes were, but I could have sworn that they were as red as our old red rooster. Anything that had red eyes always did scare me. Goose pimples jumped out all over me. My old heart started running around inside me like a scared lizard.

"Rowdy," I whispered, in a shaky voice, "that's an animal all right, but I've never laid eyes on anything that looked like that before, and I don't like the looks of it."

I had just about decided that my monkey-catching days were over, and was getting ready to get away from there, when I remembered what my grandpa had told me about the hundred-dollar monkey. He had said that it was different that the other monkeys, and that thing I was looking at sure didn't look like those other monkeys.

Just then the big monkey let out another cry, and running to the end of the limb, he leaped high in the air. I was so startled by this I stood up. I thought sure that he had sprouted wings and was flying away. Instead, he lit in the branches of the bur oak tree, and using those long arms, he started dropping down from limb to limb and landed on the ground between the little monkeys and my traps.

This all happened so fast it left me a little bit breathless. I thought squirrels could move around in the timber, but they couldn't do anything that monkey couldn't do. Every move he made was as sure as Daniel Boone's musket, and as smooth as the dasher in an old churn.

All the time this had been going on, the little monkeys hadn't made a sound. They just stood there in a bunch, watching every move the big monkey made.

About that time one of them decided that as long as there were some apples around, he may as well have one. He left the bunch, and with his skinny tail sticking straight in the air, he started toward my traps.

The big monkey saw this and went all to pieces. He started jumping up and down, and making deep, grunting noises as if he were talking to the little monkey. The little monkey seemed to understand what the big monkey was saying. He squealed like someone had stepped on his tail and scurried back to the others.

It was hard for me to believe what I had seen. Yet it was as plain as the stripes in a rainbow. That big monkey

had known that the little monkey was in danger, and, in his monkey talk, he had simply told him so.

"Rowdy," I whispered, "did you see what that monkey was doing? He was talking to that little monkey, that's what he was doing. Grandpa didn't tell me that they could talk to each other."

As if he were proud of the fact that he had knocked me out of a two-dollar reward, the big monkey then did something that all but caused me to swallow my Adam's apple. Looking straight at my hiding place, he pealed his lips back, opened his mouth, and let out another one of those squalls. When he did, I got a good look at his fighting tools.

I had thought that our old mules had big mouths and teeth, but they were nothing compared to what that monkey had. To me, it looked as if you could have thrown a pumpkin straight down his throat and never scratched the peeling on one of his long teeth.

"Rowdy," I whispered, "did you see those teeth? You'd better think twice before you jump on him. He could eat you up—collar and all."

Old Rowdy didn't seem to be the least bit scared. If I had said, "Sick 'em!" he would have torn out of those elders like a cyclone. He may have taken a whipping, but there would have been a lot of monkey hair flying around while it was going on.

I didn't have to worry about the big monkey jumping on us. Instead, he turned, and still making those deep grunting noises, he walked up within two feet of a trap and stopped. For several seconds, he just stood there, looking at the apple and all around at the ground. He kept making funny little noises, as if he were talking to himself.

The strain was almost more than I could stand. My insides got all knotted up and I felt like I was going to bust wide open. If the monkey hadn't done something about then, I think I would have. Instead of stepping in my trap, he just reached out with one of those long arms, took hold of the apple, and pulled on it until the nail came out.

Holding the apple in his paw about like I would if I were eating one, he opened his huge mouth, took one bite, and tossed what was left to the little monkeys.

This caused a loud commotion. The little monkeys started fighting over the apple. I never heard so much squealing and chattering. In no time there wasn't as much as a seed left.

I sat there as if I were frozen to the ground and watched that big monkey walk all around the bur oak, taking the apples and never stepping in a trap. One bite from each apple seemed to be all he wanted. What was left was tossed to the little monkeys.

When the last apple had disappeared, the big monkey did something that made me wonder if I wasn't seeing things. He started turning somersaults and rolling around on the ground. At the same time, he was making the bottoms ring with a peculiar noise that he hadn't made before.

Now, I had never heard a monkey laugh and didn't even know they could; but as I sat there watching the capers of that big monkey, it didn't take me long to figure out what he was doing. He was laughing at me. I was sure of it. I even remembered the dream I had had about the hundred-dollar monkey—how every time he

came leaping by, he would stop and laugh at me.

The little monkeys seemed to know that something funny was going on. They started screeching and chattering like a bunch of squirrels in a hickory nut tree.

My neck and face got all hot. I knew I was blushing, but I couldn't help it. That was the first time I had ever had a monkey laugh at me. I looked at Old Rowdy. The way I was feeling, if he had been laughing, I would have taken a stick to him. But Rowdy wasn't laughing. He was just as serious about catching those monkeys as I was.

All at once the big monkey stopped making a fool out of himself and turned to the little monkeys. Uttering a couple of those deep grunts, he just seemed to rise up in the air like fog off the river and disappeared in the branches of the bur oak tree. The little monkeys followed him— zip, zip, zip—one behind the other.

After the monkeys had all disappeared, it got so still around there you could have heard a grasshopper walking. I looked at Rowdy, and Rowdy looked at me.

"Did you ever see anything like that, Rowdy?" I said. "Grandpa was right when he said that monkey was smart, but I didn't think he was that smart. Why, he knew all the time that we were here and he sat right up there on that sycamore limb and watched me set my traps. Then he stole all of my apples and laughed at me. Now, how do you like that!"

My first go-around with the monkeys left me a little discouraged—but not too much. After all, my grandpa had taught me practically all there was to know about the trapping business. I figured it was just a matter of time until I'd have them all in the sack.

Trying to act like nothing had happened, I said, "Rowdy, that monkey may not know it, but he's messing around with one of the best trappers in these Cherokee hills. If he comes back one more time, we'll see who does the laughing. Let's try the old mouse-catching trick on him. I think that will stop this laughing business."

Rowdy whined and licked my hand. That gave me a lot of confidence and I felt much better.

Taking three more of my apples, I set them up on a log. Then taking my pocketknife, I cut them in half. Walking over to where my traps were, I lifted them from their hiding places and tripped the triggers with a stick.

Untying the strings from the nails and bushes, I used the short pieces to tie half of an apple to the trigger of each trap.

I wrapped those pieces of apple to the tops of the triggers as tightly as I could, and tied the ends of the strings in hard knots. Then I reset the traps and placed them back in the holes. Very carefully, I covered each trap with leaves but left the apples in plain sight.

Backing off to one side, I took another good look at my trap setting. Every time I had set a trap I had been proud of the way I had done it, but on that day I was especially proud. You could see the pieces of apple all right, but you sure couldn't tell there were any traps there. Not one shiny piece of metal could be seen.

"Rowdy," I said, "I don't care how smart that monkey is, if he gets one of those apples, he's going to wind up with a trap on his foot, and that's all there is to it."

All of the time I was resetting my traps I kept looking around in the trees for a monkey. I didn't see one, but I had a feeling that there were ten thousand monkey eyeballs looking right at me.

Feeling about as smart as Old Trapper Dan himself, I said, "Come on, Rowdy, I think the money will start rolling in now."

I didn't go straight back to my hiding place. Instead, I took off in another direction, circled around, and came back to it. I thought that I was being smart doing this, but I felt silly, too; because if that big monkey was sitting somewhere in the top of a sycamore tree, he was probably watching every move I made.

I was so sure that I would catch a monkey this time, I didn't sit down on my gunny sack. I held it in my hand so that I would be ready to sack him up the instant I heard the snap of a trap.

It seemed that Rowdy and I had hardly gotten seated when here came the monkeys: leaping, squealing, and chattering.

"Boy, Rowdy," I whispered, "that sure was fast, wasn't it? They must have been waiting for us. Why, the way they're acting, they must think we're playing some kind of game. They won't think it's a game when I get a few of them in the sack."

It was a little different this time than it was before. The big monkey was the first one to touch the ground, and he was standing very close to one of my traps. The little monkeys were milling around everywhere. They didn't seem to know what was going on, but every time one got close to a trap, that big monkey would fly out of gear like a mama jaybird when I wanted to take a look at her babies.

He would scream like someone had slapped a branding iron on him, and start jumping up and down, and making those deep grunting noises. He would run at the little monkeys and scare the daylights out of them. Finally he succeeded in herding them all to one side where they bunched up and stayed.

If I had known then what that big monkey was going to do next, I wouldn't have stayed there and watched.

Again he walked over close to one of my traps and stopped. I knew that I was watching a monkey, but he still looked like a small boy, standing there, trying to figure something out. Once he even bent over so that he

could get a better look at things. Then he reached up with one of his long arms and scratched his head. When I saw him do that, I thought of my grandpa. He was always scratching his head when he had something heavy on his mind.

"Rowdy," I whispered, "I believe that monkey knows the trap is there and he's trying to figure out how he can get the apple and not get caught. I don't think he can do it. I don't care how smart he is, he's not that smart." How wrong I was.

As if he had solved the problem and was tickled to death about it, the big monkey turned a few somersaults. He stopped and started straight at my hiding place. Then he let out another one of those squalls before he reached down and picked up a long stick from the ground. Holding the stick out in front of him, still uttering those deep grunts, he started beating at the apple as if he was killing a snake.

I almost jumped out of my britches when I heard the trap snap. I sat in a trance and watched that hundred-dollar monkey spring every one of my traps the same way. Every time a trap snapped, he would look straight at my hiding place and squall.

He didn't use his teeth to tear the apples from the triggers. He simply used his fingers and untied the knots in the strings.

There was one thing I could say for that monkey. He wasn't only smart, he was very polite, too. He saw to it that the little monkeys got their share of each apple.

After it was all over and the monkeys had again disappeared in the treetops, I looked to Rowdy for some kind of understanding. I didn't get any help from him. He was just lying there with his long ears sticking straight up, looking at me as if he were the most surprised hound dog in the world.

Do the monkeys continue to outwit Jay and Rowdy? Or does Jay discover a way to capture the animals and win the reward? To find out, read the rest of the novel Summer of the Monkeys *by Wilson Rawls.*

CHECK FOR UNDERSTANDING

1. Why were there monkeys roaming free in the foothills of the Ozarks?

2. How did Jay Berry plan to take advantage of his discovery of the monkeys?

3. What surprised Jay Berry about the monkeys' behavior?

4. What do you predict will be Jay Berry's next step? Explain your answer.

WRITE ABOUT *"Hunting Monkeys in the Ozarks"*

Based on the activities of the chimpanzee, the "big monkey" in the story, what are some of the characteristics of these animals? Write a description of the chimpanzee's appearance and behavior.

THINK ABOUT IT

In the selections in this unit, the only thing we can count on is the unexpected. Surprise lies waiting at the end of most of the stories. Some of the stories create suspense immediately, as in "The Invaders." Others, like "Not Quite Martin," build up gradually, becoming stranger and stranger as the story progresses. Think about the endings of the selections in this unit. Which stories ended exactly opposite than the way you had expected? Could you predict the ending in any of the selections? Think about the story which surprised you the most. What were some of the author's techniques used to trick you?

In "Hunting Monkeys in the Ozarks", the ending is the opposite of the way the main character had intended. That is, Jay Berry Lee is fooled as well as the reader.

- In what other selections does this happen?
- In what selections does one of the characters fool the reader?

WRITE ABOUT IT

"The Invaders" creates suspense and an unexpected ending by making the reader think he is reading about a strange spaceship that lands on earth. It is not until the end that we discover it is really a story about the pilgrims landing in America as told from the viewpoint of an American Indian.

Write a short story, describing an historical event from the "unexpected" viewpoint. Try to fool the reader as the author did in "The Invaders" by leaving confusing clues and letting the reader make the wrong assumption.

READ ABOUT IT

Melvin Berger. *Disease Detectives.* T. Y. Crowell, 1978.

This book describes the true story of "detectives"—epidemiologists—on the trail of a mystifying illness in Philadelphia.

Eleanor Cameron. *The Court of the Stone Children.* Dutton, 1973.

Having just moved to San Francisco, Nina enjoys visiting one of the museums there. She finds that, oddly enough, some of the stone statues in the courtyard can come to life. These statues lead her into a mystery that is two centuries old.

Phyllis R. Fenner. *Wide-Angle Lens: Stories of Time and Space.* William Morrow, 1980.

Another collection from a well-known anthologist, the stories in this book take place in unexpected and amazing settings.

Madeleine L'Engle. *A Ring of Endless Light.* Farrar, Straus, and Giroux, 1980.

Vicky Austin finds that she has some sort of rapport with dolphins that are part of a research project.

Philipa Pearce. *Tom's Midnight Garden.* Reprinted, Harper & Row, Publishers, 1984.

In this unusual story set in England, a reluctant Tom is sent to stay with relatives during his brother's illness. One night, unable to sleep, Tom listens as the hall clock strikes eleven, then twelve, and then...thirteen? Tom finds that whenever the clock chimes the impossible hour of thirteen, he can enter a wonderful garden, a place that does not exist in the daytime.

Mary Rodgers. *Freaky Friday.* Harper & Row, 1972.

A notably unexpected event in the life of the main character occurs on the day when she wakes up to find that she had turned into her mother.

2

AGAINST
THE ODDS

*What do the expressions
"struggling against the odds" and
"fighting an uphill battle" mean?
They both refer to situations in which
the chances are good that you will
lose the struggle. The characters in
this unit struggle against the odds.
Some of them win, and some lose,
but no one walks away from the
adventure.*

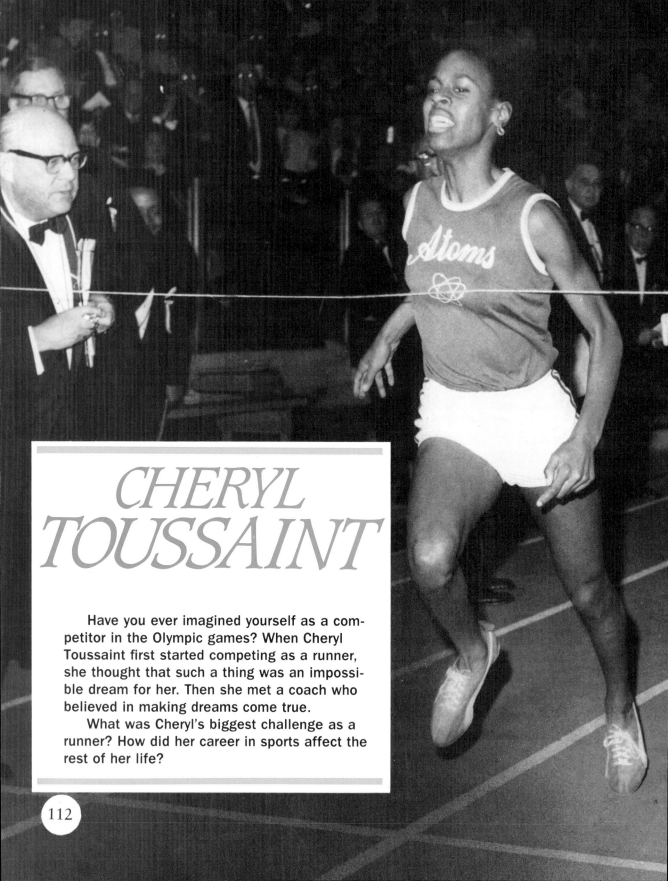

CHERYL TOUSSAINT

Have you ever imagined yourself as a competitor in the Olympic games? When Cheryl Toussaint first started competing as a runner, she thought that such a thing was an impossible dream for her. Then she met a coach who believed in making dreams come true.

What was Cheryl's biggest challenge as a runner? How did her career in sports affect the rest of her life?

In 1967 a city-sponsored group called Youth in Action held a track meet at the Boys' High School field in Brooklyn, New York. Because she had nothing better to do that day, thirteen-year-old Cheryl Toussaint went to watch the meet. Sitting in the stands with her friends, Cheryl found it all very exciting: the speed of the sprinting girls, the yells and cheers of the spectators, the highly charged atmosphere of noise, tension, and fun.

While the meet officials were arranging the order of final events, an "open" race for girls was announced. That meant that any girl present could come to the starting line and compete, even if she didn't belong to a track team. Cheryl loved to run—on the street, in the schoolyard, or in the local playground—and she wanted to enter. Still, she hesitated. The girls she had been watching in the meet looked so fast. Cheryl's friends urged her to give it a try. "Go ahead, don't be chicken," they teased. And when one said, "I dare you," Cheryl accepted the challenge.

She was wearing a dress and a pair of sandals, hardly suitable clothing for a race, so a friend who was wearing sneakers swapped footgear with Cheryl. Of course the fit wasn't exactly right, but it was the best available. Then another girl, who had changed into track shorts, lent her jeans to Cheryl. "Suited up" this way, Cheryl walked down to the starting line and waited for the race to begin.

"It was a hundred-yard dash," Cheryl remembered, "and I really didn't know what to do. I didn't even know how long a hundred yards was. I just stood at the line in someone's dungarees and someone else's sneakers. I didn't know how to start; I was standing straight up. Then the man said, 'Take your marks . . . set . . . go!' and I ran. I got second."

There were several qualifying heats being run, and Cheryl was told that the finals would be held in a while. As she waited, Cheryl began to wonder whether she should enter the finals. "For some reason, I began to hurt right around my hip area, and I didn't understand it. So, I told my friends that I didn't think I'd run. They began the teasing routine again, saying that I was chicken and that I was copping out because I didn't think I was going to win, and that kind of thing. Well, that did it. I went back on the track, ran the final, and took fourth place. That wasn't bad, but the thing that got me was that the three girls ahead of me were all Atoms. I was so impressed with how fast they were that all I could think of was how I could join the team, too."

The Atoms Track Club of Brooklyn was an AAU (Amateur Athletic Union) team, made up of local girls who wanted to run competitively. There were many fine runners in the group, and it was beginning to develop into a real track power.

After the meet was over, Cheryl saw some Atoms runners doing exercises on the grass. Screwing up her courage, she walked over to them and asked how she could join the team. They told her that joining was easy: all she had to do was come to the practices every afternoon.

For a while, Cheryl went to Prospect Park in Brooklyn for the Atoms' daily practice. But when no one paid much attention to her, she began to doubt herself and the results of her running. "I thought that because I was putting my whole heart into it, the coach should have done more than tell me to run laps, do exercises, or practice starts," she said.

Cheryl had no way of knowing that Atoms coach Fred Thompson always treated new team members this way. It was his way of testing their willingness to work. Realizing that the tough, time-consuming practice sessions were more than many girls would endure, he would watch them without their being aware of it. Then if they stayed with it without any encouragement, he would be sure that they were ready for real coaching.

After two months as an Atom, Cheryl dropped out of the club. The memory of her one race, however, kept coming back to her—the pounding heart before the start, the wonderfully free feeling of running, the excitement of coming in ahead of others. So after six months away from the Atoms, Cheryl Toussaint returned to the club, this time to stay.

Those six months away from track had given the teenager time to think about herself, her attitude toward work, and her goals in life. Cheryl decided that she really cared about track, and she went out to the Prospect Park field ready to dig in and work, even if *nobody* paid any attention to her or praised her.

Fred Thompson had missed Cheryl during those six months, and had hoped she'd come back. He had

sent a message to Cheryl, telling her she'd always be welcome. The coach had not pressed the issue, but he was very pleased when she did return.

The season for cross-country racing (long-distance races over all kinds of terrain) was just beginning, and Fred took the Atoms to a cross-country meet on Long Island, New York. That day Cheryl officially competed for the first time as an Atom, and neither she nor the coach ever forgot it.

"Cheryl had been back training with us for only about two weeks," Thompson recalled, "but I decided to enter her in a one-mile run, just to give her some competitive experience. Of course, she wasn't really in condition, and I knew it. So, I said to her before the race, "Don't go out too fast; stay with the pack and just try to finish."

"Well, the gun went off, and before I knew it, Cheryl was a hundred yards in front of the whole field and running like mad. I said to myself, 'This kid is going to pass out!' But she just kept running. Then, with about a hundred yards to go, the oxygen debt really hit her, and she just about collapsed. She fell down, then got up and started crawling on her hands and knees. It was unbelievable! She stood up, staggered some more, got about twenty yards from the finish line and fell again. She kept on going, crawling, still with nobody near her, and then right at the wire another girl caught up and won.

"Cheryl cried like a baby. I went over and picked her up, tried to comfort her, telling her that she had nothing to be ashamed of. But she just cried. I knew, at that moment, that this girl was going to be something special. I had never seen anything like that before in my whole life."

Until Fred Thompson came into her life, nobody had ever thought of Cheryl Toussaint as something special. Shortly after Cheryl's birth on December 16, 1952, her parents separated, and Cheryl went to live with her grandmother. In the crowded schools she attended, Cheryl slipped behind grade level until, by junior high, she was classified as a "slow learner." She took Corrective Reading and Corrective Math, courses that could not make her eligible for a good academic high school.

Then Cheryl joined the Atoms, and everything in her world, including school, took on new meaning. Fred Thompson assumed the role of the father she lacked at home, demanding that Cheryl do better, scolding her when she let up, praising her when she succeeded. "Freddy always encouraged me and all the girls to try for good grades," Cheryl explained. "He'd say, 'When those report cards come in, I want to see them!' and he really meant it. He made me feel that he was just as concerned with how I was doing in school as with my running. It was almost as if he were a parent—only having had so much education himself, he really knew what was going on. I couldn't tell him that a C was okay because the teacher said so—he knew better. My mother and grandmother cared, and were concerned about my schooling, but Freddy knew what each grade meant. There was no snowing him."

With new motivation, Cheryl set to work. She begged the school authorities to let her take algebra, a foreign language, and more advanced English courses. The teachers seemed certain that Cheryl wouldn't be able to do the work, but she was insistent.

Finally, they agreed to let her carry those subjects, in addition to her remedial classes, on a one-year trial. It was grueling, but Cheryl gave it everything she had, and began to learn and do well.

"When I got my report card," Cheryl said, "not only did I feel good for myself in getting good grades, I felt proud having somebody else to show them to, somebody who really appreciated them. Freddy would say, 'Cheryl, that's good. Keep it up.' Then he started to talk about college." To Cheryl, Fred Thompson's mention of college sounded like a wild fairy tale. But she understood, as did all the Atoms, that Fred meant every word he said. He told them that if they were good enough, poverty would never stop them. For example, if they qualified for the Nationals, no matter where the competition was held, he'd see that they got there. An attorney at New York's Madison Square Garden, he would use his own salary, or borrow the money, or beg for it—but the Atoms never had to worry about how they would pay for track equipment, travel expenses, or entry fees.

Her part of the bargain, Cheryl learned, was to succeed in school (flunk and you were off the team) and to work doggedly on the track. And she stuck with the hard, two-hour practice every day. "When I first joined the team," Cheryl remembered, "it was plain exhausting. I'd come home after practice barely able to shower and eat; all I wanted to do was sleep. My grandmother was accustomed to the energetic, bouncy kid I had been, and here I was—collapsing.

"Even though it knocked me out, the running definitely helped me do better in school. I had to be very well scheduled. If I hadn't been running track every day, I'd have been at the nearest park, playing handball or softball, after school. But with those early-evening practices being so tiring, I knew I had to devote afternoons to homework if I wanted to graduate."

As her schoolwork improved, so did Cheryl's performance on the track. She loved the feeling of running and now, with coach Thompson's faith in her and her own new image of herself, she began turning in faster times and winning races. Cheryl had been running for only about a year when she qualified to compete in the U.S. trials for a place on the 1968 Olympic squad.

Looking back at that time, Cheryl later said, "I had been doing fairly well, but at that point I didn't think I was ready for the Olympics. It was enough of a thrill to know that I had made it to the trials. In a way, it was scary for me. I ran and did the best I could, coming in fifth, but I didn't make the Olympic team. I was a little disappointed, but I know now that if I had qualified for the team then, it might have been the ruination of me. Athletes can be thrown, and I've seen it happen to some when they advanced further than their emotional levels could cope with. Success too soon isn't always a good thing. Sometimes people aren't mentally ready for things, and I think I wasn't ready for the Olympics then."

Cheryl was ready to become an outstanding student, however. Fred Thompson had convinced her that she was college material and that, with a little more effort, she might earn a scholarship. With that goal firing her up even more, the "slow learner" was soon getting A's and zooming to the head of her class.

In June, 1970, Cheryl graduated from Erasmus Hall High School in Brooklyn and received an academic scholarship to New York University.

"It might sound kind of boring," Cheryl said of her teen years, "because my life was a round of sleeping, eating, classes, running, studying, and more sleeping. But I was doing what I loved and what I wanted to do, and, anyway, there were those marvelous trips every year."

As one of America's top-ranked runners, Cheryl traveled to meets throughout the United States and Europe. The overseas trips gave her an opportunity to measure herself against foreign competition. Best of all, they gave her a chance to see new places, meet people from other countries, and learn through new experiences.

Running took Cheryl to Europe many times and to the U.S. Nationals year after year. Each trip was fun and each was a challenge, but they were only preparation for Cheryl's highest athletic priority—the Olympics.

The teenage runner made the Olympic Games the focus of her entire life, even to the extent of minoring in German at college so she would be able to communicate in Munich in 1972. Only two things mattered—school and track. Being so dedicated didn't leave much free time for dating. While Cheryl went out with boys occasionally, she felt it was wrong to establish a serious relationship while she was in training.

"There was one boy," she said, "with whom I went to high school, and I saw him for about two years. But then, I was always so busy that I finally felt it wasn't fair to him or me. To go steady, I'd want to devote time to him, which would have meant taking time away from something else I'd like to do. So it just got to be a hassle. I had many friends, but on a casual basis. When I wanted to go out, I'd call a friend and suggest something, and I'd feel free to say yes or no if someone called me. I liked it that way because I wasn't misleading anyone."

Although she had a less active social life than many girls, Cheryl did not feel insecure about it—most of the time. She did, however, remember a time when it bothered her a lot. "I was about sixteen," she explained, "and going through a stage when I was always moaning that I wasn't going out enough, and that I always had to call off my dates. Looking back, I think I just couldn't differentiate between the important and the unimportant. Fortunately, I outgrew that!"

Fred Thompson encouraged Cheryl and all the Atoms to lead sensible, well-regulated lives and to take good care of their health. Cheryl always needed a lot of sleep and made sure she got enough. Weight was never a problem for her, as she naturally tended to be thin, but she tried to stick to solid foods and avoid sweets and excess starches.

"My only advice to Cheryl," Thompson said, "was to drink plenty of orange juice and stay with Grandma's food. That was what made her a healthy kid in the first place. Of course, when she was living in a college dormitory, Cheryl had to take care of herself. But by that time, she knew that the wrong foods or a lack of sleep would show in her running. She was too highly motivated to let that happen, so I never had to worry about her."

Cheryl's sights were set on the 1972 Olympic team, and nothing was more important than that. Every meet counted, because every race was a rehearsal for the big one. During the indoor season in the winter of 1971-72, she was undefeated. She won the 440-yard dash at the Millrose Games, the 880-yard runs at the Maple Leaf Games in Canada and at the AAU Indoor Track and Field Championships, and the 800-meter run at the Olympic Invitational Track Meet. She was faster every time out, and everything seemed to be falling into place.

Then the outdoor season began, and Cheryl had to run a time outdoors that would qualify her for the U.S. Olympic team. She began to

press, and lost her concentration on the track. Coach Thompson tried to calm her, to reassure her that a good running time depended on good competition, and that she would make the team. Soon she had qualified as a runner on the metric mile relay team. But she still hadn't qualified in her individual event, the 800 meters. And the summer was growing short.

Fred took Cheryl to Ohio, where there were to be two meets that would give her the opportunity to qualify. On the day of the first meet, Madeline Manning Jackson, the one woman who might have challenged Cheryl and made her run a fast time, became ill. With nobody challenging her, Cheryl won the race, but her time still wasn't fast enough. At the second meet, Thompson was depending on Nancy Shafer, another top American runner, to push Cheryl to go all-out. But in the 95-degree heat on the day of the race, Nancy faded away, and from the first turn, Cheryl ran alone. Again she missed running a qualifying time.

Cheryl went to the Olympic training camp with just one last chance to make the team in an individual event. "On the day of the race," Fred Thompson recounted, "I sneaked in, so that Cheryl wouldn't see me. I hid behind a tree and watched her run. When she had done it, qualifying, I came out and she saw me. Well, we both cried and cried in relief. It was really down to the wire on that one."

Then she was off to Munich and the 1972 Olympics. Her first event was the 800-meter run, her specialty. In the qualifying heat, she followed Fred Thompson's advice never to fall farther back than third—with disastrous results. She failed to qualify and was out of competition for the medals. "If she'd been in any other heat, my instructions would have been fine," Mr. Thompson said afterward. "But the girls in her heat went out so fast that Cheryl was thrown off her normal pace and didn't make it. It was my mistake, and I'll never stop blaming myself. If Cheryl had run her usual race, pacing her first quarter more slowly, she'd have made it to the semifinals and then, maybe, to the finals."

The night after the race, Thompson went looking for Cheryl in Olympic Village and found her in tears, broken-hearted at what she considered her failure. Fred consoled her, reminding her that she was the youngest one in the event, that her running career was just beginning, and that there would be another Olympics for her. Besides, the relay

race was yet to come. Cheryl still had one more chance to win a medal.

On September 9, 1972, the first women's 4 × 400-meter relay in Olympic history was set to be run. The U.S. teams of Mabel Ferguson, Madeline Jackson, Cheryl Toussaint, and Kathy Hammond had to do well in their heat to qualify for the finals. Cheryl, running the third leg of the relay, waited to receive the baton from Madeline Jackson.

"I turned," Cheryl said, recreating the situation, "and reached for the stick. I was just starting to run with it when a girl from another team fell in front of me. My first reaction was to rear back, so I wouldn't trip over her—but you never stop. I dashed around her, only to have *another* runner step on the heel of my left shoe. Half my shoe was tied on tightly, but the other half was crushed under my heel. 'I can't believe it,' I thought. 'Here I am in the Olympics, and my shoe is coming off!'

"If I had stopped to pull it up, my teammates would have killed me, and I'd have felt awful because that was our opportunity to win a medal. So I just ran. I'd gone another ten yards or so when the shoe flew up in the air. I just kept running, dazed, wondering if my shoe had hit anyone, if the people in the stands and on TV could see my bare foot, and if they were asking what that girl was doing out there without a shoe.

"There had been two teams ahead of us when I got the stick; but somehow, before I knew it, I had passed their runners. Then I saw where I was, and I felt stunned at getting there. All I'd been thinking was that my shoe had come off, that this was the Olympics, and these things don't happen. But it did."

She may have done it the hard way—but she'd done it. Cheryl and her teammates had made it to the relay finals. "I was really confident," Cheryl said of the finals. "Nothing more could happen after that shoe thing. So when I received the baton pass, I just ran and ran until I couldn't run any more. We took second place, behind East Germany.

"Getting up there on the victory stand with my teammates, I realized that I was going to come home from my first Olympics with a silver medal. Of course, I wish we had won, but that doesn't mean I wasn't thrilled by being up there. And anyway, there was Montreal in 1976 to look forward to, and maybe a gold medal."

After the 1972 Olympics, Cheryl came home and continued to concentrate on school and track. She

graduated from college with a B+ average in 1974 and got a job with the Federal Reserve Bank in its management program. And, at the same time, she started working toward the 1976 Olympics.

Cheryl collected many trophies and prizes in her running career, but the greatest reward track gave to the skinny girl from Bedford-Stuyvesant was a chance at a whole new life. For Cheryl, being one of Freddy's Atoms spelled the difference between being nobody and being somebody very special.

Fred Thompson might have known it all along, but Cheryl didn't realize just how special she was until February 5, 1970, when she set the first of her several world records. "It was in Toronto, Canada," she recalled, "at the Maple Leaf Invitational Indoor Games. I had never run the 600-yard event before in my life,

but I felt prepared because I had been training well.

"There were so many girls in the event that it was split into two heats, both to count as finals. That meant you could win your heat and still lose the race if the girls in the other section had faster times. I was in the second section and my goal was to beat the time of the winner in the first heat.

"There were three and three-quarter laps to run in all, and, with about two laps left, I heard Freddy yelling, 'Go! Go! What are you waiting for?' And I went!

"I won my heat, then walked around the track to where Freddy and my teammates were waiting. It was funny, everybody was jumping up and down and smiling and reaching out to me. I looked at them and asked, 'Did I win?' What I meant was, did I beat the fastest time of the first heat? They just kept smiling. Then Freddy said, 'Look up at the clock.' So I looked and the clock read 1:22.2. I said, 'That's nice, I won.' Freddy kept looking at me and said very calmly, 'I think it's a new world record.'

"I thought he was kidding, until they announced it over the loudspeaker. Then the tears came. I was so excited, and I couldn't believe it. I just could never imagine that *I* had really broken a world record—me, who'd never run a 600 before, who had never, never thought of myself as a world-record-holder. It was too much for me to understand. Freddy was overjoyed, and I was, too. I can't even express all the feelings I had. They told me to jog a victory lap, and I went around the track crying, with my mind in a total fog. At that moment, I felt as if I'd never be tired, as if I could run forever.

"That night, after I'd calmed down a little, I thought about it. Lots of people break world records, but *me*—wow! I thought about how lucky I was to be an Atom, and of all the things it had given me, and it was so wonderful."

CHECK FOR UNDERSTANDING
1. How did Cheryl Toussaint first become involved in running?
2. What was Cheryl's biggest challenge as a runner?
3. Why was Fred Thompson such a successful coach?
4. How did her career in sports affect the rest of Cheryl's life?
5. Cheryl described herself as "lucky to be an Atom." Do you think that luck was the key to her success? Explain.

WRITE ABOUT *"Cheryl Toussaint"*
Imagine that you are a sportscaster on radio or television. Choose one of the races that Cheryl or Fred described so vividly in the selection. Write a commentary describing the race to your audience.

TO JAMES

by FRANK HORNE

Do you remember
how you won
that last race . . . ?
how you flung your body
at the start . . .
how your spikes
ripped the cinders
in the stretch . . .
how you catapulted
through the tape . . .
do you remember . . . ?
Don't you think
I lurched with you
out of those starting holes . . . ?
Don't you think
my sinews tightened
at those first
few strides . . .

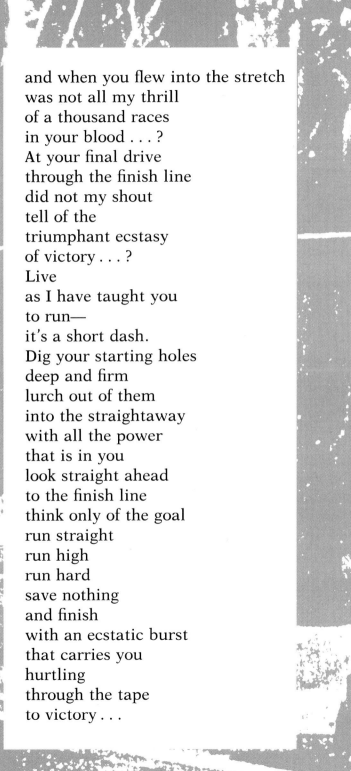

and when you flew into the stretch
was not all my thrill
of a thousand races
in your blood . . . ?
At your final drive
through the finish line
did not my shout
tell of the
triumphant ecstasy
of victory . . . ?
Live
as I have taught you
to run—
it's a short dash.
Dig your starting holes
deep and firm
lurch out of them
into the straightaway
with all the power
that is in you
look straight ahead
to the finish line
think only of the goal
run straight
run high
run hard
save nothing
and finish
with an ecstatic burst
that carries you
hurtling
through the tape
to victory . . .

VOCABULARY · LANGUAGE

Multiple-Meaning Words

I really care about track

I think I'm on the right track.

How many *other* meanings can you think of for the word *track?* Here are three: "footprints or pawprints," "metal rails on which trains run," and "to bring dirt into a room on one's feet."

The word *track* is a good example of a word that has **multiple meanings,** or many definitions. Several words of this kind appeared in the last selection, "Cheryl Toussaint." You may have noticed some of them as you read. A few are given below.

dash   lap   pack   leg   heat   trials

For each of these words, think of *one* definition that is related to running and *another* definition that has a different meaning.

When a word has more than one meaning, you can usually determine the appropriate definition by the setting, or *context,* in which the word appears. Clues in the sentence or passage will help you determine the meaning of the word.

126

Sometimes, however, you may find that context clues alone cannot help you figure out the meaning of a word. In those cases, look up the word in the dictionary. Refer to the definitions and the sentences that illustrate them. Then choose the right meaning.

The next selection you are going to read, "The Adventure of the Speckled Band," Act I, contains many examples of words that have more than one meaning. Helen Stoner, for example, says of her stepfather:

> He narrowly escaped a capital sentence. As it was, he suffered a long term of imprisonment, and then returned to England, a morose and disappointed man.

Below are two definitions for three words in the passage that have multiple meanings. By using context clues, select the appropriate definition for each word.

capital **1.** money, property, or wealth.
2. punishable by death.

sentence **1.** a group of words that expresses a complete thought.
2. a decision by a judge on the punishment of a criminal.

term **1.** a particular word or expression.
2. a period of time.

As you read "The Adventure of the Speckled Band," you will discover that a dying woman's final words offer an important clue to who her murderer is. Be on the lookout for these words. You will find that one of them has multiple meanings—which adds to the mystery.

THE SPECKLED BAND

by ARTHUR CONAN DOYLE
Adapted for radio by Michael and Mollie Hardwick

A crime is committed in a locked room, with no access in or out. Who could be responsible? This is one of the most challenging situations to be found in detective fiction.
In this selection, we hear of a lady who dies in a locked room.
What are Julia Stoner's dying words? How does Sherlock Holmes propose to go about preventing another death?

The most famous detective in the world wore a checked deerstalker cap and carried a large magnifying glass. His dazzling powers of observation filled his devoted friend and companion, Dr. Watson, with bewildered admiration. His name was Sherlock Holmes. Sherlock Holmes and Dr. Watson were the creations of the English writer Sir Arthur Conan Doyle.

CHARACTERS

SHERLOCK HOLMES
a detective residing at 221B Baker Street, London
DR. WATSON, *his friend and associate*
HELEN STONER, *a young lady in distress*
DR. GRIMESBY ROYLOTT, *Miss Stoner's stepfather*
JULIA, *Helen's sister*

ACT I

Death in a Locked Room

WATSON: (*narrating*) My friend Sherlock Holmes worked rather for the love of his art than for the acquirement of wealth. He refused to associate himself with any investigation which did not tend towards the unusual—even the fantastic. Glancing over my notes of seventy-odd cases, I cannot recall any with more singular features than the Case of the Speckled Band. I might have placed them on record before, but for a promise of secrecy from which I've only been freed in the last month by the untimely death of the lady to whom I gave it. There have been widespread rumors as to what really did happen, so it is perhaps as well to bring the facts to light at once. (*slight pause*) It began early one morning in April, 1883.

(*sound of door opening*)

HOLMES: Watson! Wake up, Watson!

WATSON: (*grunting and yawning*) Eh? What on earth?

HOLMES: Come along, Watson. It's a quarter past seven.

WATSON: Quarter past . . . ! Holmes, you . . .

HOLMES: (*chuckling*) Yes, I know it's a little before my usual time.

WATSON: A little! What is it? A fire?

HOLMES: No. A client. It seems that a young lady has arrived in a considerable state of excitement.

WATSON: Aha!

HOLMES: Now, when young ladies wander about the Metropolis at this hour of the morning and wake sleepy people up out of their beds, I presume that it is something very pressing which they have to communicate. Should it prove to be an interesting case, I'm sure you would wish to follow it from the outset.

WATSON: My dear fellow, I wouldn't miss it for anything. Young woman, eh? Just give me a few minutes to dress and I'm ready.

(**Fade out. Fade in** *sitting-room. Sound of door opening.*)

HOLMES: Good morning, madam. My name is Sherlock Holmes.

HELEN: Good morning, Mr. Holmes.

HOLMES: This is my intimate friend and associate, Dr. Watson.

WATSON: Good morning, ma'am.

HELEN: Good morning, Doctor.

HOLMES: You may speak as freely before Dr. Watson as before myself.

(*door closes*)

HOLMES: Ah, I'm glad to see Mrs. Hudson, my housekeeper, has had the good sense to light the fire. Pray draw up to it, madam, and I shall order you a cup of hot coffee. You are shivering.

HELEN: No coffee, thank you, Mr. Holmes. It's not the cold which is making me shiver.

HOLMES: What then?

HELEN: It is fear, Mr. Holmes. It is terror.

WATSON: Good heavens!

HOLMES: You must not fear. We shall soon set matters right.

WATSON: Yes, certainly.

HOLMES: You have come in by train this morning, I see.

HELEN: You know me, then?

HOLMES: No, but I observe the second half of a return ticket in the palm of your left glove. You must have started early, and yet you had a good ride in a dogcart, along heavy roads, before you reached the station.

HELEN: Mr. Holmes, I don't . . .

HOLMES: There is no mystery, my dear madam. The left arm on your jacket is spattered with mud in no less than seven places. The marks are perfectly fresh. There is no vehicle save a dogcart which throws up mud in that way, and then it's only when you sit on the left-hand side of the driver.

HELEN: Well, you're perfectly right. I started from home before six. I reached Leatherhead at twenty past, and I came in by the first train to Waterloo. Sir, I can stand this strain no longer. I shall go mad if it continues.

WATSON: Calm yourself, dear lady.

HELEN: I have no one to turn to . . . no one, save the one who cares for me, and he can be of little aid. I have heard of you, Mr. Holmes, from Mrs. Fairintosh.

HOLMES: Fairintosh? Ah, yes, the case was before your time, I think, Watson . . . concerned with an opal tiara.

WATSON: Certainly don't remember it.

HELEN: Mr. Holmes, do you think you could help me too, at least by throwing a little light through the darkness which surrounds me? At present it's out of my power to reward you for your services, but in a month or two I shall be married and have control of my own income, and then I—

HOLMES: Madam, I shall be happy to devote the same care to your case as I did to that of your friend. My profession is its own reward, but you are at liberty to defray what expenses I may be put to whenever it suits you to do so.

HELEN: You are very kind, Mr. Holmes.

HOLMES: Now I beg you to lay before us everything that may help in forming an opinion about this matter.

HELEN: The real horror of my situation seems to be that my

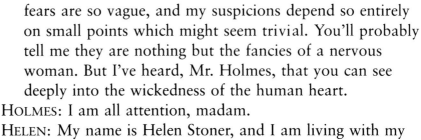

fears are so vague, and my suspicions depend so entirely on small points which might seem trivial. You'll probably tell me they are nothing but the fancies of a nervous woman. But I've heard, Mr. Holmes, that you can see deeply into the wickedness of the human heart.

HOLMES: I am all attention, madam.

HELEN: My name is Helen Stoner, and I am living with my stepfather, Dr. Grimesby Roylott, of Stoke Moran, on the western border of Surrey.

WATSON: One of the oldest Saxon families in England, I believe?

HELEN: And at one time amongst the richest, too. But in the last century four successive heirs wasted the fortune. All that was left was a few acres of ground and the two-hundred-year-old house. The last squire dragged out his existence there in the horrible life of an aristocratic pauper. But his only son, my stepfather, saw that he must adapt himself to the new conditions and took a medical degree. Then he went out to Calcutta and established a large practice. However, in a fit of anger after his house had been robbed, he beat his native butler to death.

WATSON: Good heavens!

HELEN: He narrowly escaped a capital sentence. As it was, he suffered a long term of imprisonment, and then returned to England, a morose and disappointed man.

HOLMES: When did Dr. Roylott marry your mother, Miss Stoner?

HELEN: While he was in India. My mother was the young widow of Major General Stoner, of the Bengal Artillery. My sister Julia and I were twins, and we were only two years old at the time of my mother's remarriage.

HOLMES: I see.

HELEN: My mother had a considerable sum of money . . . not less than a thousand a year. She bequeathed it to Dr. Roylott entirely while we resided with him, with a provision that a certain annual sum should be allowed to each of us in the event of our marriage. Shortly after our return to England—that was about eight years ago—my mother was killed in a railway accident near Crewe.

WATSON: (*sympathetic exclamations*)

HELEN: Dr. Roylott then abandoned his attempts to establish himself in practice in London, and he took us to live with him in the ancestral house at Stoke Moran. (*slight pause*) About this time, a terrible change came over our stepfather.

HOLMES: A change?

HELEN: Yes. Instead of making friends and exchanging visits with our neighbors, he indulged in ferocious quarrels with anyone crossing his path. There was a series of disgraceful brawls, and two of them ended in the police court. My stepfather became the terror of the village. He's a man of immense strength and absolutely uncontrollable anger.

HOLMES: Is there any history of violence or violence of temper in his family, to your knowledge?

HELEN: There is, indeed. I think in my stepfather's case it's even worse, as he lived so long in the tropics. Only last week he threw the local blacksmith over a parapet into a stream. It was only by paying over all the money I could get together that I was able to avert another public exposure.

WATSON: Terrible, terrible!

HELEN: His only friends now are the wandering gypsies. He gives them leave to camp on what's left of the family estate and sometimes wanders away with them for weeks on end. Oh, and he has his animals.

WATSON: Bit of a farmer, then?

HELEN: Nothing like that, I'm afraid. He has a passion for Indian animals. At this moment he has a cheetah and a baboon wandering quite freely over the grounds. They are feared by the villagers almost as much as their master.

133

But to continue . . . You can imagine that I and my poor sister Julia had no great pleasure in our lives. No servant would stay with us, and for a long time we did all the house work. She was only thirty at the time of her death, but her hair had already begun to whiten, even as mine has.

HOLMES: Your sister is dead, then?

HELEN: She died just two years ago. We had an aunt living near Harrow whom we were occasionally allowed to visit. When Julia went there at Christmas two years ago she met a Marine major, and got engaged to him. My stepfather learned of the engagement when my sister returned, and offered no objection to the marriage. But within a fortnight of the day which had been fixed for the wedding, this terrible event occurred.

HOLMES: Miss Stoner, pray be precise as to details at this point.

HELEN: It is easy for me to be so, for every event of that dreadful time is seared into my memory. The manor house, as I have already said, is very old. Only one wing is now inhabited. The bedrooms are on the ground floor. The first is Dr. Roylott's, the second was my sister's, and the third my own. There's no communication between them, but they all open out into the same corridor. Do I make myself plain?

HOLMES: Perfectly so.

WATSON: Yes, yes.

HELEN: The windows of all three rooms open out upon the lawn. That fatal night Dr. Roylott had gone to his room early. We knew that he was not asleep because my sister was troubled by the smell of his strong Indian cigars. She left her room, therefore, and came into mine. We chatted about her approaching wedding. At eleven P.M. she rose to leave me.

(**Fade out. Fade in** *voices of two young women.*)

JULIA: Helen darling . . .

HELEN: Yes, dear?

JULIA: Tell me, have you ever heard anyone whistle in the dead of night?

HELEN: Whistle? No, never.

JULIA: I suppose you don't whistle in your sleep?

HELEN: Certainly not! But why are you asking?

JULIA: Because during the last two nights, at about three A.M., I've kept hearing a low, clear whistle. It wakes me up. I can't tell where it comes from. It seems to be from the next room, or perhaps from the lawn. I thought I would just ask you whether you had heard it.

HELEN: No, I haven't. It must be those gypsies in the plantation.

JULIA: Yes, very likely. And yet if it were on the lawn, I wonder you didn't hear it also.

HELEN: Ah, but I've less on my mind than you. And I sleep more heavily than you.

JULIA: (*laughing*) Well, I don't suppose it matters. Good night, darling.

HELEN: Good night, Julia, dear.

(*Sounds of door closing, key turning in lock.* **Fade out** *on Helen yawning.* **Fade in** *conversation in Baker Street sitting room.*)

HOLMES: Just one moment, Miss Stoner. You locked the door after your sister?

HELEN: Yes, I did.

HOLMES: Was it your custom always to lock yourselves in at night?

HELEN: Always.

HOLMES: Why was that?

HELEN: Well, I mentioned that Dr. Roylott keeps a cheetah and a baboon. We wouldn't have felt safe unless our doors were locked.

HOLMES: Ah, quite so. Pray continue, please.

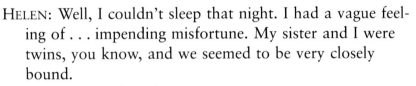

HELEN: Well, I couldn't sleep that night. I had a vague feeling of . . . impending misfortune. My sister and I were twins, you know, and we seemed to be very closely bound.

WATSON: Yes. Often the case.

HELEN: It was a wild night, with the wind howling and rain beating against the windows. Suddenly, over all the hubbub, I heard the wild screams of a terrified woman. I knew it was my sister's voice. I rushed into the corridor. Just as I opened my door I seemed to hear a low whistle and then a clanging sound, as if a mass of metal had fallen. My sister's door was unlocked, and it seemed to swing slowly open upon its hinges. I was rooted to the spot, not knowing what was about to issue from it. Then, by the light of the corridor lamp, I saw my sister coming out, with her face blanched with terror and her hands groping for help.

(*Quick* **fade out** *and* **fade in** *of young women's voices.*)

HELEN: Julia!

JULIA: (*groan*)

HELEN: What is it? What's happened?

JULIA: Oh, Helen! It was . . . it was the band! The speckled band!

HELEN: The speckled band?

JULIA: The . . . the . . . (*She falls, with a choking sob.*)

HELEN: Julia! Oh, darling! (*moving off, calling*) Stepfather! Stepfather, come quickly, please!

(**Fade out. Fade in** *Baker Street sitting-room.*)

HELEN: When he reached my sister's side, she was unconscious. She slowly sank and died without recovering consciousness. And that was the dreadful end of my beloved sister.

WATSON: A terrible story, ma'am.

HOLMES: One moment. You are sure about this whistle and the metallic sound? Could you swear to it?

HELEN: That was what the country coroner asked me at the inquiry. It's my strong impression that I heard it.

WATSON: Of course, there was the noise of the gale. I suppose the old house creaked a bit.

HELEN: It's possible that I was deceived. I don't know.

HOLMES: Was your sister dressed?

HELEN: No, she was in her nightdress. In her right hand we found the charred stump of a match, and a matchbox in her left.

HOLMES: Showing that she had struck a light and looked around when she was alarmed. That is important.

WATSON: What conclusions did the coroner come to, Miss Stoner?

HELEN: He was unable to find any satisfactory cause of death. The evidence showed that Julia's door had been fastened on the inside, and the windows were blocked with old-fashioned shutters with broad iron bars. They were fastened every night. The walls were carefully sounded, and they were found to be quite solid all round. The floor was also examined, with the same result.

HOLMES: The chimney?

HELEN: It's wide, but heavily barred.

WATSON: Then your sister was quite alone when she met her end?

HOLMES: Were there any marks of violence on her?

HELEN: None.

HOLMES: How about poison?

HELEN: The doctors examined her for it, but there was nothing.

HOLMES: Miss Stoner, what do you think this unfortunate lady died of?

HELEN: It's my belief, Mr. Holmes, she died of pure fear and nervous shock.

HOLMES: And what do you think frightened her?

HELEN: That's what I can't imagine.

WATSON: You said there were gypsies about the place. Were there any at the time?

HELEN: Yes, Dr. Watson. There are nearly always some.

WATSON: Mm!

HOLMES: What did you gather from this allusion to a speckled band?

HELEN: I've thought sometimes it was merely the wild talk of delirium. But it may have referred to some band of people.

WATSON: The gypsies!

HELEN: It had crossed my mind. I don't know whether the spotted handkerchiefs some of them wear over their heads might be described as speckled bands.

HOLMES: These are very deep waters. Pray go on with your narrative.

HELEN: Two years have passed since then, Mr. Holmes. My life has been lonelier than ever, until just lately. However, a dear friend whom I've known for many years has done me the honor to ask me to marry him. His name is Percy Armitage. We're to be married during the next few weeks.

WATSON: If I may offer my congratulations?

HELEN: Thank you, Doctor.

HOLMES: What is your stepfather's view?

138

HELEN: Oh, he's offered no opposition whatever.

HOLMES: I see.

HELEN: But two days ago some repairs were started in the west of the building. My bedroom wall is affected, so I had to move into the room in which my sister died. I'm sleeping in the very bed in which she slept. So you can imagine my terror last night as I lay awake, thinking of her awful fate, when I suddenly heard that same low whistle which had occurred just before her death.

WATSON: Great heavens!

HELEN: I sprang up and lit the lamp, but nothing was to be seen in the room. I was too shaken to go to bed again, though. I got dressed, and as soon as it was daylight I slipped down to the Crown Inn and got a dogcart to drive me to Leatherhead. My one object was to see you, Mr. Holmes, and ask your advice.

HOLMES: You have done wisely, Miss Stoner. But have you told me everything?

HELEN: Yes, I have.

HOLMES: I fancy you have not.

HELEN: Mr. Holmes!

HOLMES: You are shielding your stepfather.

HELEN: I don't understand. What do you mean?

HOLMES: If you will permit me to turn back the fringe of your sleeve . . . thank you.

WATSON: Great heavens!

HOLMES: You have been cruelly treated, madam.

HELEN: (*flustered*) He . . . he is a hard man. Perhaps he hardly knows his own strength.

HOLMES: This is very deep business. There are a thousand details I should like to know before I decide on our course of action. But we haven't a moment to lose. Now if we were to come to Stoke Moran today, would it be possible for us to see these rooms without your stepfather's knowledge?

HELEN: Yes. As it happens he was speaking of coming into town today on some important business. He will probably be away all day, and there should be nothing to disturb you. We have a housekeeper now, but she is old and foolish. I could easily get her out of the way.

HOLMES: Excellent! You are not averse to this trip, Watson?

WATSON: By no means, Holmes.

HOLMES: Then we shall both come. What are you going to do yourself, Miss Stoner?

HELEN: Now that I'm in town there are one or two things that I'd like to do. I shall go back by the noon train, so as to be there in time for your coming.

HOLMES: Then you may expect us early in the afternoon. I, too, have some small business matters to attend to first. Won't you wait and have breakfast, though?

WASTON: Yes, do.

HELEN: No, thank you. I must go. My heart is lightened already, gentlemen. (*going*) I shall look forward to seeing you again this afternoon.

WATSON: (*moving off*) Allow me . . .
(*sound of door opening and closing*)

WATSON: Well, Holmes?

HOLMES: And what do you think of it all, Watson?

WATSON: Dark and sinister, that's what I think of it.

HOLMES: Dark enough and sinister enough.

WATSON: But, Holmes. If she's correct in saying the floors and walls are sound, and the door and window and chimney impassable, then her sister must have been absolutely alone when she met her death.

HOLMES: Death in a sealed room, in other words?

WATSON: Then, what about these nocturnal whistles? And what she said about a speckled band?

HOLMES: I was hoping you were going to provide me with those answers, Watson.

WATSON: Well, you'll have to hope again. I haven't a notion.

HOLMES: Dear me!

WATSON: Have you?

HOLMES: We have whistles at night, a band of gypsies on very friendly terms with a doctor who has a financial interest in preventing his stepdaughter's marriage. We have a dying reference to a speckled band, and the fact of a metallic clang which might have been caused by one of those metal bars on the shutters falling back into place. If we combine these ideas, I think there is good ground to believe that the mystery may be cleared along those lines.

WATSON: But what did the gypsies do, then?

HOLMES: I cannot imagine.

WATSON: Neither can I. I can see plenty of obstacles to any theory involving them.

HOLMES: And so can I. It's precisely for that reason that we're going to Stoke Moran today. I want to see just how much can be explained away.
(disturbance outside door)

HOLMES: What in the name of . . .
(door flung open)

ROYLOTT: Which of you is Holmes?

HOLMES: My name, sir. But you have the advantage of me.

ROYLOTT: I am Dr. Grimesby Roylott of Stoke Moran.

HOLMES: Indeed, doctor. Pray take a seat.

ROYLOTT: I will do nothing of the kind. My stepdaughter has been here. I have traced her. What has she been saying to you?

HOLMES: It *is* a little cold for the time of year.

ROYLOTT: What has she been saying to you?

HOLMES: But I have heard that the crocuses promise well.

ROYLOTT: Ha! You think you can put me off, do you? I know you, you scoundrel! I have heard of you before. You are Holmes the meddler.

HOLMES: *(chuckles)*

ROYLOTT: Holmes the busybody!

HOLMES: (*chuckles louder*)

ROYLOTT: Holmes the Scotland Yard troublemaker.

HOLMES: (*laughs heartily*) Your conversation is most entertaining, Dr. Roylott. When you go out, close the door. There's a decided draft.

ROYLOTT: I will go when I have had my say. Don't you dare to meddle with my affairs. I know the girl has been here. I'm a dangerous man to fall foul of. (*moving off*) See here.

(*rattle of fire irons*)

ROYLOTT: I'll show you how I can bend a poker, and how I could bend you for two pins. (*grunts with effort*) There!

(*clatter as poker is hurled to floor*)

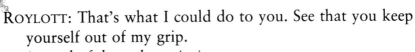

ROYLOTT: That's what I could do to you. See that you keep yourself out of my grip.

(*sound of door slamming*)

WATSON: Well, really.

HOLMES: (*laughing*) He seems a very amiable fellow. (*moving off*) I'm not quite so bulky myself, but if he'd stayed I might have shown him that my grip is not much more feeble than his own.

(*Clatter of poker being retrieved. Holmes grunts with effort.*)

HOLMES: There you are . . . quite straight again.

WATSON: I say, Holmes!

HOLMES: And fancy his having the insolence to confuse me with the official detective force! However, the incident gives zest to our investigation.

WATSON: I hope the dear little lady won't suffer from allowing this brute to trace her.

HOLMES: Let's hope not. And now, Watson, we shall order breakfast. Afterwards I shall walk down to Doctors' Commons, where I hope to get some data which may help us in this matter.

(**Fade out.**)

CHECK FOR UNDERSTANDING

1. How did Sherlock Holmes know that Helen Stoner had traveled to London by dogcart and by train?
2. Why did Helen Stoner want Holmes's help?
3. What were Julia Stoner's dying words?
4. What possible causes of Julia's death were mentioned? Which one do you think was the most probable? Explain.
5. How did Sherlock Holmes propose to go about preventing another death?
6. How would you describe Dr. Roylott?

WRITE ABOUT *Act I of "The Speckled Band"*

Imagine that you are Helen Stoner. Write a letter to a close friend in which you describe your impressions of Sherlock Holmes and Dr. Watson.

Drawing Conclusions

Maria Vargas, a police detective, entered her home one night and discovered Henry and Gertrude lying dead on the floor. A glass bowl lay beside them and a large puddle of water covered the carpet. She concluded from her observations that Henry and Gertrude had died of suffocation. It was obvious to her that Timothy was responsible for their deaths—*and that he was at that very moment hiding somewhere in the house!*

Detective Vargas had all the evidence she needed to draw an accurate conclusion about what had happened. The location of Henry and Gertrude made the cause of death apparent. The position of the bowl revealed the murderer. In order to draw the same conclusions, you must infer what Detective Vargas already knew: Henry and Gertrude were goldfish and Timothy was a cat.

Logic, combined with your own experience, can help you to **draw conclusions** when you are reading. All you need do is to pay close attention to the facts and details that the author provides.

Detective stories require the reader to deduce three facts about a suspect in order to draw a conclusion: the motive, the means by which the crime was accomplished, and the opportunity the suspect had to commit the crime. Which of these three facts is revealed by this passage from "The Adventure of the Speckled Band"?

> **HELEN:** My mother had a considerable sum of money...not less than a thousand a year. She bequeathed it to Dr. Roylott entirely while we resided with him, with a provision that a certain annual sum should be allowed to each of us in the event of our marriage.

Did Dr. Roylott have a reason for wanting Julia to die on the eve of her marriage? Since he would lose a portion of his income at the time of her marriage, he did have a motive for her murder. This does not mean that Dr. Roylott actually committed the crime. It means only that he could possibly be the murderer.

What about the means and the opportunity? Helen Stoner told Holmes that there was no communication among the three bedrooms. Yet she also told him:

> That fatal night Dr. Roylott had gone to his room early. We knew that he was not asleep because my sister was troubled by the smell of his strong Indian cigars. She left her room, therefore, and came into mine.

Note the facts that Helen revealed: (1) Julia smelled Dr. Roylott's cigar smoke in her room. (2) Julia left her room and came to Helen's room—*where there was no smell of cigar smoke.* Therefore, there *had* to be a passageway of some sort between Dr. Roylott's room and Julia's room, and none between Julia's room and Helen's room. There is simply no other logical explanation that matches the facts the reader has been given.

As you read the second act of "The Adventure of the Speckled Band," look closely at the details that Holmes uncovers, especially those he points out to Watson. Ask yourself what possible connection those details might have to the untimely death of Julia Stoner. Like Sherlock Holmes, use your knowledge and imagination to draw logical conclusions.

THE SPECKLED BAND
ACT II

The Key to the Mystery

Sherlock Holmes often repeated this advice. "When you have eliminated the impossible, whatever is left—no matter how improbable—must be true." Holmes set about solving the locked-room mystery by inspecting the scene of the crime.

What clues lead Holmes to the true solution to the mystery? What is the speckled band?

(**Fade in** *Baker Street sitting room. Sound of door closing.*)

WATSON: Ah, Holmes! Wondered if you'd be back for lunch.

HOLMES: Not quite one P.M., I think.

WATSON: What have you got there?

HOLMES: Some rather interesting notes. I've been examining the will of the deceased wife.

WATSON: Roylott's?

HOLMES: Yes. The total income at the time of his wife's death was little short of eleven hundred pounds. Agricultural prices have fallen since then though, so it's not much more than seven hundred and fifty pounds now. Each daughter could claim an income of two hundred and fifty pounds in case of marriage. So, if both girls had married, our strong man would have had a mere pittance left.

WATSON: I see. Even one marriage would have cut his income by a good third.

HOLMES: Exactly. My morning's work has proved that he has the very strongest motives for standing in the way of anything of the sort. And now, Watson, this is too serious for dawdling, especially as the old man knows that we are interesting ourselves in his affairs. I think we must forgo lunch and take a cab to Waterloo.

WATSON: Very well, if you say so.

HOLMES: I'd be much obliged if you would slip your revolver into your pocket. An Eley's No. 2 is an excellent argument with gentlemen who can twist steel pokers into knots. I think that and a toothbrush are all we shall need. (**Fade out. Fade in** *sound of voices.*)

HELEN: Mr. Holmes, Dr. Watson. I've been waiting so eagerly for you. It's all turned out splendidly. Dr. Roylott has gone to town, and it's unlikely he'll be back before evening.

HOLMES: We had the pleasure of making the doctor's acquaintance ourselves.

HELEN: Where?

WATSON: He came to our rooms. Threw his weight about a bit too. Trying to warn us off.

HELEN: He followed me, then?

HOLMES: So it appears.

HELEN: What will he say when he returns?

HOLMES: He had better be on his guard. He may find there is someone more cunning than himself on his track. You must lock yourself in safely tonight. If he tries violence, we shall take you away to your aunt's. But now, we must make the best use of our time.

HELEN: Yes, of course.

HOLMES: If you will kindly take us at once to the rooms we are to examine.

HELEN: If you'll follow me, then. (**Fade out. Fade in** *sound of steps in hall.*)

HOLMES: And this, I take it, is the room in which you are now sleeping?

HELEN: Yes. This is where my sister met her death.

HOLMES: Dr. Roylott's room is on one side of it, and your old room on the other?

HELEN: That's so.

HOLMES: You are sleeping in here only while alterations are going on, I believe you said?

HELEN: Well . . .

WATSON: There doesn't seem much need for those alterations. It's a solid enough wall.

HELEN: There is none. I believe it was simply an excuse to move me from my room.

HOLMES: Ah! Now, if I may examine the room itself.

HELEN: Yes. Please come in.

(sound of door opening)

HOLMES: I see. Now, as both you and your sister locked your doors at night, your rooms were quite unapproachable from the corridor.

HELEN: Yes.

HOLMES: And there are the shutters you close over the windows at night.

WATSON: Strong enough, by the look of them. Solid iron hinges. Nowhere to get a knife through to raise the bar.

HOLMES: I believe you're correct, Watson (*moving slightly off*) Well, what else have we? What is that over the bed? A bell rope?

HELEN: Yes. It rings in the housekeeper's room.

HOLMES: It looks newer than the other things here.

HELEN: Yes. It was only put there a couple of years ago.

HOLMES: Oh? Your sister asked for it, I suppose?

HELEN: No. I never heard of her using it. We always used to get what we wanted for ourselves.

HOLMES: Indeed! Care to give it a tug, Watson?

WATSON: Certainly. What about the, er, housekeeper?

HELEN: She won't hear it, Dr. Watson. She's in the wash-house, well out of our way this afternoon.

WATSON: (*moving off*) Right. (*slight pause*) Hello, that's funny.

HOLMES: What is it, Watson?

WATSON: Doesn't seem to work. No give in it at all.

HOLMES: Let me see. (*slight pause*) Mm! This bell rope is a dummy.

HELEN: You mean it won't ring?

HOLMES: No. It is not even attached to a wire.

WATSON: Very strange.

HOLMES: And very interesting. Look. You can see it's fastened to a hook just above the little opening of the ventilator.

HELEN: How very absurd! I never noticed that before.

HOLMES: Hm! There are one or two very singular points about this room. For instance, do you notice that the ventilator connects with the adjoining room?

WATSON: Good heavens!

HOLMES: What a fool a builder must be to ventilate one room from another when he could just as easily have cut the ventilator through the outside wall to the fresh air.

HELEN: The ventilator was quite a recent addition, too.

HOLMES: Done about the same time as the bell rope, I fancy.

HELEN: Yes. There were several little changes carried out about that time.

HOLMES: They seem to have been of a most interesting character—a dummy bell rope and a ventilator which doesn't ventilate. With your permission, Miss Stoner, we shall now carry our researches into the next apartment . . . Dr. Roylott's own room.

(*sound of steps as they move to the other room*)

HOLMES: Sparsely furnished, I see.

HELEN: Yes.

HOLMES: And a safe. What's in it?

HELEN: My stepfather's business papers.

HOLMES: Oh! You've seen inside then?

HELEN: Only once, some years ago. It was full of papers.

HOLMES: There isn't a cat in it, for example?

WATSON: Cat in a safe, Holmes?

HELEN: No. Of course not.

HOLMES: Well, look at this. What's a saucer of milk doing here?

HELEN: Well, I don't understand. We don't keep a cat. But there are a cheetah and a baboon.

HOLMES: Well, a cheetah is just a big cat, and yet I dare say a saucer of milk wouldn't go very far in satisfying its wants. There is one point I should like to determine.

WATSON: What's that, Holmes?

HOLMES: The seat of this wooden chair here. Just get my lens onto it. (*slight pause*) Hm! That's quite settled, then.

WATSON: What . . .

HOLMES: (*slightly off*) Hello! Here is something interesting.

WATSON: Looks like a dog leash.

HOLMES: Curled upon itself and tied to make a loop of a whipcord. What do you make of that, Watson?

WATSON: Well, it's a common enough object. But I don't know why it should be tied like that.

HOLMES: That isn't quite so common, is it? Ah, me! It's a wicked world, and when a clever man turns his brain to crime it is the worst of all. I think I have seen enough now, Miss Stoner. With your permission we shall walk out upon the lawn.

HELEN: Certainly. (*sounds of steps as they leave house*)

HOLMES: It is very essential, Miss Stoner, that you should absolutely follow my advice in every respect. Your life may depend upon your compliance.

HELEN: I assure you I am in your hands.

HOLMES: In the first place, my friend and I must spend the night in your room.

WATSON: Holmes . . . !

HELEN: I don't . . .

HOLMES: Yes, it must be so. Let me explain. I believe that is the village inn over there?

HELEN: Yes, that is the Crown.

HOLMES: Very good. Your windows would be visible from there, I think?

HELEN: Certainly.

HOLMES: You must confine yourself to your room with a headache when your stepfather comes back. When you

hear him retire for the night, you must open the shutters on your window, undo the hasp, put your lamp there as a signal to us, and then withdraw from the room with everything you're likely to want. You must go into the room which you used to occupy. I've no doubt that you could manage there for one night?

HELEN: Oh, yes, easily.

HOLMES: The rest you will leave in our hands.

HELEN: But what will you do?

HOLMES: We shall come over from the inn and spend the night in the room you have left, and we shall investigate the cause of this noise which has disturbed you.

HELEN: Mr. Holmes, I believe you have already made up your mind.

HOLMES: Perhaps I have.

HELEN: Then for pity's sake tell me what was the cause of my sister's death?

HOLMES: I should prefer to have clearer proof before I speak. And now, Miss Stoner, we must leave you. If Dr. Roylott returned and saw us, our journey would be in vain. Watson and I must make our way to the Crown and engage a room commanding a view of this part of Stoke Moran Manor House. Goodbye, Miss Stoner. Be brave.

HELEN: Thank you Mr. Holmes. I have complete faith in you.

(**Fade out. Fade in** *sound of voices in room at inn.*)

WATSON: (*off*) Now he is shaking his fists at the boy. Didn't open the gates quick enough for him. Ah, there he goes. (*distant sound of horsetrap driving away*)

HOLMES: Well, so the good doctor returns.

WATSON: And in a very nasty mood, if you ask me, Holmes.

HOLMES: You know, Watson, I really have some scruples about taking you with me tonight. There is a distinct element of danger.

WATSON: Can I be of assistance?

HOLMES: Your presence might be invaluable.

WATSON: Then I shall certainly come.

HOLMES: It is very kind of you.

WATSON: You speak of danger, Holmes. You've evidently seen more in those rooms than I did.

HOLMES: No. I imagine you saw as much as I. But I fancy I may have deduced a little more.

WATSON: I didn't notice anything remarkable except the bell rope.

HOLMES: You saw the ventilator, too?

WATSON: Yes. But I don't think it's such a very unusual thing to have a small opening between two rooms. I mean, it's so small that a rat could hardly get through.

HOLMES: Before we even came to Stoke Moran I knew we should find a ventilator.

WATSON: My dear Holmes!

HOLMES: Oh, yes, I did. You remember in her statement she said that her sister was troubled by the smell of Dr. Roylott's cigar in her room?

WATSON: Yes.

HOLMES: Well, of course, that suggests at once that there must be a communication between the two rooms.

WATSON: Ah!

HOLMES: It could only be a small one, or it would have been remarked on at the coroner's inquiry. Therefore, I deduced a ventilator.

WATSON: Pretty obvious, I suppose.

HOLMES: Oh, yes!

WATSON: But what harm can there be in that?

HOLMES: Well, there is at least a curious coincidence of dates. A ventilator is made, a bell rope is hung, and a lady who sleeps in the bed dies. Did you observe anything peculiar about that bed?

WATSON: No.

HOLMES: It was clamped to the floor.

WATSON: What?

HOLMES: The lady could not move her bed. It must always be in the same relative position to the ventilator and to the rope.

WATSON: Holmes! Now I'm beginning to see.

HOLMES: Capital!

WATSON: We're only just in time to prevent another horrible crime!

HOLMES: Horrible and subtle. When a doctor does go wrong, he is the first of criminals. He has nerve and he has knowledge. Palmer and Pritchard were among the heads of their profession. This man strikes even deeper, but I think, Watson, that we shall be able to strike deeper still. But we shall have horrors enough before the night is over. For goodness sake, let us have a quiet pipe and turn our minds for a few hours to something more cheerful. (**Fade out. Fade in.**)

WATSON: Holmes! There's the light from the manor house. Her signal.

HOLMES: About eleven o'clock. Come along, then. And keep a sharp lookout for that baboon.

WATSON: And the cheetah! I shall be a good deal happier when we're in that room.

HOLMES: Now come along.

(**Fade out. Fade in** *sound of wind.*)

HOLMES: (*speaking low*) Now, Watson, there is the window. She has left it open for us. We must get in as quickly as possible and close the shutters without a sound. We must sit without a light. He would see it through the ventilator.

WATSON: Yes. I understand.

HOLMES: Do not go to sleep. Your life may depend on it. Have your pistol ready in case we should need it. I will sit on the side of the bed, and you in the chair.

WATSON: Right.

HOLMES: I've brought a candle and matches with me. We shall have to turn out her lamp as soon as we enter, so that he'll think that she's gone to bed. But if anything happens I have my candle ready to light. Now, my dear Watson, is everything understood?

WATSON: Perfectly.

HOLMES: Good. Let's get in, then.

(*Rustle of shrubbery, then slight noises as men climb through window.*)

HOLMES: (*whispers*) Excellent. Now put out the lamp, Watson. Good. Now then, quite still, not a sound.

WATSON: (*whispers*) Holmes—something's happening. A lantern's been lit in the next room.

HOLMES: Yes, I see. Listen!

(*slight hissing comes and goes several times*)

WATSON: What is it?

(*low whistle from next room*)

HOLMES: Right, Watson. Stay where you are. (*Match struck and candle lit. Holmes leaps to his feet and lashes several times at the bell rope with his cane.*)

HOLMES: (*shouting*) You see it, Watson? You see it?

WATSON: I can't . . .

HOLMES: Ah! It's getting away!

WATSON: What is it, Holmes? I can't see . . .

ROYLOTT: (*screams in the next room*)

HOLMES: Quickly, Watson. Into the next room.
(*sound of running feet*)

WATSON: What does it mean, Holmes?

HOLMES: Get your pistol out, and into Roylott's room
quickly.

ROYLOTT: (*moans with pain as they enter*)

WATSON: Look at him—look at his head! Wrapped around
it!

HOLMES: The band—the speckled band!

ROYLOTT: (*gives a final strangled cry and is silent*)

HOLMES: It's a swamp adder, the deadliest snake in India. He's dead already.

WATSON: Great heavens!

HOLMES: Violence does, in truth, recoil upon the violent. The schemer falls into the pit which he digs for another.

WATSON: Shall I shoot it?

HOLMES: No, this noose in the dog leash will do it. It's obviously intended for this. Just slip it around the reptile's neck—like that—and if you will be so good as to open the safe door a little wider we'll pop it inside— like that. Now close the door quickly.

WATSON: With the greatest pleasure!

(*clang of door*)

HOLMES: And now we must remove Miss Stoner to some place of shelter and let the country police know what has happened.

(**Fade in** *conversation in train compartment.*)

WATSON: But Holmes, what made you suspect you would find a snake?

HOLMES: When I examined the room, it became clear to me that whatever danger threatened could not come either from the window or the door. The discovery that the bell rope placed behind the ventilator was a dummy, and that the bed was clamped to the floor, instantly made me suspicious that the rope was there as a bridge. The idea of a snake occurred to me instantly, and when I coupled it with my knowledge that Dr. Roylott was a fancier of creatures from India, I felt sure I was on the right track.

WATSON: Yes, of course. I see.

HOLMES: The idea of using a form of poison which could not possibly be discovered by any chemical test was just such a one as would occur to a clever and ruthless man who had had an Eastern training. From his point of view, also, the speed with which such a poison would take effect would be an advantage. It would be a sharp-eyed

coroner indeed who could distinguish the two little dark punctures which would show where the poison fangs had done their work.

WATSON: That's quite so. Miss Stoner made no mention of anything like that having being discovered.

HOLMES: I'm sure they weren't.

WATSON: Well, what about the whistle?

HOLMES: That was the next thing I thought about. He would put the snake through the ventilator with the certainty that it would crawl down the rope and land on the bed. He couldn't be sure that it would bite the occupant of the bed. She might escape every night for a week before she fell a victim. Therefore, he had to be able to recall the snake before the morning light or she would have seen it. He trained it—probably by the use of the milk which we saw—to come back to him when he whistled to it.

WATSON: Bit of a snake charmer, eh?

HOLMES: Something of the kind. Well, I had come to these conclusions before I had even entered his room. You remember I examined his chair with my lens?

WATSON: What was all that, then?

HOLMES: Simply to confirm to myself that he had been in the habit of standing on it in order to reach the ventilator. When I saw the safe, the saucer of milk, and this loop of whipcord, any doubts I might still have had were dispelled.

WATSON: So the metallic clang . . .

HOLMES: Obviously her stepfather hastily closing the door of his safe on its terrible occupant.

WATSON: Holmes . . .

HOLMES: Yes, Watson?

WATSON: I'm just beginning to feel rather thankful that I didn't know any of this before we settled down in the room in the dark. When I think of that creature sliding down the bell rope toward us . . .

HOLMES: Well, at least I sat on the bed and gave you the chair.

WATSON: So you did. And you knew what to expect, too.

HOLMES: As soon as I heard the creature hiss, I knew for certain what we were up against. I don't mind admitting I was glad to get that candle lit, and to use my stick upon the brute.

WATSON: With the result of driving it through the ventilator. Was that what you wanted to do?

HOLMES: No, I wouldn't say that. Some of my blows got home upon it and must have roused its snakish temper. It fled through the ventilator and fastened upon the first person it saw. No doubt I'm indirectly responsible for Dr. Grimesby Roylott's death.

CHECK FOR UNDERSTANDING

1. What did Sherlock Holmes discover about the financial status of Dr. Roylett? Why was this discovery important?
2. What was the importance of each of these discoveries: the phony bell rope, the ventilator, the saucer of milk and the dog leash in Dr. Roylott's room?
3. What possible solutions to the mystery did Holmes eliminate as impossible?
4. What was the speckled band?
5. What clues led Holmes to the true solution to the mystery?
6. At what point, do you think, did Holmes guess the solution to the mystery? When did Watson understand the solution?

WRITE ABOUT Act II of "The Speckled Band"

Imagine that you are a police officer. Write a police report describing the circumstances of Julia Stoner's death. Be sure to consider means, motive, and opportunity.

STUDY SKILLS

Reading Textbooks: PQRST

Dr. X set up a series of experiments without first stating their purpose. He collected the data haphazardly, without any clear idea of what question the experiments were meant to answer. Finally, the experiments were carried out in no particular order and the results were not noted in any way.

What would happen if Dr. X tried to perform these experiments without following a plan? What are the chances that such experiments would be successful? Would the chances of success be greater if Dr. X set up the experiments with specific questions in mind, performed the steps in order, and kept track of the results? Why?

Having a method to follow, a plan with clearcut steps and a definite order, can increase your chances of success in many kinds of situations. You saw in Unit 1 how important it is to know the purpose for which you are reading. The purpose determines the way you will read. When you are reading to acquire and retain information, for example, you need to read more slowly and carefully than when you are reading for pleasure. You can do more than slow down your reading rate, though. You can use a method that will help you understand and remember what you read: **PQRST**.

The **PQRST** method consists of five steps:

P **P**review
Q **Q**uestion
R **R**ead
S **S**tudy
T **T**est

Step 1. You **preview** the material to get a general idea of what it is about. Start by reading the *title* and the *introduction*, if there is one. Then read all the *headings* and any *questions* that appear at the end. In addition, read any words that are underlined or printed in boldface or italic type. These are *key words* and name important concepts in the text. Finally, look at the *pictures* and read the *captions*.

Step 2. The second step in PQRST is to use the headings and key words to make up **questions** that you will try to answer as you read the text. The model at the bottom of this page shows you two questions based on the sample text on page 162. The first question is drawn from two of the key words. The second question is drawn from a heading. Preview the sample on page 162. Then use a heading and one or more key words to make up new questions.

Step 3. Step three in PQRST is to **read** the text, looking for answers to the questions you developed. As you read, look too for important ideas that were not included in headings or key words. Add questions about these ideas to your list. Read the sample on page 162 and add another question to your list.

Step 4. After you have finished reading, **study** the material by writing the answer to each of your questions. Then check the text to make sure that your answers are correct and complete. Write the answers to your questions based on the sample.

Step 5. Finally, **test** yourself by covering the answer column of your paper and asking yourself the questions again. As you answer each question, check the answer you wrote on your paper to be sure you remembered all the important details. Follow this procedure with your questions about the sample.

Heading or Key Word	Question	Answer
fossils/remains	What are fossils remains of?	
Types of Fossils	What are the four types of fossils?	

FOSSIL FORMATION

Scientists have long relied on *fossils* to give them information about the past. Fossils are remains of animals and plants that were buried in the earth. A fossil can be an animal, part of an animal, a plant, or even a footprint from the past. Fossils are the only evidence we have of what existed in prehistoric times.

Types of Fossils

Fossils can be classified by the way they were preserved. Fossils can be impressions of objects or animals, actual objects or animals, or material that replaced the original object or animal. The four main kinds of fossils are *petrified* fossils, molds and casts, prints, and whole animals and plants.

Classifying Fossils

Petrified fossils occur when the remains of plants or animals have turned to stone or have been replaced with minerals. To form a fossil of stone, the pockets of air around the plant or animal are filled with minerals. The minerals then strengthen the remains. This is known as *permineralization*. In some cases, water dissolves the plant or animal, and minerals take their place. This is known as *mineralization*.

When a plant or animal is buried in mud, clay, or other material that hardens, a mold or cast can form. Water dissolves away the organism, leaving a hollow the shape of the organism.

Prints are usually molds of thin objects, such as leaves, or footprints made by animals or people. When soft mud in which a print is made hardens into stone, the print is preserved.

The fourth type of fossil occurs when the whole animal or plant is preserved. This type of fossil is very unusual and most often is found in ice or tar, where the preservation happens rapidly. Most organisms decay too quickly to be preserved in this way.

Using What You Have Learned

Use the PQRST method to read the selection entitled "Amazing Allies" on page 176. Remember to follow the following five steps.

P **Preview** the material.

Q Make up **questions.**

R **Read** to find the answers to the questions.

S **Study** the material by writing the answers and checking them in the text.

T **Test** yourself by answering the questions again.

Heading or Key Word	Question	Answer
fossils/remains	What are fossils remains of?	
Types of Fossils	What are the four types of fossils?	

Expanding Your Skills

Teach the PQRST method to someone else, preferably another student in your school. Your lesson should include a demonstration of how to make up questions based on the headings, the key words, and other ideas in the text.

Danger can bring out remarkable qualities in people. You may have read newspaper accounts of ordinary people who act heroically in a dangerous situation. In this excerpt, three animals get a chance to display their remarkable qualities in the face of danger.

Why was the mother bear bewildered? Was there any similarity in the behavior of the cat and the behavior of the mother bear?

SURPRISE ATTACK

by SHEILA BURNFORD

When their owners went on vacation and left them in the care of friends, three homesick pets—a Siamese cat, a bull terrier, and a Labrador retriever—started off on a trek through the Canadian wilderness. They were unaware of the 250 miles they needed to cross in order to rejoin their beloved family.

Faced with the odds of great distance over unfamiliar, dangerous territory, the animals join forces in order to survive. In this excerpt from The Incredible Journey, *the three had just spent their first night sleeping in the open air. The old bull terrier was accustomed to a warm bed indoors. He woke up feeling stiff and tired. He struggled the next day to keep pace with his companions.*

In the cold hour before dawn, the bull terrier woke, then staggered painfully to his feet. He was trembling with cold and was extremely hungry and thirsty. He walked stiffly in the direction of the pool nearby, passing on his way the cat, who was crouched over something held between his paws. The terrier heard a crunching sound as the cat's jaws moved, and, wagging his tail in interest, moved over to investigate. The cat regarded him distantly, then stalked away, leaving the carcass; but to the terrier it was a disappointing mess of feathers only. He drank long and deeply at the pool and on his return tried the feathers again, for he was ravenous; but they stuck in his gullet and he retched them out. He nibbled at some stalks of grass, then, delicately, his lips rolled back over his teeth, he picked a few overripe raspberries from a low bush. He had always liked to eat domestic raspberries this way, and although the taste was familiar, it did nothing to appease his hunger. He was pleased to see the young dog appear presently. He wagged his tail and licked the other's face, then followed resignedly when a move was made towards the direction of the road. They were followed a few moments later by the cat, who was still licking his lips after his feathery breakfast.

In the gray light of dawn the trio continued down the side of the road until they reached a point where it took a right-angled turn. Here they hesitated before a disused logging trail that led westward from the side of the road, its entrance almost concealed by overhanging branches. The leader lifted his head and appeared almost as though he were searching for the scent of something, some reassurance; and apparently he found it, for he led his companions up the trail between the overhanging trees. The going here was softer; the middle was overgrown with grass and the ruts on either side were full of dead leaves. The close-growing trees which almost met overhead would afford more shade when the sun rose higher. These were all considerations that the old dog needed, for he had been tired today even before he started, and his pace was already considerably slower.

Both dogs were very hungry and watched enviously when the cat caught and killed a chipmunk while they were resting by a stream in the middle of the day. But when the old dog advanced with a hopeful wag of his tail, the cat, growling, retreated into the bushes with his prey. Puzzled and disappointed, the terrier sat listening to the crunching sounds inside the bushes, saliva running from his mouth.

A few minutes later the cat emerged and sat down, daintily cleaning his whiskers. The old dog licked the black Siamese face with his panting tongue and was affectionately patted on the nose in return. Restless with hunger, he wandered up the banks of the creek, investigating every rock and hollow, pushing his hopeful nose through tunnels of withered sedge[1] and into the yielding earth of molehills. Sadly he lay down by an unrewarding blueberry bush, drew his paws down tightly over his blackened face, then licked the dirt off them.

The young dog, too, was hungry; but he would have to be on the verge of starvation before the barriers of deep-rooted Labrador heredity would be broken down. For generations his ancestors had been bred to retrieve without harming, and there was nothing of the hunter in his make-up; as yet, any killing was abhorrent to him. He drank deeply at the stream and urged his companions on.

The trail ran high over the crest of this hilly, wooded country, and the surrounding countryside below was filled with an overwhelming beauty of color; the reds and vermillions[2] of the occasional maples; pale birch, and yellow poplar, and here and there the scarlet clusters of mountain ash berries against a rich dark-green background of spruce and pine and cedar.

[1] a marsh grass
[2] bright red

Several times they passed log ramps built into the side of the hill, picking their way across the deep ruts left by the timber sleighs below; and sometimes they passed derelict buildings in rank, overgrown clearings, old stables for the bush horses and living quarters for the men who had worked there a generation ago. The windows were broken and sagging and weeds were growing up between the floorboards, and even one old rusted cookstove had fireweed springing from the firebox. The animals, strangely enough, did not like these evidences of human occupation and skirted them as far as possible, hair raised along their backs.

Late in the afternoon the old dog's pace had slowed down to a stumbling walk, and it seemed as if only sheer determination were keeping him on his feet at all. He was dizzy and swaying, and his heart was pounding. The cat must have sensed this general failing, for he now walked steadily beside the dogs, very close to his tottering old friend, and uttered plaintive worried bleats. Finally, the old dog came to a standstill by a deep rut half-filled with muddy water. He stood there as if he had not even the strength to step around it. His head sagged, and his whole body was trembling. Then, as he tried to lap the water, his legs seemed to crumple under him and he collapsed, half in and half out of the rut. His eyes were closed, and his body moved only to the long, shallow, shuddering breaths that came at widening intervals. Soon he lay completely limp and still. The young dog became frantic now; he whined, as he scratched at the edge of the rut, then nudged and pushed with his nose, doing everything in his power to rouse the huddled, unresponsive body. Again and again he barked, and the cat growled softly and continuously, walking back and forth and rubbing his whole length against the dirty, muddied head. There was no response to their attention. The old dog lay unconscious and remote.

The two animals grew silent, and sat by his side, disturbed and uneasy; until at last they turned and left him, neither looking back—the Labrador disappearing into the bushes where the crack of broken branches marked his progress farther and farther away; the cat stalking a partridge which had appeared at the side of the trail some hundred yards away and was pecking unconcernedly at the sandy dirt. But at the shrill warning of a squirrel, it flew off across the trail with a sudden whirr into the trees, while the cat was still some distance away. Undaunted, still licking his lips in anticipation, the cat continued around a bend in the trail in search of another, and was lost to sight.

The shadows lengthened across the deserted track, and the evening wind sighed down it to sweep a flurry of whispering leaves across the rut, their brown brittleness light as a benison[3] as they drifted across the unheeding white form. The curious squirrel peered in bright-eyed wonder from a nearby tree, clucking softly to itself. A shrew ran halfway across, paused and ran back; and there was a soft sound of wings as a whisky-jack landed and swayed to and fro on a birch branch, tilting his head to one side as he looked down and called to his mate to come and join him. The wind died away—a sudden hush descended.

Suddenly, there was a sound of a heavy body pushing through the undergrowth, accompanied by a sharp cracking of branches, and the spell was broken. Chattering shrilly in alarm and excitement, the squirrel ran up the trunk of the tree

3 a blessing

169

and the whisky-jacks flew off. Now onto the trail on all fours scampered a half-grown bear cub, round furry ears pricked and small deep-set eyes alight with curiosity in the sharp little face as he beheld the old dog. There was a grunting snuffling sound in the bush behind the cub; his mother was investigating a rotten tree stump. The cub stood for a moment and then hesitatingly advanced toward the rut where the terrier lay. He sniffed around, wrinkling his facile[4] nose at the unfamiliar smell, then reached out a long curved black paw and tapped the white head. For a moment the mists of unconsciousness cleared and the old dog opened his eyes, aware of danger. The cub sprang back in alarm and watched from a safe distance. Seeing that there was no further movement, he loped back and cuffed again with his paw, this time harder, and watched for a response. Only enough strength was left in the old dog for a valiant baring of his teeth. He snarled faintly with pain and hatred when his shoulder was raked by the wicked claws of the excited cub, and made an attempt to struggle to his feet. The smell of the drawn blood excited the cub further; he straddled the dog's body and started to play with the long white tail, nibbling at the end like a child with a new toy. But there was no response; all conscious effort drained, the old dog no longer felt any pain or indignity. He lay as though asleep, his eyes veiled and unseeing, his lip still curled in a snarl.

[4] flexible

Around the bend in the trail, dragging a large dead partridge by the wing, came the cat. The wing sprang back softly from his mouth as he gazed at the scene before him. In one split second a terrible transformation took place; his blue eyes glittered hugely and evilly in the black masked face, and every hair on the wheat-colored body stood upright so that he appeared twice his real size; even the chocolate-colored tail puffed up as it switched from side to side. He crouched low to the ground, tensed and ready, and uttered a high, ear-splitting scream; and as the startled cub turned, the cat sprang.

He landed on the back of the dark furred neck, clinging with his monkeylike hind legs while he raked his claws across the cub's eyes. Again and again he raked with the terrible talons, hissing and spitting in murderous devilry until the cub was screaming in pain and fear, blinded with blood, making brushing movements with his paws to dislodge the unseen horror on his back. His screams were answered by a thunderous roar as the huge black she-bear crashed through the bushes and rushed to the cub. She swiped at the clinging cat with a tremendous paw. But the cat was too quick for her and with a hiss of fury leaped to the ground and disappeared behind a tree. The unfortunate cub's head received the full force of the blow and he was sent spinning across the track and into the

bushes. In a blind, frustrated rage, maddened by the cries of her cub, the mother turned for something on which to vent her fury, and saw the still figure of the old dog. Even as she lumbered snarling towards him the cat distracted her attention with a sudden leap to the side of the track. The bear halted, then reared up to full height for attack, red eyes glinting savagely, neck upstretched and head weaving from side to side in a menacing, snakelike way. The cat uttered another banshee[5] scream and stepped forward with a stiff-legged, sideways movement, his squinting, terrible eyes fixed on his enormous adversary. Something like fear or indecision crept into the bear's eyes as the cat advanced; she shuffled back a step with lowered head. Slow, deliberate, purposeful, the cat came on—again the bear retreated, bewildered by the tactics of this terrible small animal, distraught by her cub's whimpering, slowly falling back before the relentless inch-by-inch advance. Now the cat stopped and crouched low, lashing his tail from side to side—the bear stopped too, shifting her weight uneasily before the spring that must follow, longing to decamp but afraid to turn her back. A sudden crackle of undergrowth turned the huge animal into a statue, rigid with apprehension—and when a great dog sprang out of the bush and stood beside the cat, teeth bared

[5] a spirit

and snarling, every hair on his russet back and ruff erect, she dropped to all fours, turned swiftly and fled towards her cub. There was a last growl of desperate bravado from the bush and a whimpering cry; then the sounds of the bears' escape receded in the distance. Finally all was quiet again; the curious squirrel leaped from his ringside seat and scrambled farther down the trunk of the tree.

The cat shrank back to his normal size. His eyes regained their usual cool, detached look. He shook each paw distastefully in turn, glanced briefly at the limp, muddied bundle by his feet, blood oozing from four deep parallel gashes on the shoulder, then turned and sauntered slowly down the track towards his partridge.

The young dog nosed his friend all over, his lips wrinkling at the rank bear smell, then attempted to stanch the wounds with his rough tongue. He scratched fresh leaves over the bloodstained ones, then barked by the old dog's head; but there was no response, and at last he lay down panting on the grass. His eyes were uneasy and watchful; the hairs still stood upright in a ridge on his back, and from time to time he whined in perplexity. He watched the cat drag a large gray bird almost up to the nose of the unconscious dog, then slowly and deliberately begin to tear at the bird's flesh. He growled softly, but the cat ignored him and continued his tearing and eating.

Presently, the enticing[6] smell of raw, warm meat filtered through into the old dog's senses. He opened one eye and gave an appreciative sniff. The effect was galvanizing; his muddied half-chewed tail stirred and he raised his shoulders, then his forelegs, with a convulsive effort, like an old work horse getting up after a fall.

He was a pitiful sight—the half of his body that had lain in the rut was black and soaking, while the other was streaked and stained with blood. He looked like some grotesque harlequin.[7] He trembled violently and uncontrollably throughout the length of his body, but in the sunken depths of the slanted black-currant eyes there was a faint gleam of interest—which increased as he pushed his nose into the still-warm bundle of soft gray feathers. This time there was no growling rebuff over the prey; instead, the cat sat down a few yards away, studiedly aloof and indifferent, then painstakingly washed down the length of his tail. When the end twitched he pinned it down with a paw.

The old dog ate, crunching the bones ravenously with his blunt teeth. Even as his companions watched him, a miraculous strength slowly seeped back into his body. He dozed for a while, a feather hanging from his mouth, then woke again to finish the last morsel. By nightfall he was able to walk over to the soft grass at the side of the track, where he lay down and blinked happily at his companions, wagging his pitiful tail. The Labrador lay down beside him, and licked the wounded shoulder.

An hour or two later the purring cat joined them, carelessly dropping another succulent[8] morsel by his old friend's nose. This was a deer mouse, a little creature with big eyes and long hind legs like miniature kangaroo. It was swallowed with a satisfying gulp, and soon the old dog slept.

[6] tempting
[7] a clown
[8] tasty

174

But the cat purring against his chest and the young dog curled at his back were wakeful and alert most of the remaining night; neither moved from his side.

CHECK FOR UNDERSTANDING

1. What did the Labrador retriever and the bull terrier have in common?

2. Which of the three animals was best adapted for survival in the wild? Explain.

3. Why was the mother bear bewildered?

4. Was there any similarity in the behavior of the cat and the behavior of the mother bear? If so, what?

5. Do you think that the cat and the dogs will complete their journey? Would their experience with the bears have helped them in any way? Explain.

WRITE ABOUT *"Surprise Attack"*

Write a description of the surprise attack as it might have seemed to the bears.

Amazing Allies

by ALAN DEVOE

Teamwork. Is it something that only human beings understand? Some scientists are trying to discover whether or not animals can demonstrate teamwork as well.

What makes the behavior of the animals in Dr. Tsai's experiment so remarkable? According to the author, why is "good will" good biology?

A flash of bright blue in the woods caught the eye of biologist Hilbert Siegler of the Texas Game Commission. Then a second spot of blue stirred, as another jay sailed on silent wings to the same branch. The newcomer, holding a piece of food in its beak, hopped closer to the first bird. Turning eagerly, the first jay lifted its head and accepted hungrily the gift its visitor poked down into its throat.

Siegler was astonished. In fledgling season, young birds often continue coaxing food from their parents even after they have grown up. In courting season, bird swains often bring food to the female birds they are wooing. But this wasn't the season for fledglings, nor was it courting time. This was the dead of winter.

Hastily the wildlife expert raised his binoculars and got the answer. The receiver of the bounty was an adult jay. The lower part of its beak had been broken off nearly at the base. It had no way to pick up food.

176

A chimpanzee, a tree-dwelling ape, is smaller and more intelligent than a gorilla.

FAMILIAR FRIENDS

Nature's creatures are often competitive. But these instincts are balanced by another kind of drive. Nature does not implant just the single message: Take care of yourself. There is a second instinct: Cooperate. It is as vital as the breath of life.

Every creature has a need for companionship as biologically important as food and drink. Testing tadpoles, zoologists have found that even these humble creatures are so deeply influenced by social need that a solitary tadpole can heal an injured part of its body only slowly, but if it is placed with other tadpoles its healing powers speed up almost miraculously. University of Chicago scientists have discovered that when mice are raised in contact with other mice, they grow faster than mice reared on an identical diet in isolation.

Animals often develop teamwork into a partnership. R. M. Yerkes, an authority on apes, gave a chimpanzee a heavy box of food with a complicated lid-fastener. Sniffing delightedly, the chimp tried to drag away the box so he could work at leisure on the task of getting it open. It was too heavy, so he sought out another chimp, tapped him on the shoulder, and gestured for help. Together, the two easily moved the box, worked at opening it, and shared the feast.

A chimpanzee, given food when apes in nearby cages were left unfed, has been seen to pass a share of his food through the bars. Sharing sometimes extends to giving help. An ape with a sliver in its finger goes to another ape, and the "doctor" works as hard at the job as a human doctor.

The coatis of Central and South America, long-nosed relatives of raccoons, swing through the jungle tree-tops in bands, hunting for small prey. A favorite delicacy is the iguana, the big lizard. But an iguana would be a tough customer for a small coati to tackle up among the twig tips, so hunting coatis split into two groups. One goes aloft and scares dozing iguanas out of the branches. As the lizards fall, they are grabbed and overpowered by an army of coatis deployed on the ground.

A coyote can streak along over the prairie in top bursts of speed at about thirty-five miles an hour, but a jackrabbit can hit close to forty-five. Coyotes sometimes organize a relay race to defeat the challenge of such arithmetic. Coyote Number One, when it gets tired, drives the rabbit on an angle toward a piece of cover. Out pops Coyote Number Two to take over the chase, angling off on a new diagonal.

Resting up and getting back its wind, Coyote Number One is presently ready to cut in again. This continues until the rabbit is exhausted.

Crows and ravens demonstrate the rewards of teamwork. Frances Pitt, a British naturalist, owned a raven pair, Ben and Joe, whose teamwork in dealing with visiting cats was characteristic. Ben would approach the cat from the front, parading nonchalantly close. Fascinated by what looked like an easy meal, the cat would fail to observe that Joe was mincing around to the rear. A moment later a black beak would close on the cat's tail. Meowing in outrage, the cat would whirl around to see Joe waddling away across the yard, while Ben seized the tail now presented to him. On a good day Ben and Joe could get a cat to turn in circles like a top. I have seen a trio of crows work a team play of this sort so effectively with a great horned owl that it fell off a branch.

RARE FRIENDS

Such group teamwork is not unusual among creatures of the same species, but scientists are now discovering that the sense of kinship can be trained among animals of different species. The elephants in Ringling Brothers—Barnum & Bailey's Circus and the circus cat, Midnight, were as devoted to each other as if they all had been kittens together. At the Philadelphia Zoo a few years ago the keepers had a problem with an unapproachable rhinoceros, until they gave him the only available companion they could think of risking in the cage: a domestic goat. Almost overnight the rhino's disposition began to change. Before long he would take all the high-spirited butting the goat cared to inflict and come back for more. He had discovered companionship.

This instinct can cut across even the lines of supposedly "incurable" hostilities. A Chinese biologist, Dr. L. S. Tsai, would put a cat and a rat in a cage near a food compartment that had a transparent shutter. This could be opened by pressure on two buttons in the cage. But both had to be pressed at the same time, one by each animal. Again and again, rats and cats learned to put aside their distrust of each other. Faced with a common problem, they worked successfully together to solve it.

This urge toward constructive cooperation touches first the individual, then expands to family, then widens to the group, then, at least in human beings, becomes the ideal of good will. Wherever naturalists have peered deeply into the mysteries of nature's world, they have found the same moving message.

Our human ideals are not a dream. They are good biology.

CHECK FOR UNDERSTANDING
1. According to the author, what instinct balances competition in nature?
2. Why do you think the ravens behaved as they did to the visiting cats?
3. What made the behavior of the animals in Dr. Tsai's experiment so remarkable?
4. According to the author, why is "good will" good biology?
5. After reading "Surprise Attack" and "Amazing Allies," what generalization can you make about the behavior of animals?

WRITE ABOUT *Amazing Allies*
Which example of teamwork among animals seems the most surprising and remarkable to you? Write a paragraph explaining what you find to be most surprising about it. Then suggest situations that either support or contradict the example.

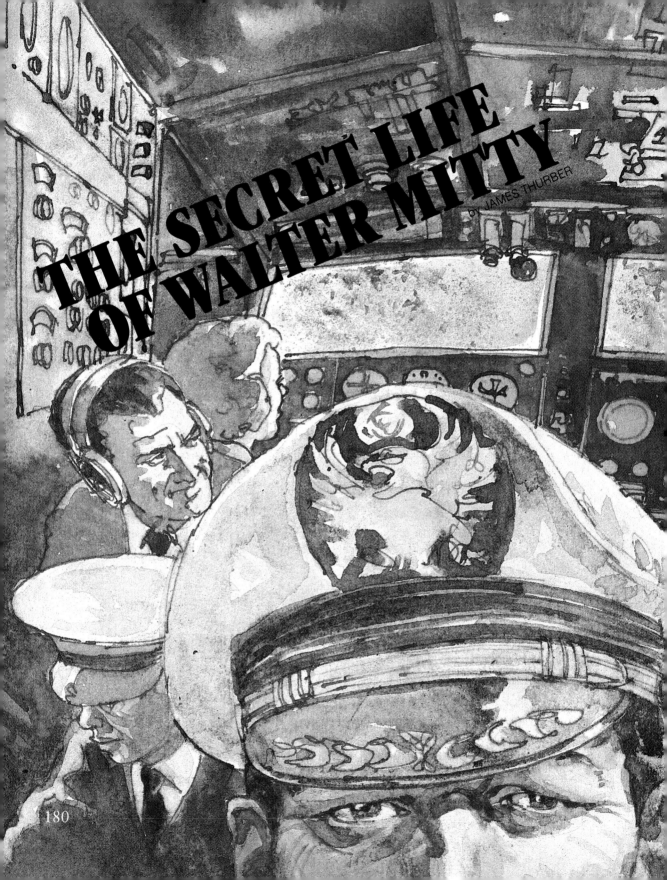

THE SECRET LIFE OF WALTER MITTY

BY JAMES THURBER

In just one day, the hero in this story experiences the thrill of defying the odds many times. This adventurer has found the secret of success. Where did Walter Mitty's adventures take place? In what roles does Walter Mitty see himself?

"We're going through!" The Commander's voice was like thin ice breaking. He wore his full-dress uniform, with the heavily braided white cap pulled down rakishly over one cold gray eye.

"We can't make it, sir. It's spoiling for a hurricane, if you ask me."

"I'm not asking you, Lieutenant Berg," said the Commander. "Throw on the power light! Rev her up to 8,500! We're going through!" The pounding of the cylinders increased: ta-pocketa-pocketa-pocketa-*pocketa-pocketa*. The Commander stared at the ice forming on the pilot window. He walked over and twisted a row of complicated dials. "Switch on No. 8 auxiliary!" he shouted.

"Switch on No. 8 auxiliary!" repeated Lieutenant Berg. "Full strength in No. 3 turret!"

The crew, bending to their various tasks in the huge, hurtling eight-engined Navy hydroplane, looked at each other and grinned. "The Old Man'll get us through," they said to one another. "The Old Man's not afraid of anything. . . ."

"Not so fast! You're driving too fast!" said Mrs. Mitty. "What are you driving so fast for?"

"Hmm?" said Walter Mitty. He looked at his wife, in the seat beside him, with shocked astonishment. She seemed grossly unfamiliar, like a strange woman who had yelled at him in a crowd.

"You were up to fifty-five," she said. "You know I don't like to go more than forty. You were up to fifty-five."

Walter Mitty drove on toward Waterbury in silence, the roaring of the SN202 through the worst storm in twenty years of Navy flying fading in the remote, intimate airways of his mind. "You're tensed up again," said Mrs. Mitty. "It's one of your days. I wish you'd let Dr. Renshaw look you over."

Walter Mitty stopped the car in front of the building where his wife went to have her hair done. "Remember to get those overshoes while I'm having my hair done," she said.

"I don't need overshoes," said Mitty.

She put her mirror back into her bag. "We've been all through that," she said, getting out of the car. "You're not a young man any longer." He raced the engine a little. "Why don't you wear your gloves? Have you lost your gloves?" Walter Mitty reached into a pocket and brought out the gloves. He put them on, but after she had turned and gone into the building and he had driven on to a red light, he took them off again.

"Pick it up, brother!" snapped a cop as the light changed, and Mitty hastily pulled on his gloves and lurched ahead. He drove around the streets aimlessly for a time, and then he drove past the hospital on his way to the parking lot.

. . . "It's the millionaire banker, Wellington McMillan," said the pretty nurse.

"Yes?" said Walter Mitty, removing his gloves slowly. "Who has the case?"

"Dr. Renshaw and Dr. Benbow, but there are two specialists here, Dr. Remington from New York and Mr. Pritchard-Mitford from London. He flew over."

A door opened down a long, cool corridor and Dr. Renshaw came out. He looked distraught and haggard. "Hello, Mitty," he said. "We're having a terrible time with McMillan, the millionaire banker and close personal friend of President Roosevelt. Ostreosis of the ductal tract. Tertiary. Wish you'd take a look at him."

"Glad to," said Mitty.

In the operating room there were whispered introductions: Dr. Remington, Dr. Mitty. Mr. Pritchard-Mitford, Dr. Mitty. "I've read your book on streptothricosis," said Pritchard-Mitford, shaking hands. "A brilliant performance, sir."

"Thank you," said Walter Mitty.

"Didn't know you were in the States, Mitty," grumbled Dr. Remington. "Coals to Newcastle,[1] bringing Mitford and me up here for a tertiary."

"You are very kind," said Mitty.

A huge, complicated machine, connected to the operating table with many tubes and wires, began at this moment to go pocketa-pocketa-pocketa. "The new anesthetizer is giving way!" shouted an intern. "There is no one in the East who knows how to fix it!"

"Quiet, man!" said Mitty, in a low, cool voice. He sprang to the machine, which was now going pocketa-pocketa-queep-pocketa-queep. He began fingering delicately a row of glistening dials. "Give me a fountain pen!" he snapped. Someone handed him a fountain pen. He pulled a faulty piston out of the machine and inserted the pen in its place. "That will hold for ten minutes," he said. "Get on with the operation."

A nurse hurried over and whispered to Renshaw, and Mitty saw the man turn pale. "Coreopsis has set in," said Renshaw nervously. "If you would take over, Mitty?"

Mitty looked at him and at the craven figure of Benbow, and at the grave, uncertain faces of the two great specialists. "If you wish," he said. They slipped a white gown on him; he adjusted a mask and drew on thin gloves; nurses handed him shining . . .

"Back it up, Mac! Look out for that station wagon!" Walter Mitty jammed on the brakes. "Wrong lane, Mac," said the parking-lot attendant, looking at Mitty closely.

"Gee. Yeh," muttered Mitty. He began cautiously to back out of the lane marked "Exit Only."

[1] an unnecessary effort. The expression arose because Newcastle, England, was noted for producing coal, and so bringing coals to Newcastle was unneccessary.

183

"Leave her sit there," said the attendant. "I'll put her away." Mitty got out of the car. "Hey, better leave the key."

"Oh," said Mitty, handing the man the ignition key. The attendant vaulted into the car, backed it up with insolent skill, and put it where it belonged.

They're so cocky, thought Walter Mitty, walking along Main Street; they think they know everything. Once he had tried to take his tire chains off, outside New Milford, and he had got them wound around the axles. A man had had to come out in a wrecking car and unwind them—a young, grinning garage man. Since then Mrs. Mitty always made him drive to a garage to have the chains taken off. The next time, he thought, I'll wear my right arm in a sling; they won't grin at me then. I'll have my right arm in a sling and they'll see I couldn't possibly take the chains off myself. He kicked at the slush on the sidewalk. "Overshoes," he said to himself, and he began looking for a shoe store.

When he came out into the street again, with the overshoes in a box under his arm, Walter Mitty began to wonder what the other thing was his wife had told him to get. She had told him twice, before they set out from their house for Waterbury. In a way he hated these weekly trips to town—he was always getting something wrong. Tissues, he thought, shaving cream, razor blades? No. Toothpaste, toothbrush, bicarbonate, carborundum, initiative, and referendum? He gave it up. But she would remember it. "Where's the what's-its-name?" she would ask. "Don't tell me you forgot the what's-its-name?" A newsboy went by shouting something about the Waterbury trial.

. . . "Perhaps this will refresh your memory." The district attorney suddenly thrust a heavy automatic at the quiet figure on the witness stand. "Have you ever seen this before?"

Walter Mitty took the gun and examined it expertly. "This is my Webley-Vickers 50.80," he said calmly. An excited buzz ran around the courtroom. The judge rapped for order.

"You are a crack shot with any sort of firearms, I believe?" said the district attorney insinuatingly.

"Objection!" shouted Mitty's attorney. "We have shown that the defendant could not have fired the shot. We have shown that he wore his right arm in a sling on the night of the fourteenth of July."

Walter Mitty raised his hand briefly and the bickering attorneys were stilled. "With any known make of gun," he said evenly, "I could have killed Gregory Fitzhurst at three hundred feet *with my left hand*." Pandemonium broke loose in the courtroom. A woman's scream rose above the bedlam and suddenly a lovely, dark-haired girl was in Walter Mitty's arms. The district attorney struck at her savagely. Without rising from his chair, Mitty let the man have it on the point of the chin. "You miserable cur!" . . .

"Puppy biscuit," said Walter Mitty. He stopped walking and the buildings of Waterbury rose up out of the misty court-room and surrounded him again.

A woman who was passing laughed. "He said 'Puppy biscuit,'" she said to her companion. "That man said 'Puppy biscuit' to himself."

Walter Mitty hurried on. He went into a grocery store, not the first one he came to but a smaller one farther up the street. "I want some biscuit for small, young dogs," he said to the clerk.

"Any special brand, sir?"

The greatest pistol shot in the world thought for a moment. "It says 'Puppies Bark for It' on the box," said Walter Mitty.

His wife would be through at the hairdresser's in fifteen minutes, Mitty saw in looking at his watch, unless they had trouble drying it. Sometimes they had trouble drying it. She didn't like to get to the hotel first; she would want him to be there waiting for her as usual. He found a big leather chair in the lobby, facing a window, and he put the overshoes and the

puppy biscuit on the floor beside it. He picked up an old magazine and sank down into the chair. "Can Germany Conquer the World through the Air?" Walter Mitty looked at the pictures of bombing planes and of ruined streets.

. . . "The cannonading has got the wind up frightened[2] in young Raleigh, sir," said the sergeant.

Captain Mitty looked up at him through tousled hair. "Get him to bed," he said wearily. "With the others. I'll fly alone."

"But you can't, sir," said the sergeant anxiously. "It takes two men to handle that bomber, and Von Richtman's circus is between here and Saulier."

"Somebody's got to get that ammunition dump," said Mitty. "I'm going over." War thundered and whined around the dugout and battered at the door. There was a rending of wood and splinters flew through the room. "A bit of a near thing," said Captain Mitty carelessly.

"The box barrage is closing in," said the sergeant.

"We only live once, Sergeant," said Mitty, with his faint, fleeting smile. "Or do we?" Captain Mitty stood up and strapped on his huge Webley-Vickers automatic.

The pounding of the cannon increased; there was the rat-tat-tatting of machine guns, and from somewhere came the menacing pocketa-pocketa-pocketa of the new flame throwers. Walter Mitty walked to the door of the dugout humming. He turned and waved to the sergeant. "Cheerio!" he said. . . .

Something struck his shoulder. "I've been looking all over this hotel for you," said Mrs. Mitty. "Why do you have to hide in this old chair? How did you expect me to find you?"

[2] frightened. The expression is used more often in Britain than in America.

"Things close in," said Walter Mitty vaguely.

"What?" Mrs. Mitty said. "Did you get the what's-its-name? The puppy biscuit? What's in that box?"

"Overshoes," said Mitty.

"Couldn't you have put them on in the store?"

"I was thinking," said Walter Mitty. "Does it ever occur to you that I am sometimes thinking?"

She looked at him. "I'm going to take your temperature when I get you home," she said.

They went out through the revolving doors that made a faintly derisive whistling sound when you pushed them. It was two blocks to the parking lot. At the drugstore on the corner she said, "Wait here for me. I forgot something. I won't be a minute."

She was more than a minute. It began to rain, rain with sleet in it. Walter Mitty stood against the wall of the drugstore.

. . . He put his shoulders back and his heels together. With that faint, fleeting smile playing about his lips, he faced the firing squad; erect and motionless, proud and disdainful, Walter Mitty the Undefeated, inscrutable to the last.

CHECK FOR UNDERSTANDING

1. Where did Walter Mitty's adventures take place?

2. In what roles did Walter Mitty see himself?

3. Describe Mrs. Mitty. Was she the only person who intimidated Walter?

4. What qualities did Walter dream of possessing? Refer to specific fantasies to support your answer.

5. If someone were described to you as a "Walter Mitty," what sort of person do you think he or she might be?

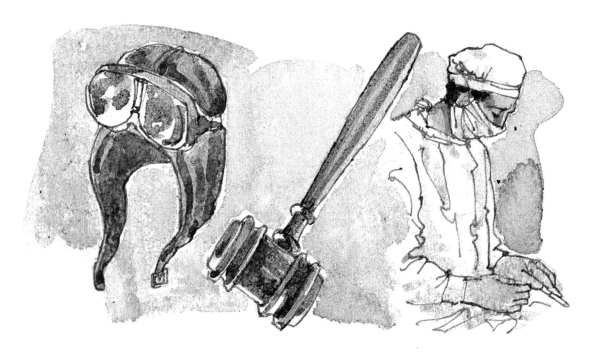

WRITE ABOUT *"The Secret Life of Walter Mitty"*

What about the secret life of Mrs. Walter Mitty? Choose one event in the selection in which Mrs. Mitty appears. Write a short adventure in which the heroic Mrs. Mitty defies the odds.

THE DELIGHT SONG OF TSOAI-TALEE

by N. SCOTT MOMADAY

I am a feather in the bright sky.
I am the blue horse that runs in the plain.
I am the fish that rolls, shining, in the water.
I am the shadow that follows a child.
I am the evening light, the luster of meadows.
I am an eagle playing with the wind.
I am a cluster of bright beads.
I am the farthest star.
I am the cold of the dawn.
I am the roaring of the rain.
I am the glitter on the crust of the snow.
I am the long track of the moon in a lake.
I am a flame of four colors.
I am a deer standing away in the dusk.
I am a field of sumac and the pomme blanche.
I am an angle of geese upon the winter sky.
I am the hunger of a young wolf.
I am the whole dream of these things.

You see, I am alive, I am alive.
I stand in good relation to the earth.
I stand in good relation to the gods.
I stand in good relation to all that is beautiful.
I stand in good relation to the daughter of Tsen-tainte.
You see, I am alive, I am alive.

LITERATURE

Setting

Setting is the background against which the story takes place—the time and place in which a story happens. Writers may put their characters in the past, present, or future. The time setting could be a particular day, a season of the year, or a period in history. The characters might live in actual places or imaginary ones. The place setting could be on a mountaintop, at sea, in a cave, or on the surface of the moon.

Often the setting in a short story is more important than just a place and time for the plot to unfold. In some stories, nearly everything that happens depends on the setting. As in "The Adventure of the Speckled Band," setting shapes the plot by causing events to occur. For example, Sherlock Holmes was able to solve the mystery of the speckled band by carefully studying every detail of the setting of the murder.

> HOLMES: When I examined the room, it became clear to me that whatever danger threatened could not come either from the window or the door. The discovery that the bell-rope placed behind the ventilator was a dummy and that the bed was clamped to the floor instantly made me suspicious that the rope was there as a bridge.

The reader learns that the murderer trained a snake to crawl down the rope, land on the bed, and bite the occupant. The setting, then, influences the action of the story.

Sometimes the setting can help the reader understand the characters in a story by revealing something about their personalities. For example, one character's house could be described as immaculately clean and orderly, with fresh flowers and white curtains. Another character might live in a house that is littered with trash and dirty laundry. Each character's setting reflects his or her own personality traits.

The setting can also be used to create an atmosphere that will arouse a particular emotion or response in the reader. For example, if a character is walking down a street and the writer describes the setting as a "dark, deserted street hemmed in by gray, empty buildings," the reader feels a sense of anxiety and loneliness. If the same character walks down a busy street on a sunny day and a band is playing on a street corner, a feeling of happiness is created.

In "Battling the Grasshoppers," a story about a young pioneer couple, we immediately feel the plight of David and Molly when we learn the setting.

> She walked through grasshoppers thick as spray around her knees. They crunched sickeningly under her feet; she could not avoid stepping on them. Grasshoppers were in her hair, in her sleeves, in her skirts. Her ears tried to shut out the whirring of their wings.
>
> Mechanically she cared for the baby. At the usual time she cooked supper. That night she fed the horses and led them to water. David was cutting slough grass and piling it on the burned strip around the wheat field.

What impression of Molly do you get from reading the paragraph?

What clues in the passage indicate when and where the story takes place?

As you read "Battling the Grasshoppers," watch how the unusual setting of the story shapes the plot and reveals the characters' personalities.

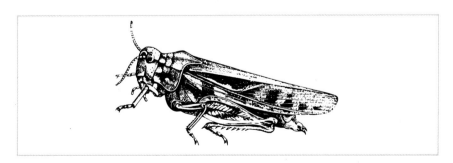

YOUNG PIONEERS

ROSE WILDER LANE

Just·A·Taste

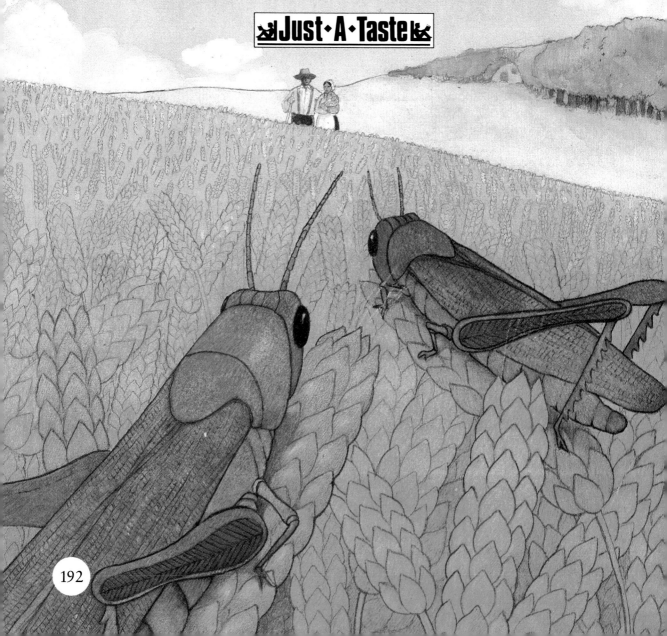

The pioneers of the American West faced many hardships. One of the greatest threats came from a seemingly harmless source.

What threatens the crops? What do Molly and David do to save their wheat?

Molly and her husband David were homesteaders. They had filed a claim on a large tract of prairieland. If they were able to live there for five years, the land would belong to them.

This year's crop of wheat promised to be a large one. David and Molly were confident that the harvest would earn enough money to see them through the rugged winter on the prairie. Who could foresee that something as seemingly harmless as a grasshopper could threaten their success?

BATTING THE GRASSHOPPERS

The descent of the grasshoppers was, mercifully, a nightmare. It was a horror, but it was unbelievable. Some saving resistance in David and Molly refused to believe it. They refused to believe that they would not save the wheat.

The windless day encouraged them. They could control the fires they lighted. Surely the grasshoppers, with hundreds of miles of prairie before them, would avoid flames. Before the winged creatures had ceased to fall from the sky, David had driven the snorting, trembling horses thrice around the wheat field. Three furrows of upturned earth protected the wheat from the fire he set in the wild grass.

It was Molly's part to follow the fire along the strip of plowed ground, to keep the flames from crawling or leaping into the wheat. David had the harder task of fighting the fire in the grass. If it escaped him, the whole country would be burned over; nothing, then, could keep the grasshoppers out of the field. But there was no wind.

The fire ran merrily crackling, sending up waves of fiercer heat into the heat of the sun. All the glassy air was in motion. Back and forth Molly ran, gasping, beating at wisps of burning grass, stamping them into the earth with her feet. For moments together she lost sight of David. The smoke came in gusts, stinging her eyes, her throat. With the smell of the clean smoke there was another, oilier smell; grasshoppers, caught by the licking heat, fell wingless into the fire. Their bodies burst with soft, popping sounds.

It seemed that this madness of fighting had never begun, would never end. There had never been and would never be anything but this fierce, relentless, and desperate battle. Yet it ended. The last clump of burning grass smoldered on blackened ground.

Molly dissolved in trembling. Having nothing to lean against, she swayed and the firm earth held her. It was good to lie on.

David came striding to her and glanced quickly to see that she was all right. He was grimy with smoke, his eyelashes were gone and the hair was scorched from his arms.

"They don't seem to be eating anything," he said huskily, and coughed. "Maybe it was a false alarm."

Molly sat up, then got to her feet, steadying her knees. The wheat stood as before, golden-green and beautiful, with a whirring of grasshoppers over it.

"You go in and rest," David said. "I'm going to keep up a good thick smudge. That'll do the trick!"

She walked through grasshoppers thick as spray around her knees. They crunched sickeningly under her feet; she could not avoid stepping on them. Grasshoppers were in her hair, in her sleeves, in her skirts. Her ears tried to shut out the whirring of their wings.

Mechanically she cared for the baby. At the usual time she cooked supper. That night she fed the horses and led them to water. David was cutting slough grass and piling it on the burned

strip around the wheat field. Thick smoke rose and spread in
the motionless air.

Molly kept supper warm for a long time. At last she let it
grow cold. She lay down without undressing and slept a little.
David came in at last, too tired and restless to eat. He was angry
when she urged him to rest.

"I'm not a baby! Losing a little sleep won't hurt me!" he
said.

She went with him to the wheat field. In the starlight they
stirred the heaps of smoldering grass, buried the flames under
masses of dampened stalks, kept the heavy smoke pouring into
the air.

Dawn came murky through the smoke hanging above the
wheat field. When the sun's first rays struck across the prairie,
a sound rose from it. It was a small, vast sound of innumerable
tiny jaws nibbling, crunching. A trembling began in the wheat

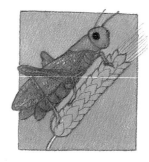

field. Tall stalks shivered; here and there one moved as if it were struggling. It swayed and leaned crookedly against its fellows.

David shouted hoarsely and plunged into the field. They had never gone into the wheat, not even to examine it, unwilling to break down one precious stalk. Now David trampled them down, he tore them up by armfuls, shouting, "Molly, quick! Come help! Quick!"

Smudges placed thickly through the field might save some of it. David raved, "Fool! Fool! Why didn't I do this sooner?"

It was like tearing their own flesh, to tear up the roots of the wheat, to pile up heaps of the ripening grain and set fire to it. They worked in the smoke, in the heat, destroying the thing they wanted to save. A sacrifice of part might save the rest. They trampled down the thick stalks, they cleared spaces, they smothered the flames of burning wheat with the earth on its roots.

At the edge of the field Molly heard again that sound of nibbling. She stood and looked at the wheat. Scores of stalks were moving jerkily, as if they were struggling. The nibbling sound came from the whole prairie. It was not so loud as the flight of grasshoppers before her skirts, but it was continuous. It did not grow louder or softer; it did not stop. The prairie grasses had everywhere a restless movement, not made by any breeze. It sickened her to feel grasshoppers crushing to slime on the soles of her shoes.

Outside the door of the dugout she took off her shoes. In the doorway she took off her dress and petticoat and shook the grasshoppers out of them. Then she fetched water from the creek and mixed a generous drink of vinegar, molasses, and water to take to David.

He drank gratefully, draining the last drop from the little pail. It quivered in his hand. The nibbling sound was all around them, and looking into his bloodshot eyes, she found courage to say:

"David, you might as well rest. It's no—"

He shouted, "I'll save it or die trying! I'm not licked yet. Don't *you* turn against me!" He dashed the pail on the ground and left her as though he hated her.

Molly picked up the pail. Between the smudge fires, patches of the wheat were still standing. Their tops lay in ridges, like grass lodged by the wind. Each blade and every bearded head of grain quivered a little. Before Molly's eyes, one tall stalk fell, then another, and a hollow in the ridged tops slid lower. A whir of grasshoppers shot up from it.

What she feared was that David would be killed by sunstroke.

Every hour she carried a cool drink to him. She took him food, but he would not stop to eat. His wild look frightened her. She could not persuade him to leave the field where he was working in the heat, under the blazing sun. That evening she did the chores again, and went to the field determined to make David rest. He would not listen to her. But the sun was sinking at last.

The baby had the colic; she could not leave him again. She fed him peppermint water and patiently walked up and down, while he yelled on her shoulder. She carried him up the path and looked at smoke rising luridly in the starlight. Every step crushed the loathsome grasshoppers, and even in the night she could hear their nibbling.

Next morning the baby slept, exhausted. Molly took tea and bread to David. He drank thirstily and choked down a few mouthfuls of bread.

"We'll save some of it," he said, looking at the ravaged field. "Not much, but some. I figure near a tenth of it's still standing. They can't take all of it, you know. It isn't possible. Some of it's bound to be left. Enough for flour and seed. If we just have seed—I can get time on those debts, if I put in a crop. I'll save enough for seed. If I just keep up this smudge."

Molly felt a little hope. If even a few stalks were left, here and there, she and David could gather each one carefully. They

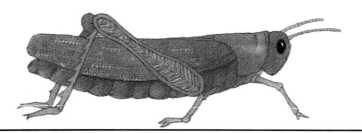

could live that winter on game and the sod potatoes, and put in another crop in the spring.

Then the rising sun struck her shoulders with its heat. Time did not seem to be passing; it stood still, quivering a little under the cruelty of the sun, trembling a little to the ceaseless, metallic nibbling.

That afternoon the grass was no longer standing on the prairie. It lay as if mowed, and still it was restlessly shaken. Bringing a pail of water from the creek, Molly halted and stared at the little plum trees. Not a leaf was left. She went into the dugout and set about mixing the vinegar and molasses for David's drink. The doorway behind her darkened. She was still an instant, then turned.

David's eyes were red in his sooty face. He straightened his shoulders and tried to speak robustly through a raw throat:

"Well, Molly, I—I can't—" His mouth twisted and he said brutally, "The wheat's gone. Every spear." He dropped heavily onto the bench.

Molly had known this would happen; she had known it when the first wheat stalk fell. She had known it when the nibbling began. Now it had happened, and something within her cried out that it could not be true.

"Why don't you say something?" David raged at her. And covered his face with his hands.

Molly turned away instantly. She mustn't let him break down.

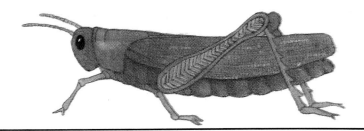

"I guess if there isn't any wheat, we'll get along without it," she said equably. "You've got along all right without it so far."

But they had never been in debt before.

She measured the molasses, poured the vinegar, stirred the mixture round and round. "I'm mixing up some vinegar and water. You'd better wash up and drink it while it's nice and cool."

To her surprise, she began to cry. Her mouth writhed uncontrollably and tears ran from her eyes. She went on stirring till she heard David at the washbasin, then she dried her face and blew her nose.

David wiped his blistered arms gingerly, ran the comb through his wet hair, and drained the cup she handed him. "Molly, that hits the spot!"

"You're hot and tired," she answered. Even in the dugout the maddening, ceaseless sound of nibbling gnawed at their ears.

Tears brimmed his raw lids. He drew her against him where he sat on the bench. She felt the sob shake his body when he turned his face against her shoulder, and she knew that, as she had clung to him when the baby was born, he was clinging to her in this misery too great to bear alone.

"There, there," she said. "It's all right. I was afraid you'd get sunstroke. We're going to be all right."

"Oh, Molly, if I hadn't been such a fool! Those debts I ran up—How'll I ever pay—in debt almost two hundred dollars—Not even flour for this winter; not even seed."

"Never mind now. You'll manage all right. You're tired; you're worn out. You'll feel better when you've had some sleep."

He slept heavily, exhausted. Next morning his face was creased and his eyes swollen. After he had done the chores and eaten breakfast, she persuaded him to lie down again. He fell asleep at once, and Molly sat quiet in order not to disturb him. Her head was heavy and she let it sink against her arm on the table. Dozing, she was all the time aware of David in the bunk, of the baby on the floor. Her eyes opened and she saw the baby absorbed in his own pink feet. He frowned intently, staring with slightly crossed eyes at the inexplicable things wavering about him, and patiently he tried to lay hold of the toes that eluded his uncertain grasp.

Suddenly Molly was aware of a new sound—a rasping, clicking, scratching sound. It crawled up her spine and over her scalp. She started to her feet, and saw the top of the door jamb rippling like a snake. The clean black line was scaly, and rippling, pouring inward.

She snatched up the baby, wrapped him in her apron, covered him with her arms. Then she saw the thing clearly. The grasshoppers were coming into the dugout. The ridged long backs jostled one another. Hundreds, thousands of hard, triangular heads, knobbed with eyes, pointed with nibbling jaws, were coming downward, turning, moving inward over the door jamb.

200

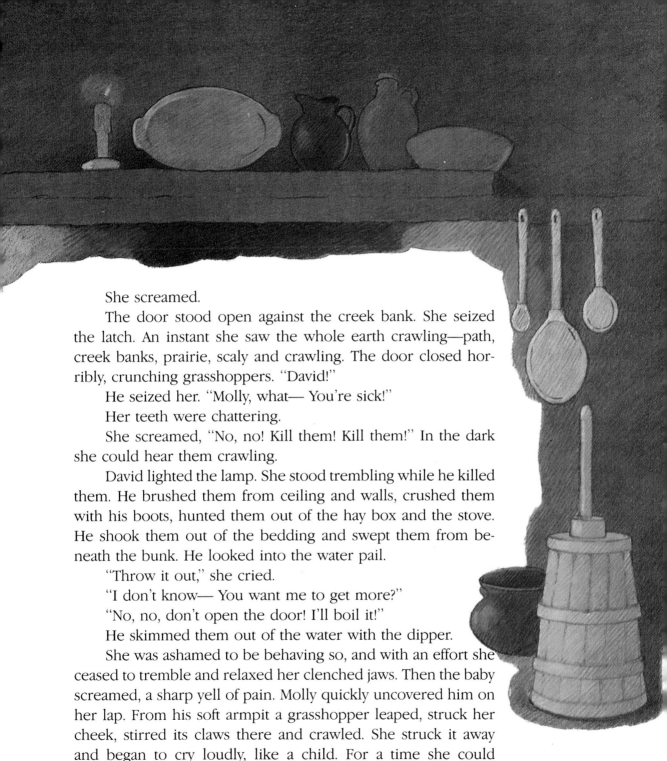

She screamed.

The door stood open against the creek bank. She seized the latch. An instant she saw the whole earth crawling—path, creek banks, prairie, scaly and crawling. The door closed horribly, crunching grasshoppers. "David!"

He seized her. "Molly, what— You're sick!"

Her teeth were chattering.

She screamed, "No, no! Kill them! Kill them!" In the dark she could hear them crawling.

David lighted the lamp. She stood trembling while he killed them. He brushed them from ceiling and walls, crushed them with his boots, hunted them out of the hay box and the stove. He shook them out of the bedding and swept them from beneath the bunk. He looked into the water pail.

"Throw it out," she cried.

"I don't know— You want me to get more?"

"No, no, don't open the door! I'll boil it!"

He skimmed them out of the water with the dipper.

She was ashamed to be behaving so, and with an effort she ceased to tremble and relaxed her clenched jaws. Then the baby screamed, a sharp yell of pain. Molly quickly uncovered him on her lap. From his soft armpit a grasshopper leaped, struck her cheek, stirred its claws there and crawled. She struck it away and began to cry loudly, like a child. For a time she could not stop crying, even in David's arms. When she was

quiet, they heard the grasshoppers crawling on the paper windowpane. Grasshoppers were a mottled shadow crawling steadily downward across it, and by that they knew that the whole earth was still crawling in the sunlight outside.

All that night the creatures crawled, and all the next day. David slipped out to take care of the horses. When he came back, Molly did not ask him any questions. They sat all day in the dugout behind the closed door.

"The railroad's left," David said. "This won't stop the railroad. I'll go back to work on it for a while. Oh, we're not licked yet by a long ways! We'll make out all right."

"Of course we will," Molly said. "We always have."

She knew how he hated to go back to work on the railroad. It had been different when they were starting out. Now for a year he had had his own land; he had been independent. It was hard to go back to obeying other men's orders for wages. But it couldn't be helped. When they were silent, they could hear the claws on the paper pane.

Later that afternoon the oiled paper shone clear. David opened the door.

As mysteriously as they had come, the grasshoppers were going. They had ceased to crawl, they had left the ground. A translucent cloud, colored like mother-of-pearl, swept northwestward across the sun.

After experiencing the destructiveness of a swarm of grasshoppers, some settlers decided to give up their land. But Molly and David were ready to re-establish themselves on their prairie homestead. Read the rest of the novel Young Pioneers *by Rose Wilder Lane in order to find out how well they succeeded.*

CHECK FOR UNDERSTANDING
1. What threatened the crops?
2. What did David and Molly do in order to save their wheat?
3. Why would saving even a small part of the crop help the homesteaders next year?
4. How did Molly's reaction to the loss of the wheat differ from David's?
5. Do you predict that the plans Molly and David made for keeping their homestead will work? Give reasons for your answer.

WRITE ABOUT *"Battling the Grasshoppers"*
How would the homesteaders explain the disaster to a friend or relative who had never seen a swarm of grasshoppers? Write a letter, from either David or Molly, describing their experiences with the grasshoppers.

THINK ABOUT IT

Think about the various characters in the stories you have just read. How do some of these characters go "against the odds"?

- Cheryl Toussaint, who was classified as a "slow learner," but who "liked to run," beat the odds by winning an academic scholarship to college and going on to the 1972 Olympics and other competitions where she set several world records.
- Sherlock Holmes manages to solve an seemingly impossible murder mystery by his careful observation and intelligence.
- Three pets were able to survive a "surprise attack" during a dangerous journey through the Canadian wilderness.
- Walter Mitty overcomes his boring, humdrum life by daydreaming and imagining himself as courageous Navy commander, a brilliant surgeon, a defendant in a murder trial.
- David and Molly go against nature's odds by battling thousands of grasshoppers singlehandedly at their ranch.

Each character was willing to go "against the odds" for a different reason. Each had a specific goal in mind. What were the different goals of the characters mentioned above?

WRITE ABOUT IT

All of us have had some experience in battling the odds on some level. It may not have been as dramatic as "Battling the Grasshoppers," for example, but it may have been just as difficult. Perhaps you managed to win a swim meet against an older, stronger team, or you passed an especially difficult math test by studying diligently for days.

Write a paragraph describing an experience in which you went against the odds—and overcame them. Be sure to include your feelings and your motivation during that time, as well as how you managed to triumph in the end.

READ ABOUT IT

Joan W. Blos. *Brothers of the Heart*. Charles Scribner's Sons, 1985.

This historical novel reveals the difficulties faced by pioneers in the Michigan wilderness. Shem Perkins is taught the ways of survival by the elderly Mary Goodhue, of the Ottawa tribe.

William Kotzwinkle. *Trouble in Bugland: A Collection of Inspector Mantis Mysteries*. David R. Godine, Publisher, 1983.

The Sherlock Holmes of the insect world, Inspector Mantis solves cases in much the same way as his human counterpart. The Inspector even has his own version of Watson in the faithful Dr. Hopper. Other characters include Professor Channing Booklouse, Mrs. Inchworm, and the Duchess of Doodlebug.

William Judson. *Cold River*. New American Library, 1976.

Lizzy enjoys hiking and camping with her father and brother. She finds, however, that her survival skills may not be enough to see her through one of the worst snowstorms within memory.

Jack London. *The Call of the Wild*. Watermill Press, 1980. First published in 1903.

This classic tale describes the conflicting loyalties of the sled-dog Buck. Treated badly by one owner, Buck is saved by a new master. He is torn between his desire to run free and his loyalty to the human being who is kind to him.

Robert M. McClung. *The True Adventures of Grizzly Adams*. William Morrow, 1985.

In the mid-1800s, an eccentric, independent man named John Adams became known for catching grizzly bears—and befriending them.

Scott O'Dell. *Island of the Blue Dolphins*. Houghton Mifflin, 1960.

An unusual and inspiring story, this book recounts the survival of a young Indian girl on an island off the coast of California. Karana learns how to survive on her own—for eighteen years.

3

THE HUMAN KIND

Consider the human kind. How do we appear to each other? How do we reveal our feelings and personalities? And how do we appear to animals? In this unit, we see ourselves from the perspectives of artists, biographers, and even animals, among others.

People usually have good reasons for choosing friends and enemies. You can tell a lot about a person by the friends and enemies they have chosen. What role does Grandfather La Belle play in Little Little's life? What is the convention for TADpoles and PODs?

LITTLE
LOOKS

by M. E. KERR

When she was five months old, Little Little La Belle weighed fifteen pounds, two ounces, and was two feet, one inch tall. At age ten, she stood only three feet, three inches tall, and had not grown any taller by her eighteenth year.

She lived in La Belle, New York, a town founded by her family. It was inhabited by standard-sized people, including Little Little's parents and her sister, who was called Cowboy because she loved horses so much.

Little Little tried not to measure herself by other people's yardsticks, but it was not always easy.

When I was growing up, it was my grandfather La Belle who gave me names like Richard Gibson, famous painter and most famous miniaturist in all the world . . . Toulouse-Lautrec, whose paintings were priceless and in every major museum . . . Attila the Hun, who led an army of half a million across Europe . . . Croesus, king of Lydia in Asia Minor, from whom we get the expression "rich as Croesus" . . . and Richebourg, a spy in the French Revolution. On and on.

"All little people!" he would bellow. "All famous!"

When I asked him where the female dwarfs were, he said they were buried in history along with other notable ladies. He said they were there all right, he just didn't happen to know about them.

He'd done a lot of research in the La Belle library and seemed always to have new names for me of other important dwarfs, with one omission.

"Why don't you ever tell me about Tom Thumb?" I asked him.

"Oh, Tom Thumb," he answered disdainfully.

"I've been reading a lot about him. He was very successful. He was a general and . . ."

"He was a general of nothing! He was given the title General by a fellow who had a circus, P. T. Barnum! He wasn't a real general."

"But he was the most famous dwarf in the world, wasn't he?"

"He was paraded around."

"He met Queen Victoria[1] and the Duke of Wellington[2] and the Prince of Wales.[3] He even met President Lincoln."

"He might have done all that without being a dwarf."

"How?"

"*How?*" My grandfather said. "By using what he had up here"—tapping his forehead with his finger—"instead of letting someone exploit him!"

"What does 'exploit' mean, Grandfather?"

"It means to utilize for profit. This Barnum fellow made a lot of money satisfying the public's curiosity about what someone different looks like. He turned Tom Thumb into a sideshow!"

"Didn't he pay him?"

"Oh, he paid him. But that's no way to live your life, Little Little, and he's no example to follow!"

Long after I needed to be burped, my grandfather would hold me in his arms tightly, jiggling me up and down the way you do a baby, and reciting into my ear:

If you can't be a pine on top of the hill,
Be a scrub in the valley—but be
The best little scrub by the side of the rill;
Be a bush if you can't be a tree.

They were soothing words to hear, being danced around my room, until I grew old enough to think them over and decide that the idea of being a bush wasn't all that appealing, and for me, anyway, not the answer.

Whenever our family went anywhere, we were always stared at because of me. There were always what Cowboy and

[1] (1819–1901) the ruler of Britain and its colonies from 1837 to 1901.
[2] (1769–1852) a British general.
[3] (1841–1910) the eldest son of Queen Victoria.

I called "peepers" in the hotel dining room, or the motel lobbies. Wherever we went, we'd see them looking over the tops of their newspapers or menus, stealing glances when they thought we weren't watching, sometimes just plain staring at us as though we'd just piled out of a flying saucer direct from Mars.

"Jeepers, creepers, look at all the peepers," Cowboy would remark.

She'd try her best to laugh it off, but she'd get red and start cracking her knuckles, and I'd wish I'd just eaten in my room, or not gone on the trip at all. . . .

Except when we were all tooling along together in the car, I never really saw the sights when we went places. I saw the sightseers see me.

I used to daydream that I was from an all-dwarf family. I would imagine my mother, father, grandparents, and Cowboy all shrunk to my size, living in a little house, locked in against a larger world, laughing at them and sharing their tyranny with other La Belles.

Although in various ways and straight out I was told by my mother I would not grow to be as tall as other people, it did not sink in until my little sister grew bigger than I was.

In every room of our house, there is a chair my size.

When Cowboy was very young, she would always try to sit in my chairs. For a time, my father added other small chairs to appease Cowboy, until she was too big to be comfortable in them.

When she stopped sitting in the little chairs around the house, I grabbed at them ecstatically, as though they were cake and the other hungry cake-eater in the house had suddenly dropped out of the contest.

Then came the day Cowboy no longer needed to be lifted to the drinking fountain outside Lathrop's on Main Street, and no longer needed to stand on the box to wash her hands in the bathroom sink.

The picture was coming into focus.

My mother answered all my questions in tears, and my father never gave up the idea of measuring me by the long, yellow tape measure fixed to the kitchen wall.

Cowboy, during that period, let me have things of hers she really wanted for herself.

One summer, my grandfather took me to Pennsylvania.

We were approaching a motel and I was seated beside him in his black car, strapped to my kiddyride, about to have a "surprise"—his only explanation for this weekend trip in the dead of August.

My grandfather, Reverend Warren La Belle, is a cream puff whose soft sweet center isn't immediately visible. If you

know him, you know it's there, but he is a big man with craggy features and bushy eyebrows, who barks out his sermons and frowns his way through most days.

He isn't a man you question about a surprise he's planned, and I didn't ask any questions as we took that unusual journey together.

The first thing I saw was a red-white-and-blue banner over the coned roof of The Pennsylvania Dutch Inn, saying:

WELCOME TADpoles AND PODs!

"What are 'TADpoles and PODs,' Grandfather?" I finally ventured. We were driving up a circular road, heading toward the parking space behind the motel.

"You'll see, Little Little."

213

Then, coming into view, coming out of cars and around the sides of cars, falling from the heavens for all I knew, were others like me, redheaded, blond, blue-eyed, brown-eyed, straight, twisted, beautiful, ugly, in-between . . . a world of me.

My grandfather parked and turned off the ignition. "We're at a convention, Little Little. 'TAD' stands for 'The American Diminutives,' and TADpoles are the children."

"And 'PODS'?"

"Parents of Diminutives." He looked down at me, watching me watch out the car window.

"Where did they all come from?" I said.

"Their homes. Same as you."

Then he put his hand over mine. "Your mother and your father were against this, Little Little. You know how they are where you're concerned. They'd keep you under glass, if they could, to protect you. Your mother, particularly. She's afraid you'll see others who aren't in as good shape as you are, and it'll upset you. Well, I see people my size lame and twisted, too, and so should you. This isn't a perfect world, Little Little, far from it. We're all mixed in together. Right now you've got the world in a miniature, in more ways than one. Want to have a look?"

The pool at the motel had been drained of most of its water, since the only guests that weekend were TADpoles and PODs. The deep end was only about four feet, and the shallow end one foot.

My grandfather made himself at home with the PODs after I changed into my bathing suit. I could hear him behind me, up on the lawn, his deep voice pontificating and his laughter thundering louder than anyone's.

I looked around shyly and finally spotted a girl playing with a large, red rubber ball, in the water by the swimming pool ladder, down at the deep end. She was a most amazing looking girl with the kind of gossamer, blond hair angels have, perfect skin tanned from the sun, and dancing, dark eyes that flashed with her wide, white smile.

I was as vain about my swimming as I was about my own blond hair, which was longer than hers and straight, not curly like hers. I swam vigorously toward her with my best strokes, then grabbed hold of the side and took off my cap, tossing my hair.

When I told her my name, she said, "If you're going to swim, you have to wear your cap. It's a rule."

"Well, I'll just hold on here for a while. I'm from New York."

"Your hair is touching the water."

"It always gets a little wet anyway."

"It shouldn't touch the water. It's against the rules."

"What's your name?" I asked.

"My hair isn't touching the water because I can stand at this end," she answered.

We looked at each other for a moment, and I heard the shouts of the other kids and the soft rock being pumped through the loudspeakers. I saw her dark eyes hardening ever so slightly, although the smile stayed on her mouth.

"Maybe I should get out and put my cap back on," I said.

"I'd say so." She moved out of my way so I could climb the ladder.

As I reached for the rung she said, "I'm four foot one. I can stand at this end."

She wasn't finished.

"You'd better not swim down at this end if you can't touch bottom."

"I'm a good swimmer."

"But I'm really not one of you," she said. "You'd better go meet the others."

She was the first one like me I'd ever talked to.

Later, as I made friends with the others, they told me her name was Eloise Ficklin, and she never made friends with TADpoles who were perfectly formed.

"She's a repudiator, that's what we call her kind."

"I call her mean."

"She hates coming to these conventions but her parents make her come. She wants to pass, to pretend she's just short, so she picks out TADpoles who aren't like her at all, and claims she's helping out. The more you're like her, the less she'll like you."

My grandfather said to me that night, "Well, you have learned something about prejudice today, Little Little. The people at the top of the ladder don't pick on the one way at the bottom. They pick on the one on the rung next to them. The person way at the bottom picks on the person on the ground. There's always someone to look down on, if looking down on someone is your style."

"I really hate her," I said. "No one's ever treated me that way, and I'd never treat anyone that way."

"Oh, you may get around to it," my grandfather said. "No one looks up all the time. When things get tough, your eyes drop, Little Little. Just remember to raise them back up before you've lost your direction."

"What about having an enemy? Is that looking down on someone?"

"Enemies you look square in the eye, as you do friends. You don't make too much of them or too little. You see them for what they are."

"Then Eloise Ficklin is my first enemy."

"Sounds like you made a good choice," my grandfather said.

Eloise Ficklin now stars on television as Dora, The Dancing Lettuce Leaf, in the commercial for Melody Mayonnaise.

217

CHECK FOR UNDERSTANDING

1. Why did Grandfather La Belle tell Little Little about all the famous little people in history?
2. When Little Little was traveling with her family, how did the "little looks" people gave her make Little Little feel?
3. What was the convention for TADpoles and PODs?
4. With what cruel words did Eloise Ficklin reject Little Little?
5. What role did Grandfather La Belle play in Little Little's life?
6. Whom does the author admire more, Little Little or Eloise? How can you tell?

WRITE ABOUT *"Little Looks"*

This story includes many facts about Diminutives. Using the information in the story, write an article describing Diminutives.

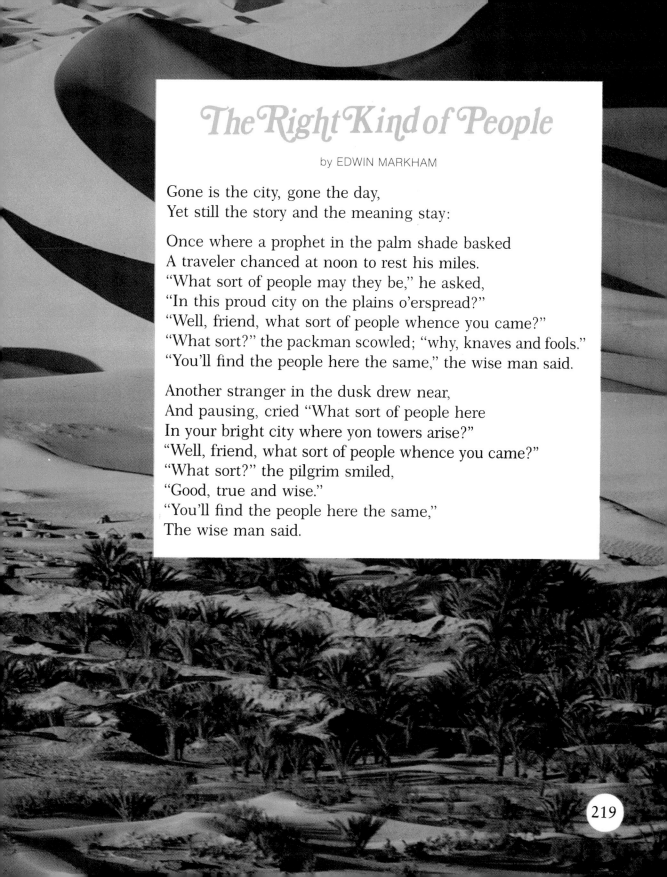

The Right Kind of People

by EDWIN MARKHAM

Gone is the city, gone the day,
Yet still the story and the meaning stay:

Once where a prophet in the palm shade basked
A traveler chanced at noon to rest his miles.
"What sort of people may they be," he asked,
"In this proud city on the plains o'erspread?"
"Well, friend, what sort of people whence you came?"
"What sort?" the packman scowled; "why, knaves and fools."
"You'll find the people here the same," the wise man said.

Another stranger in the dusk drew near,
And pausing, cried "What sort of people here
In your bright city where yon towers arise?"
"Well, friend, what sort of people whence you came?"
"What sort?" the pilgrim smiled,
"Good, true and wise."
"You'll find the people here the same,"
The wise man said.

COMPREHENSION

Characters' Actions

" I weep for you, the Walrus said:
'I deeply sympathize.'
With sobs and tears he sorted out
Those of the largest size,
Holding his pocket-handkerchief
Before his streaming eyes."

"I like the Walrus best," said Alice: "because he was a *little* sorry for the poor oysters."

"He ate more than the Carpenter, though," said Tweedledee. "You see he held his handkerchief in front, so that the Carpenter couldn't count how many he took: contrariwise."

In *Through the Looking Glass,* the Walrus and the Carpenter took the oysters for a walk and then ate them. The Walrus *seemed* sorry, but Alice, lacking sufficient information, did not interpret his "grief" properly.

In "Little Looks," Eloise Ficklin was cruel to Little Little when they met. Little Little was mystified by her behavior until she learned that Eloise was a "repudiator" who never made friends with perfectly formed TADpoles. If she had not talked to the other TADpoles, Little Little would never have understood why she had been treated so badly.

Authors reveal the reasons for **characters' actions** in many ways. Sometimes the reasons are stated clearly. At other times, they are merely suggested. Like Alice and Little Little, you must discover these reasons in order to evaluate a character's actions.

Sometimes a person's feelings are not stated outright; their feelings are only suggested. Read Little Little's account of the time when she realized that she would not grow taller.

My mother answered all my questions in tears, and my father never gave up the idea of measuring me by the long yellow tape measure fixed to the kitchen wall.

The passage suggests that Little Little's parents have not accepted the fact that Little is a dwarf.

How does this passage help you to understand the parents' opposition to Grandfather La Belle's "surprise"? Does this make their overprotectiveness seem more understandable?

The way a person feels about something is often revealed by one or two words. Notice that Grandfather La Belle answered "disdainfully" when Little Little asked him about Tom Thumb.

A person's typical behavior also helps you to evaluate his or her actions. What does this description tell you about Grandfather La Belle?

> My grandfather, Reverend Warren La Belle, is a cream puff whose soft sweet center isn't immediately visible. If you know him, you know it's there, but he is a big man with craggy features and bushy eyebrows, who barks out his sermons and frowns his way through most days.

Suppose Grandfather La Belle "bellowed" at Little Little. What do you know about him that would explain his behavior?

As you read the next story, look for information that reveals motives. Notice how the characters behave typically and be aware of the one-word clues that tell you how a character feels about what he or she is doing.

Jean-August-Dominique Ingres, *M. Bertin*, 1832.

LOOKING AT FACES

by GILES WATERFIELD

What can photographs or portraits of people reveal about them? Even if you do not know the people in the portraits, you can often tell something about their personalities by looking at their faces and the surroundings.

This article includes a series of seven portraits. What details in a portrait help the artist to reveal the subject's personality? To which of the seven portraits does the viewer have to bring the most imagination? Why?

A person's face tells us more about its owner than any other part of the body. It shows what mood someone is in, how old they are, and a good deal about their character. It is not surprising, then, that artists interested in people should often choose to concentrate on their faces.

Some of the pictures in this article are by great portraitists whose aim has been to capture as good a likeness as possible. These are placed alongside faces remolded by the vivid imaginations of the artists. The result is a strikingly varied portrait gallery.

PUBLIC AND PRIVATE FACES

The first three paintings show the different ways in which a person in a portrait seems either involved with the spectator, or principally interested in his or her own thoughts. One might think that the difference between a public face and a private one is that in a public face the eyes look directly at you, as though trying to reach you, while the eyes of a private face will be turned away. In fact the eyes of these people are almost all staring straight out of their pictures. But the effect that they make is varied.

A Two-sided Face

This is a portrait of Monsieur Bertin. He was editor of one of the most important political newspapers in France in the early nineteenth century and a well-known figure. At this time

Leonardo da Vinci, *Ginevra de' Benci,* 1480.

he was not a young man. But he still had the energy of youth. The artist, Ingres, wanted to paint Bertin in as natural a position as possible. Certainly he looks as he must have in life, with his waistcoat crumpled, and hair ruffled. When you see this painting—a large one—it makes a strong impact. The sitter seems to loom out of the portrait, overpowering the spectator with his bulk and the directness of his gaze.

It is a remarkable face. One side seems to smile ironically. The other is severe and formidable. There is no attempt to disguise his double chin. But Bertin does not need to be made handsome. Everything in the picture—the way he is sitting, the brown and yellow coloring, the extraordinary hands which appear to echo his facial expression—contributes to his personality.

Lady of the Sad Eyes

Here is the face of Ginevra de'Benci. The juniper tree at the back is a pun on her name. *Ginevra* is the Italian for "juniper." This portrait expresses a strong sense of sadness. We

Grant Wood, *American Gothic,* 1930.

224

often judge whether people are cheerful or depressed by their mouths. A smile, for example, is an easily recognizable signal. In this portrait, it is not only the mouth which reveals the lady's feelings. Cover the lower part of the face, and look at her eyes. You can see that, with their brooding gaze and heavy lids, they show the same emotion.

The artist was Leonardo da Vinci, best known for his *Mona Lisa*. You can recognize his work from various clues: the hair, for instance. In his writing, Leonardo compared curls of hair to the swirls of water. You can see here how he expressed this idea in his painting. Most of all, we can recognize his sitters from the strange, withdrawn look he gives them.

The Pioneering Spirit

The two other people on this page come from a different society altogether. This is a fairly recent picture called *American Gothic*, by Grant Wood. The title, refers to the clapboard house and also, perhaps, to the people themselves. *Gothic* means something medieval, or very old. These are pioneers, from the early days of the United States, who worked hard on the land to make a living for themselves. The man's face, with his clear eyes, straight mouth, and broad chin, expresses the qualities of determination, courage, and honesty.

Look at the pitchfork which the man holds in his fist like a weapon. The shape is repeated more than once, on the dungarees, and even on the roofs of the houses. This is perhaps the artist's way of linking the man to his work and his surroundings.

The face of the woman is less calm. She stands behind her father, and looks in a different direction. Her clothes are more decorative, less practical, than her father's. Her elegant brooch seems out of place. Does she share her father's convictions? Or do the lines around her chin and eyes show that she feels differently about her life?

RE-MAKING FACES

So far all the faces you have seen have been recognizable views of people as you expect to see them. Here is something different. One of these faces is a carved wooden mask from Africa. We do not know exactly when it was made, or by whom. The other is a painting by one of the most famous artists of the twentieth century, Picasso. Though the purpose of these two works is not the same, the approach has something in common. The two artists are not interested in

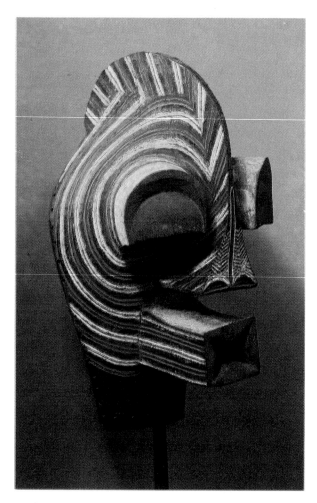

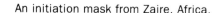
An initiation mask from Zaire, Africa.

tiations. Every boy at a certain age moved from childhood to adulthood, and this event was marked by special ceremonies. These often included dances. The people initiating the children would be disguised in raffia* cloaks and masks. These masks were precious and magical. It was thought that they were the incarnations of the magic spirits and dead heroes of the tribe, and so the masks were not made to look like humans.

Weeping Picture

Picasso, who was Spanish, was one of the first European artists to take an interest in African art. It very much influenced his own. He learned that it was not necessary to paint people according to the old rules. But that an artist could often express feelings more powerfully by distorting the sitter's face. Here he paints a woman dressed in ordinary clothes. As the title suggests, the point of this picture is to indicate the emotion she is suffering. Everything contributes: her crumpled face, her twisted mouth and agonized eyes, the tension in her fingers, the strange coloring. Though the picture may not be "like" the woman, it *is* like a woman weeping.

showing faces "realistically"—that is, as people ususally look. Instead, they are reinterpreting faces. They are making something out of the features (eyes, nose, and mouth) for a particular reason. The impact that each work of art makes is strong.

A Mask with Strange Powers

The mask comes from Zaire. It belonged to the Songe tribe and had a particular purpose. It was used for ini-

* a strong fiber obtained from the leaves of a palm tree

Pablo Picasso, *Woman Weeping*, 1937.

SELF-PORTRAITS

Vincent van Gogh's picture, painted in 1890, is a self-portrait. Van Gogh was a man of strange and unstable character. His paintings were too unusual for the people of his own time to accept. But he is now thought of as one of the greatest European artists. His portrait is ruled, as you would expect, by the face, but everything contributes to the mood.

Look at the way the background is painted, with twisting, boldly colored, restless lines, even for the coat. The same applies to the head. This face is very tense, and full of violence. The paint is put roughly on the canvas. It gives a feeling of the skin's texture, and contributes to the uneasiness of the picture. So it is difficult to let your eyes stop on any surface. Again, the eyes are especially strong. Each seems to stare in a different direction, suggesting the pain, and also the strength, of this man in torment.

Taking an Honest Look

This painting is by Rembrandt. He died in 1669, at the age of sixty-six. He painted this picture in that year.

Vincent van Gogh, *Self-portrait*, 1890.

227

Rembrandt van Rijn, *Self-portrait,* 1669.

By this time he was poor and lonely. This and his other late portraits show his sadness. He seems to be looking into the distance. What his face expresses, through the lines, the tension round the mouth, and above all the eyes, is the weight of his long life and sad experience.

Only the face has any importance. Many of the outlines are blurred. We feel that the flesh is crumbling, and almost that we could touch it.

Of course, often artists will paint themselves in a self-confident and cheerful mood, as Rembrandt showed himself as a young man. But many of the best self-portraits are those where artists have studied their own character and painted what they have seen.

CHECK FOR UNDERSTANDING

1. Are the paintings of Rembrandt and Van Gogh portraits of public faces or private faces? Explain.
2. What details in a portrait help the artist to reveal the subject's personality?
3. To which of the seven portraits did the viewer have to bring the most imagination? Why?
4. What if Picasso had been able to paint a portrait of Van Gogh? What physical characteristics might he have emphasized? What characteristics of Van Gogh's personality might he have tried to show?

WRITE ABOUT *"Looking at Faces"*

Imagine that you could have your portrait painted by one of the artists represented in this article. Which artist would you choose? Why? Write a paragraph explaining your choice. Then describe what your portrait might be like.

REMBRANDT'S
late self-portraits

by ELIZABETH JENNINGS

You are confronted with yourself. Each year
The pouches fill, the skin is uglier.
You give it all unflinchingly. You stare
Into yourself, beyond. Your brush's care
Runs with self-knowledge. Here

Is a humility at one with craft.
There is no arrogance. Pride is apart
From this self-scrutiny. You make light drift
The way you want. Your face is bruised and hurt
But there is still love left.

Love of the art and others. To the last
Experiment went on. You stared beyond
Your age, the times. You also plucked the past
And tempered it. Self-portraits understand,
And old age can divest,
With truthful changes, us of fear and death.
Look, a new anguish. There, the bloated nose,
The sadness and the joy. To paint's to breathe,
And all the darknesses are dared. You chose
What each must reckon with.

PORTRAIT
by a neighbour

by EDNA ST. VINCENT MILLAY

Before she has her floor swept
    Or her dishes done,
Any day you'll find her
    A-sunning in the sun!

It's long after midnight
    Her key's in the lock,
And you never see her chimney smoke
    Till past ten o'clock!

She digs in her garden
    With a shovel and a spoon,
She weeds her lazy lettuce
    By the light of the moon,

She walks up the walk
    Like a woman in a dream,
She forgets she borrowed butter
    And pays you back cream!

Her lawn looks like a meadow,
    And if she mows the place
She leaves the clover standing
    And the Queen Anne's lace!

my cousin
AGATHA

by RAMÓN LÓPEZ VELARDE
*translated from the
Spanish by Cheli Durán Ryan*

My godmother used to ask my cousin Agatha
to spend the day with us,
and my cousin used to arrive
wrapped in a contradictory magic
of starch and odious ritual
mourning.

Agatha entered, rustling
starch, and her green eyes
and warm red cheeks
protected me from the dreadful
black . . .
  I was only a child
who knew the O by its roundness
and Agatha, who knitted
mildly, persistently, in the echoing corridor,
sent little unknown shivers
up my spine.

(I think I owe her, too, my crazy
but heroic habit of talking alone.)

At dinner, in the restful twilight
of the dining room,
I was slowly bewitched by the brittle
intermittent ring of plates,
and the lilt that was like a caress
in my cousin's voice.
  Agatha was
(rosy cheeks, green eyes, black mourning)
a polychrome* basket of colors,
crammed with apples and grapes,
on the ebony of an old cupboard.

232

* (pol'ē krōm') having several colors

an old
CHARCOAL SELLER

by PO CHÜ-YI
Translated from the Chinese by Eugene Eoyang

An old charcoal seller
Cuts firewood, burns coal by the southern mountain.
His face, all covered with dust and ash, the color of smoke,
The hair at his temples is gray, his ten fingers black.
The money he makes selling coal, what is it for?
To put clothes on his back and food in his mouth.
The rags on his poor body are thin and threadbare;
Distressed at the low price of coal, he hopes for colder weather.
Night comes, an inch of snow has fallen on the city,
In the morning, he rides his cart along the icy ruts,
His ox weary, he hungry, and the sun already high.
In the mud by the south gate, outside the market, he stops to rest.
All of a sudden, two dashing riders appear;
An imperial envoy, garbed in yellow (his attendant in white),
Holding an official dispatch, he reads a proclamation.
Then turns the cart around, curses the ox, and leads it north.
One cartload of coal—a thousand or more catties*!
No use appealing to the official spiriting the cart away:
Half a length of red lace, a slip of damask
Dropped on the ox—is payment in full!

* A catty is a unit of weight that in China
  equals a bit more than a pound.

233

Connotations

> "...painted, with twisting, boldly colored restless lines...
>
> The paint is put roughly on the canvas..."

These excerpts from "Looking at Faces" describe the way Vincent van Gogh painted to produce special feelings. These words create an image in your mind of how van Gogh painted. In many ways, writers are like artists. Unlike artists, however, writers use *words* rather than paint to obtain desired feelings. Certain words are very well suited to this purpose. They have the power to arouse feelings such as anger or joy. Like the vivid brush strokes of the artist, words can bring about desired emotions.

You have probably come across many such words in your reading. *Hero* and *coward* are examples. We say that words such as these have a particular **connotation,** that is, they bring to mind feelings or judgments that go beyond the word's dictionary definition.

A word may have a **positive** connotation such as *hero,* or a **negative** connotation such as *coward.* Some words are considered **neutral.** Of course, what a word connotes, or brings to mind, may vary from one person to another. Most people, however, would probably agree on the following connotations.

POSITIVE CONNOTATION	NEGATIVE CONNOTATION
thrifty	stingy
determined	stubborn
courageous	foolhardy

The following words are found in "Looking at Faces." For each, decide if the word has a positive or a negative connotation, or if it is neutral.

pioneers	brooding	spectator
violence	self-confident	extraordinary
elegant	cheerful	tension
house	unstable	withdrawn

Look up the first word above, *pioneer,* in the dictionary. Notice how the word's **denotation,** its dictionary definition, differs from its connotation.

In the following selection, "Harriet Tubman," you will read part of a letter written by Frederick Douglass. In it, he states:

> "...I have received much encouragement at every step of the way...I have had the applause of the crowd and the satisfaction that comes of being approved by the multitude, while the most that you have done has been witnessed by a few trembling, scared, and footsore bondsmen and women, whom you have led out of the house of bondage..."

Which words in the passage above have a positive connotation? Which have a negative connotation?

As you read "Harriet Tubman," you will discover words such as *slavery, freedom,* and *leadership.* What connotation does each of these words have? See how many words with a strong connotation you can find in the selection.

Courageous fighters, like Harriet Tubman, often risk their lives defending what they believe in. What qualities make Harriet Tubman a good military scout and intelligence agent? What does Harriet Tubman's appearance in 1854 tell you about her life?

Harriet Tubman

by LANGSTON HUGHES

"Then we saw the lightning, and that was the guns. Then we heard the thunder, and that was the big guns. And then we heard the rain falling, and that was the drops of blood falling. And when we came to get in the crops, it was dead men we reaped." So the escaped slave, Harriet Tubman, described one of the battles of the war between the North and South in which she took part, for she was in the thick of the fighting. Before the war, like Frederick Douglass, Harriet Tubman devoted her life to the cause of freedom, and after the war to the advancement of her people.

Like Douglass she was born a slave, one of eleven daughters and sons. No one kept a record of her birth, so the exact year is not known. But she lived so long, and so much was written about her, that most of the other facts of her life are accurately recorded. She was a homely child, willful, wild, and constantly in rebellion against slavery. Unlike Phillis Wheatley* or Douglass, Harriet had no formal education.

When she was about twenty-four years old, she married a jolly, carefree fellow named Tubman. He did not share her concern for leaving the slave country. A few years later, when her old master died, Harriet heard that she and two of her brothers were to be sold. They decided to run away together. It was too dangerous to tell anyone. Harriet had no chance to let even her mother know directly. But on the evening that she was leaving, she went about the fields and the slave quarters singing,

When that old chariot comes,
I'm goin' to leave you.
I'm bound for the Promised Land . . .
And the way she sang that song let her friends and kinfolks know that, to Harriet, the Promised Land right then meant the North, not heaven. That night she left the Brodas Plantation on the Big Buckwater River, never to return. Before dawn her brothers became frightened, and went back to the slave huts before their absence was discovered. But Harriet went on, alone, through the woods by night, hiding by day, having no map, unable to read or write, but trusting God, instinct, and the North Star to guide her. By some miracle she eventually got to Philadelphia, found work there, and was never again a slave.

But Harriet could not be happy while all her family were slaves. She kept thinking about them. So, some months later, she went back, hoping to persuade her husband to come north with her. He said he did not wish to go. However, she led others northward. And within two years of her own escape, she had secretly returned to the South three times to rescue two brothers, a sister and her children, and a dozen more slaves. The Fugitive Slave Law of 1850 made it dangerous for runaways to stop anywhere in the United States. So Harriet led her followers to Canada, where she spent winter begging, cooking, and praying for them. Then she returned to rescue nine more slaves.

During the first years of her own freedom, Harriet spent most of her time showing others how to follow in her

* (1754?–1784) African-born American poet

footsteps. Her fame as a fearless leader of "freedom bands" spread rapidly. Shortly, large rewards were offered by the slave holders for her capture. But she never was captured. And she never lost any of her followers to the slave catchers. One reason for this was that, once someone decided to go with her and started out, Harriet did not permit any turning back. Perhaps her experience with her two brothers when she first ran away accounted for this insistence. Her method of preventing frightened or weak travelers on the freedom road from returning to slavery, and perhaps being whipped into betraying the others, was simple. Harriet Tubman carried a pistol. When anyone said he could not, or would not, go on, Harriet pulled her gun from the folds of her dress and said, "You *will* go on—or you'll die." The strength, or the courage, to continue was always forthcoming when her faltering companions looked into the muzzle of Harriet's gun. Through swamp and thicket, rain and cold, they went on toward the North. Thus, everyone who started out with Harriet Tubman lived to thank her for freedom.

Long before the War Between the States came, many slaves were escaping. And so many white people in the North were helping them, that the routes to freedom became known as the "Underground Railroad." Secret "stations" where escaping slaves might be hidden, warmed, and fed were established in homes, barns, and sometimes even churches along the way. The Quakers were especially helpful and active in this regard. And a strong Anti-Slavery Society supported such activities. Slave owners were losing thousands of dollars worth of slaves by escape every year. Harriet Tubman became known as a

"conductor," on the Underground Railroad. She was not the only "conductor," but she was the most famous, and one of the most daring. Once she brought as many as twenty-five slaves in a single band to freedom.

Harriet had a great sense of humor. She enjoyed telling the story herself of how, not being able to read, she once sat down and went to sleep on a park bench, right under a sign offering a big reward for her capture. When she began to make speeches to raise money for the cause of freedom, she often told jokes, sang, and sometimes even danced. She might have been a great actress, people said. Without make-up she could hollow out her cheeks and wrinkle her brow to seem like a very old woman. She would make her body shrink and cause her legs to totter when she chose to so disguise herself. Once, making a trip to rescue some relatives, she had to pass through a village where she was known. She bought two hens. She tied them by their feet and hung them, heads down, around her neck. Then she went tottering along. Sure enough, a slave catcher came up the street who might, she thought, recognize her, tottering or not. So she unloosed the squalling chickens in the middle of the street, and dived after them, purposely not catching them so she could run down the road in pursuit and out of the slave catcher's sight, while all the passers-by laughed.

Sometimes, knowing that her band of fugitives was pursued by angry masters, she would get on a train headed south . . . because nobody would suspect that runaway slaves would be going south. Sometimes she would disguise the women in her party, and herself, as men. Babies would be given a sleeping medicine to keep them quiet, and then wrapped like bundles. Sometimes she would wade for hours up a stream to throw the hounds off scent. In the dark of night, when there was no North Star, she would feel the trunks of trees for the moss that grows on the northern side. That would serve as a guide toward freedom. Some people thought that Harriet Tubman led a charmed life because, within twelve years, she made nineteen dangerous trips into the South rescuing slaves. She herself said, "I never ran my train off the track. And I never lost a passenger."

Her father and mother were both over seventy years of age when she rescued them. She brought her parents north, to a home she had begun to buy in Auburn, New York. At first they stayed in St. Catherines, Canada. There escaped slaves were safe, since, in 1833, Queen Victoria had declared all slavery illegal. But it was too cold for them there. And Harriet's work was not on foreign soil. She herself seemed to have no fear of being captured. She came and went about the United States as she chose. She became so famous that, although she never sought the spotlight, it was hard for her not to be recognized wherever she was. Once at a great woman's suffrage meeting, an old head wound had caused her to go sound asleep in the audience. She was recognized and awoke to find herself on the platform. Her speech for woman's rights was roundly applauded.

In those days neither blacks nor women could vote. Harriet believed both should. So, like Frederick Douglass she followed the woman's suffrage movement closely.

In appearance "a more ordinary specimen of humanity could hardly be found." But there was no one with a greater capacity for leadership than she had. Among the slaves, where she walked in secret, Harriet began to be known as Moses. And at the great public meetings of the North, as the black historian William Wells Brown wrote in 1854, "all who frequented anti-slavery conventions, lectures, picnics, and fairs could not fail to have seen a black woman of medium size, upper teeth gone, smiling countenance, attired in coarse but neat apparel, with an old-fashioned reticule or bag suspended by her side, who, on taking her seat, would at once drop off into a sound sleep. . . . No fugitive was ever captured who had Moses for a leader." She was very independent. Between rescue trips or speeches, she would work as a cook or scrubwoman. She might borrow, but she never begged money for herself. All contributions went toward the cause of freedom in one way or another, as did most of what she earned.

But when the War Between the States began, she became a nurse for the Union armies. And then as a military scout and an invaluable intelligence agent behind the lines, she was promised compensation. Technically she was not a registered nurse. And, being a woman, she could not be a soldier. Yet she carried a Union pass, traveled on government transports, did dangerous missions in Confederate territory, and gave advice to chiefs of staff. She never got paid for this, although she had been promised $1800 for certain assignments. To Harriet this made no difference until after the war. She badly needed money to care for her aged parents. Petitions were sent to the War Department and to Congress to try to get the $1800 due her. But it was never granted.

Harriet Tubman's war activities were amazing. She served under General Stevens at Beaufort, South Carolina. She was sent to Florida to nurse those ill of dysentery, smallpox, and yellow fever. She was with Colonel Robert Gould Shaw at Fort Wagner. She organized a group of nine scouts and river pilots. With Colonel Montgomery, she led a Union raiding contingent of three gunboats and about 150 black troops up the Combahee River. As reported by the Boston *Commonwealth*, for July 10, 1863, they, "under the guidance of a

black woman, dashed into the enemy's country, struck a bold and effective blow, destroying millions of dollars worth of commissary stores, cotton, and lordly dwellings, and, striking terror into the hearts of rebeldom, brought off near 800 slaves and thousands of dollars worth of property." Concerning Harriet Tubman, the article continued, "Many and many times she has penetrated the enemy's lines and discovered their situation and condition, and escaped without injury, but not without extreme hazard."

Harriet Tubman never had a farm of her own. Her generous nature caused her to give away almost all the money she ever got her hands on. There were always fugitives, or relatives, or causes, or friends in need. She was over forty years old when Abraham Lincoln signed the Emancipation Proclamation, making legal for all the freedom she had struggled to secure. She lived for almost fifty years after the war was over. Some people thought she was a hundred years old when she died in 1913. Certainly she was over ninety.

A number of books have been written about her. The first one, *Scenes in the Life of Harriet Tubman*, by Sarah H. Bradford, appeared in 1869. The proceeds from the sale helped Harriet pay for her cottage. She asked her friend,

Frederick Douglass, who had hidden her and her runaway slaves more than once in his home in Rochester, for a letter about her book. In his reply he compared their two careers.

"The difference between us is very marked. Most that I have done and suffered in the service of our cause has been in public, and I have received much encouragement at every step of the way. I have wrought in the day . . . you in the night. You, on the other hand, have labored in a private way. I have had the applause of the crowd and the satisfaction that comes of being approved by the multitude, while the most that you have done has been witnessed by a few trembling, scared, and footsore bondsmen and women, whom you have led out of the house of bondage, and whose heartfelt "God bless you" has been your only reward. The midnight sky and the silent stars have been the witnesses of your devotion to freedom and of your heroism."

Years later, a reporter for *The New York Herald Tribune* came to interview Harriet one afternoon in Auburn. He wrote that, as he was leaving, Harriet looked toward an orchard nearby and asked, "Do you like apples?"

On being assured that the young man liked them, she asked, "Did you ever plant any apples?"

The writer confessed that he had not.

"No," said the old woman. "But somebody else planted them. I liked apples when I was young. And I said, 'Some day I'll plant apples myself for other folks to eat.' And I guess I did."

Her apples were the apples of freedom. Harriet Tubman lived to see the harvest. Her home in Auburn, New York, is preserved as a memorial to her planting.

CHECK FOR UNDERSTANDING

1. How famous was Harriet Tubman in her lifetime?

2. Approximately how old was Harriet Tubman when William Wells Brown described her in 1854?

3. What qualities made Harriet Tubman a good military scout and intelligence agent?

4. What did Harriet Tubman's appearance in 1854 tell you about her life?

5. What did the author mean when he said that the apples that Harriet had planted "were the apples of freedom"?

WRITE ABOUT *"Harriet Tubman"*

Imagine that you could paint a portrait of Harriet Tubman, one that would reveal her personality. At what point in her life would you choose to show her? What details would you choose? Write a description of your portrait.

FOLLOW
THE DRINKING
GOURD

According to some historians, many traditional spirituals were actually secret messages about traveling on the Underground Railroad. The drinking gourd in this song may refer to the Big Dipper. The handle of that constellation points to the North Star, which travelers use as a guide.

FIRST VERSE
When the sun comes back and the first quail calls,
Follow the drinking gourd,
For the old man is awaiting for to carry you to freedom,
Follow the drinking gourd.

CHORUS
Follow the drinking gourd,
Follow the drinking gourd,
For the old man is awaiting for to carry you to freedom,
Follow the drinking gourd.

SECOND VERSE
The river bank'll make a mighty good road;
The dead trees'll show you the way.
Left foot, peg foot traveling on,
Follow the drinking gourd.

THIRD VERSE
The river ends between two hills,
Follow the drinking gourd.
And there's another river on the other side,
Follow the drinking gourd.

FOURTH VERSE
Where the great big river meets the little river,
Follow the drinking gourd.
The old man is waiting for to carry you to freedom,
Follow the drinking gourd.

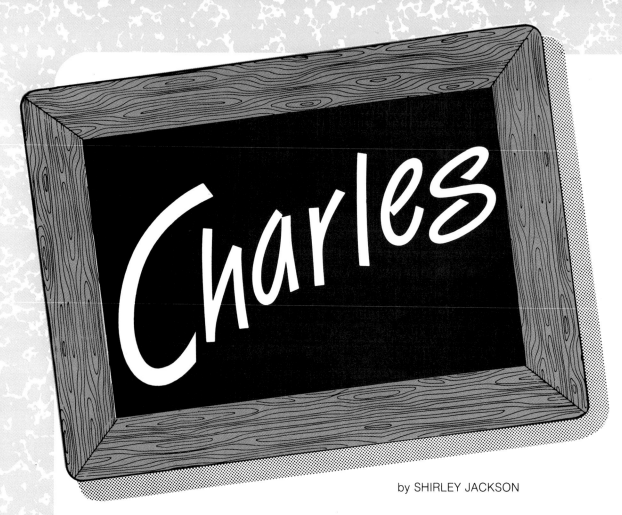

by SHIRLEY JACKSON

Everyone knows a young child who misbehaves. Sometimes the misbehavior is so outrageous that it is fascinating to watch. Laurie's parents are fascinated by their son's description of Charles. What does Laurie think the school will do about Charles? How do you think Laurie's mother felt when the teacher responded to her comment about Charles?

The day my son Laurie started kindergarten he renounced courduroy overalls with bibs and began wearing blue jeans with a belt; I watched him go off the first morning with the older girl next door, seeing clearly that an era of my life was ended, my sweet-voiced nursery-school tot replaced by a long-trousered, swaggering character who forgot to stop at the corner and wave good-bye to me.

He came home the same way, the front door slamming open, his cap on the floor, and the voice suddenly became raucous shouting, "Isn't anybody *here*?"

At lunch he spoke insolently to his father, spilled his baby sister's milk, and remarked that his teacher said we were not to take the name of the Lord in vain.

"How *was* school today?" I asked, elaborately casual.

"All right," he said.

"Did you learn anything?" his father asked.

Laurie regarded his father coldly. "I didn't learn nothing," he said.

"Anything," I said. "Didn't learn anything."

"The teacher spanked a boy, though," Laurie said, addressing his bread and butter. "For being fresh," he added, with his mouth full.

"What did he do?" I asked. "Who was it?"

Laurie thought. "It was Charles," he said. "He was fresh. The teacher spanked him and made him stand in a corner. He was awfully fresh."

"What did he do?" I asked again, but Laurie slid off his chair, took a cookie, and left, while his father was still saying, "See here, young man."

The next day Laurie remarked at lunch, as soon as he sat down, "Well, Charles was bad again today." He grinned enormously and said, "Today Charles hit the teacher."

"Good heavens," I said, mindful of the Lord's name, "I suppose he got spanked again?"

"He sure did," Laurie said. "Look up," he said to his father.

"What?" his father said, looking up.

"Look down," Laurie said. "Look at my thumb. Gee, you're dumb." He began to laugh insanely.

"Why did Charles hit the teacher?" I asked quickly.

"Because she tried to make him color with red crayons," Laurie said. "Charles wanted to color with green crayons so

Charles was a bad boy today...

he hit the teacher and she spanked him and said nobody talk to Charles but everybody did."

The third day—it was the Wednesday of the first week—Charles bounced a see-saw on to the head of a little girl and made her bleed, and the teacher made him stay inside all during recess. Thursday Charles had to stand in a corner during story-time because he kept pounding his feet on the floor. Friday Charles was deprived of blackboard privileges because he threw chalk.

On Saturday I remarked to my husband, "Do you think kindergarten is too unsettling for Laurie? All this toughness, and bad grammar, and this Charles boy sounds like such a bad influence."

"It'll be all right," my husband said reassuringly. "Bound to be people like Charles in the world. Might as well meet them now as later."

On Monday Laurie came home late, full of news. "Charles," he shouted as he came up the hill; I was waiting anxiously on the front steps. "Charles," Laurie yelled all the way up the hill, "Charles was bad again."

"Come right in," I said, as soon as he came close enough. "Lunch is waiting."

"You know what Charles did?" he demanded, following me through the door. "Charles yelled so in school they sent a boy in from first grade to tell the teacher she had to make

Charles keep quiet, and so Charles had to stay after school.
And so all the children stayed to watch him."

"What did he do?" I asked.

"He just sat there," Laurie said, climbing into his chair at
the table. "Hi, Pop, old dust mop."

"Charles had to stay after school today," I told my husband. "Everyone stayed with him."

"What does this Charles look like?" my husband asked
Laurie. "What's his other name?"

"He bigger than me," Laurie said. "And he doesn't ever
wear a jacket."

Monday night was the first Parent-Teachers meeting, and
only the fact that the baby had a cold kept me from going; I
wanted passionately to meet Charles's mother. On Tuesday
Laurie remarked suddenly, "Our teacher had a friend come to
see her in school today."

"Charles's mother?" my husband and I asked simultaneously.

"Naah," Laurie said scornfully. "It was a man who came
and made us do exercises, we had to touch our toes. Look."
He climbed down from his chair and squatted down and
touched his toes. "Like this," he said. He got solemnly back
into his chair and said, picking up his fork, "Charles didn't
even *do* exercises."

"Fresh again?" I said.

"He kicked the teacher's friend," Laurie said. "The teacher's friend told Charles to touch his toes like I just did and Charles kicked him."

"What are they going to do about Charles, do you suppose?" Laurie's father asked him.

Laurie shrugged elaborately. "Throw him out of school, I guess," he said.

Wednesday and Thursday were routine; Charles yelled during story-hour and hit a boy in the stomach and made him cry. On Friday Charles stayed after school again and so did all the other children.

With the third week of kindergarten Charles was an institution in our family; the baby was being a Charles when she cried all afternoon; Laurie did a Charles when he filled his wagon full of mud and pulled it through the kitchen; even my husband, when he caught his elbow in the telephone cord and pulled telephone, ashtray, and a bowl of flowers off the table, said, after the first minute, "Looks like Charles."

During the third and fourth weeks it looked like a reformation in Charles; Laurie reported grimly at lunch on Thursday of the third week, "Charles was so good today the teacher gave him an apple."

"What?" I said, and my husband added warily, "You mean Charles?"

"Charles," Laurie said. "He gave the crayons around and he picked up the books afterward and the teacher said he was her helper."

"What happened?" I asked incredulously.

"He was her helper, that's all," Laurie said, and shrugged.

"Can this be true about Charles?" I asked my husband that night. "Can something like this happen?"

"Wait and see," my husband said cynically. "When you've got a Charles to deal with, this may mean he's only plotting."

He seemed to be wrong. For over a week Charles was the teacher's helper; each day he handed things out and he picked things up; no one had to stay after school.

"The P.T.A. meeting's next week again," I told my husband one evening. "I'm going to find Charles's mother there."

"Ask her what happened to Charles," my husband said. "I'd like to know."

"I'd like to know myself," I said.

On Friday of that week things were back to normal. "You know what Charles did today?" Laurie demanded at the lunch table, in a voice slightly awed. "He told a little girl to say a word and she said it and the teacher washed her mouth out with soap and Charles laughed."

"What word?" his father asked unwisely, and Laurie said, "I'll have to whisper it to you, it's so bad." He got down off his chair and went around to his father. His father bent his head down and Laurie whispered joyfully. His father's eyes widened.

"Did Charles tell the little girl to say *that*?" he asked respectfully.

"She said it *twice*," Laurie said. "Charles told her to say it *twice*."

"What happened to Charles?" my husband asked.

"Nothing," Laurie said. "He was passing out the crayons."

Monday morning Charles abandoned the little girl and said the evil word himself three or four times, getting his mouth washed out with soap each time. He also threw chalk.

My husband came to the door with me that evening as I set out for the P.T.A. meeting. "Invite her over for a cup of tea after the meeting," he said. "I want to get a look at her."

"If only she's there," I said prayerfully.

"She'll be there," my husband said. "I don't see how they could hold a P.T.A. meeting without Charles's mother."

At the meeting I sat restlessly, scanning each comfortable matronly face, trying to determine which one hid the secret of

RUN

Charles. None of them looked to me haggard enough. No one stood up in the meeting and apologized for the way her son had been acting. No one mentioned Charles.

After the meeting I identified and sought out Laurie's kindergarten teacher. She had a plate with a cup of tea and a piece of chocolate cake; I had a plate with a cup of tea and a piece of marshmallow cake. We manuevered up to one another cautiously and smiled.

"I've been so anxious to meet you," I said. "I'm Laurie's mother."

"We're all so interested in Laurie," she said.

"Well, he certainly likes kindergarten," I said. "He talks about it all the time."

"We had a little trouble adjusting, the first week or so," she said primly, "but now he's a fine little helper. With occasional lapses, of course."

"Laurie usually adjusts very quickly," I said. "I suppose this time it's Charles's influence."

"Charles?"

"Yes," I said, laughing, "you must have your hands full in that kindergarten, with Charles."

"Charles?" she said. "We don't have any Charles in the kindergarten."

"Charles," "We haven't any..."

CHECK FOR UNDERSTANDING

1. Why do you think Laurie refused to wear overalls to kindergarten?
2. What did Laurie think the school would do about Charles?
3. Why did Laurie talk so much about Charles?
4. Who was Charles?
5. How do you think Laurie's mother felt when the teacher responded to her comment about Charles?

WRITE ABOUT *"Charles"*

Imagine what Laurie's mother would say to his father about the P.T.A. meeting. Write a conversation in which she tells him the latest news about Charles.

Comparing Sources of Information

Which book do you think will be more accurate?

The True Story about Kindergarten
Author A has many years of experience as a kindergarten teacher. She is familiar with the many tricks that children play on themselves and on their parents.

The True Story about Kindergarten
Author B has recently entered kindergarten. In the beginning, he experienced some difficulties in adjusting to the strict regimen. He created an imaginary friend as a way of coping with the stresses of his new life.

In Shirley Jackson's story "Charles," Laurie's parents depended on their son to tell them what was happening in the kindergarten classroom. Laurie was their only source of information. Laurie's tales of the misdeeds of Charles—the worst boy in the class—are so convincing that his parents begin to wonder how the teacher, let alone Charles' parents, can cope with him. Laurie creates the character of Charles so well that the family begins to refer to any accident or childish error as a "Charles." Not until the parent-teacher meeting does Laurie's mother find out that there is no Charles, except in Laurie's imagination.

Any newspaper reporter who wrote a story based on Laurie's information would have made a serious journalistic mistake by not checking the source of the information. If the source of the information, the person who is telling the story, is not reliable, then the story may not be reliable either. For example, a book about how pine trees are the major source of air pollution because they have a strong smell is less convincing when you find out that the writer never studied science.

Students, like reporters, are also in the business of gathering facts and deciding on the accuracy of information. Whenever you write a report for science class, prepare a debate for social studies class, or write an opinion paper for English class, you read what others have written and sometimes you quote some of their words and ideas. How can you make sure that the authors you quote are reliable?

Asking the Right Questions

To evaluate an author's ability to write accurately or objectively, read the book jacket or book reviews and try to find the answer to these questions.

- Does the writer have the right kind of education or training?

Not every writer has to have an advanced degree in the subject he or she is writing about. However, certain technical subjects should be handled only by people who have studied them. An engineering text should be written by someone who has a degree in engineering; a biology text should be written by someone who has studied biology; a book on writing should be written by someone who is a professional writer. Someone who has learned certain skills on the job can also be a reliable source if the answer to the next question is satisfactory.

- Does the writer have enough experience?

If you decided to become a dancer, you would want a teacher with lots of experience. You would not want someone who has been dancing for only one year. For the same reason, a book about the hidden dangers of deep-sea diving would be more accurate if it were written by a diver with both a science background and many years of diving experience. Because not everyone can be a professional writer, some writers describe experiences that others have had. For example, a book about what it feels like to travel in space should either be written by an astronaut or be based on interviews with astronauts.

● Does the writer have a hidden bias?

A book about why it is necessary to hunt whales would not be very objective if it were written by the captain of a whale-fishing boat. You can check for hidden bias, unobjective views, by reading the jacket copy closely. For whom does the writer work? Where did he or she go to school? What other books has the author written? Another good place to check is the Acknowledgments page in the front of the book. Authors usually thank the libraries and companies who gave them the information they use.

Using What You Have Learned

Listed below each title are two possible authors. Decide which person would make the better author.

1. *Wilderness Survival*

Charlotte Wilkinson. Ms. Wilkinson has been a resident of Barnet's Island in the Northwest Territories of Canada for thirty years. She lives in a log cabin that she built and wears clothes that she has made from the wool of the goats that she raises. Ms. Wilkinson learned medicine from a book after her husband, a doctor, died. Soon after, she took out her younger son's inflamed appendix.

Roger Mantercore. Dr. Mantercore, a recent graduate of the University of Washington, has spent two summers leading students on ten-day hiking tours of the Canadian Rockies. He is a trained botanist and photographer and wants to devote his life to helping others enjoy the wilderness.

2. *Is Exercise Good for You?*

James Bartlesson. Mr. Bartlesson is the founder of the Manitoba Rest Club, the first resort that advertises itself as the place where "No one makes you do anything you don't want to do." The author is also famous for designing the Bartlesson Chair, the complete rest system that has an overhead TV, a built-in stereo, a mini-refrigerator, and a robot that can cook.

Jonathan McGuire. Dr. McGuire, whose degree is in sports medicine, was severely injured as a young boy. After many months of hospitalization, he could barely walk. His parents started him on a program of exercises, and after two years he was able to run on the high school track team.

Expanding Your Skills

Make up jacket copy for books in a field you know something about. Read your copy aloud and ask the class to evaluate which book might be the most accurate.

Twins have interested other people throughout history. They not only look alike, but often they seem to feel the other's pain, or sense when the other is in danger. Professor Tom Bouchard has conducted a scientific study of twins. Why do you think the researchers ask the twins approximately 15,000 questions? Why does seeing one's interests, likes and dislikes, and attitudes in another person help one to understand oneself better?

A STUDY OF TWINS

by PETER WATSON

What happens to twins who are separated at birth because they are adopted by different families? Professor Tom Bouchard runs an ongoing study of twins separated at birth. The study is located, appropriately, in the Twin Cities of Minneapolis and St. Paul, Minnesota. Twins are tested, physically and psychologically, for similarities and differences. Some of the test results are of more than just scientific interest. They provide a fascinating glimpse of the special link that exists between even those twins who grow up without knowing that they are one of a pair.

JAKE AND KEITH

Jake Hellbach arrived in Minneapolis on a cold Sunday in March 1980. He had flown in from New Orleans. Hours before, his twin, Keith Heitzman, had arrived from Dallas/Fort Worth. They were the thirteenth set of twins to arrive in the city for a week's intensive testing. Jake was met by Tom Bouchard and shown to the scientist's car. Before they had driven out of the airport Jake remarked on a slight shuddering sound on the right side of the vehicle, toward the rear. It was a small knocking sound, nothing serious. It was due to an uneven tire. But that was not what made Bouchard smile. Earlier in the day, Jake's twin Keith had remarked on the *same* sound in Tom's car.

When twins arrive to take part in the Minnesota study, they are usually met at the airport by Tom Bouchard or one of his colleagues. The fact that Jake and his brother Keith had both commented on the unusual sound was only one of several coincidences that have occurred during the study. A British pair of twins turned up wearing identical jewelry. Twin men, separated for twenty-five years, arrived at the airport wearing identical shirts and identical glasses.

Tom Bouchard has been intrigued by these similarities at the airport. They have undoubtedly had an effect on him and his feeling about twins. He does not attach too much importance to what happens in the baggage claim area.

Twins who take part in the program generally arrive in Minneapolis on a Sunday. On Sunday night, Bouchard has dinner with the twins and explains the study to them. He tells them what to expect during the coming week. He warns them that they will be exhausted by their time in the Twin Cities. They sign consent forms, and the study is ready to begin.

TESTS AND MORE TESTS

The study generally begins on Monday morning. It runs almost nonstop until midafternoon the next Saturday. Evenings and the whole of Wednesday are free. But the other working days run from 8 A.M. until 5:30 P.M., a tiring schedule. During that time the twins answer approximately 15,000 questions about themselves and see several psychologists.

First, the twins give a medical history. They think of all the childhood illnesses they have had, when they had them, how sick they were, and so on. "We want to know whether they've had mumps, broken legs—everything. When, how long, and how serious!'' says Bouchard. They have a physical examination. A test of heart and regulatory systems follows. Many of the twins are nearing middle age. Certain abnormalities that are developing are sometimes spotted in these tests. For example, Barbara Herbert and Daphne Goodship both found in Minneapolis that they were developing identical heart murmurs.

An allergy test involves blood samples and some skin tests. Next comes an examination of the lungs, especially their capacity. This can be very useful in research, particularly in regard to smoking.

Professor David Lykken tests the twins' heart patterns and their brainwaves. These tests have already provided a number of intriguing sidelights. For instance, in order to have their brainwaves tested, the twins have to enter a small soundproofed booth. It is rather like a telephone booth, but without the windows. Dr. Lykken has found that a number of twins show the same reaction to the booth itself. If one twin is afraid of close spaces and is wary of entering the booth, the other twin usually has the same reaction. And where one twin does not mind the booth, the

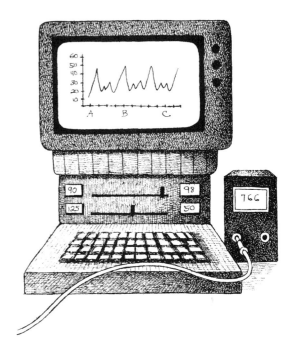

other twin doesn't either. Lykken has found also that the brainwave patterns of twins are more similar when they are apart than when they are together in the same room. Lykken also takes the twins' fingerprints, handprints, and footprints. He finds that twins tend to grow calluses on the same parts of their hands and feet. He measures head size and weight, and takes photos of all the twins.

The twins' intelligence, memories, and personalities are tested. Questions like: ''How many uses can you think of for a brick?'' are asked. Twins have to draw a house, a tree, and a person. This is to reveal different aspects of their personalities. Their common dreams are noted.

Next there are various physical tests. For example, a hand-steadiness test and a hand-eye coordination test are given. The twins also spend some time on a treadmill, to see how they react to sustained movement.

Bouchard spends Friday morning taking the twins through their lives. He puts special emphasis on how they have reacted to stresses and crises . . . exams, for example, or the death of a loved one, divorce, or being fired.

Another interview explores the twins' personal lives . . . their feelings, attitudes, important experiences, and so on. An interview with two of the doctors is videotaped. The videotape has two purposes. It allows the scientists to look at the gestures and mannerisms of the twins later on and search for similarities. It also allows other scientists to look at the twins and make their own judgments about them. Finally, the twins' handwriting is sampled. Their wives or husbands, if they have come to Minneapolis, undergo some of the psychological testing.

As with the brainwave tests, Bouchard found that twins tested in different rooms produce results that are *more* similar than when they are together in the same room. And many twins not only get the same scores on the tests. They also make the same mistakes, and finish at the same time. This sort of detail has made a deep impression on some of the twins. Many have, quite definitely, found out at Minnesota that they were more alike than they thought. They have discovered interests, likes, and dislikes. They find attitudes in each other that, because they can see them in someone else, make them understand themselves better. Making the same mistakes on the tests, as much as getting the same score, has had a big impact on several pairs of twins. It is as if seeing another's shortcomings has finally convinced them of their own. This kind of reaction is hard to analyze scientifically. But it has excited Bouchard and his co-workers.

TWO PEAS IN A POD

The first coincidence in the lives of Jake Hellbach and Keith Heitzman occurred without either of them knowing it. They were born in Algiers, a suburb of New Orleans, and adopted into different families. But, as luck would have it, the entry for Hellbach in the New Orleans phone book was in the next column to, and right opposite, that for Heitzman.

These twins are known in Minnesota for the fact that they looked more alike than any of the others. "Some identical twins, after all the years apart, don't look all that identical. But these do," Bouchard says. Both are tall, dark, and handsome men, slim and given to smiles that spread only gradually over their faces. They resemble each other so much, in fact, that during their week in Minnesota, Bouchard actually mistook Keith for Jake over lunch on Tuesday, the only time this has ever happened. "It's not only the physical similarity," says Bouchard. "But their similarity in being so quiet is also striking. They even sit with their arms folded in the same way."

After they were separated, Jake and Keith grew up on different sides of the Mississippi in Jefferson County, Louisiana, just outside New Orleans. They attended rival high schools. Jake eventually settled in Abita Springs and Keith in Metairie. Jake is now a pump mechanic and Keith a welder.

The chain of events that led to their reunion began a long time ago. While they were growing up, neither knew he was a twin. Their adoptive parents judged it best not to tell them. But Keith had always believed that he had a brother. His feeling was confirmed when he saw his birth certificate and found out he had been the first-born of a set of twin boys. Then he started looking for his brother in earnest.

The next move came when his adoptive mother contacted Bouchard. She had read about the Minnesota study in a magazine. She asked the professor to help find Keith's twin. Bouchard put one of his

assistants on to the problem, but their inquiries came to nothing. As a last resort, Keith paid for his own advertisement in the New Orleans afternoon paper, the *States-Item*. That did the trick.

After the ad appeared, the editors of the paper became interested in Keith's search, and wrote him up in an article. Jake Hellbach's adoptive mother had not seen Keith's ad. But she did see the article. That was when she told Jake that she realized Heitzman must be his twin.

Since Keith was already in touch with Bouchard it was not long before he and his brother were on their way to Minneapolis. Although they were the most similar twins Bouchard had yet encountered in terms of their bearing, manners, and habits, they did show some scientific differences. For a start Jake is left-handed. Keith is right-handed. This affected how they did some tests. For instance, in one test they had to draw a house. Jake put the door on the left, Keith on the right. Otherwise the houses were very similar. It is possible that they may be mirror-image twins. That is identical but with certain attributes—the crown of the hair, fingerprints, and so on—reversed. Bouchard is not certain yet. They were the first pair he had seen who had differed in this way. Another difference is that Jake has a bigger head, though a slightly smaller body.

Like the other twins, Jake and Keith made several intriguing discoveries about themselves at Minneapolis. Among them, both are allergic to ragweed and dust, both did poorly in school. Both avoided gym classes in school but enjoyed art. Both have a strong interest in hunting. Both have a great appetite for chocolate and other sweet things. Both dress in a similar manner and are especially fond of large cowboy hats. And both "put off until tomorrow what should be done today." These two also show perfectly what happens to many identical twins who meet after years of separation. Although it was Keith who did the looking because he always felt he had a brother, Jake had always wanted a brother. "Finding a blood brother as an adult is great, to say the least," he says now.

"They're making up for lost time," says Stacey Heitzman, Keith's wife. "There's just no separating them now." "They think the same," says Caroll Heitzman, Keith's adoptive mother. "They are both attuned to what each other is thinking. Being separated, you wouldn't imagine they would have this." And, Stacey adds, "The twins can communicate using only partial sentences no one else understands."

When they were in Minneapolis, Keith and Jake were still a source of interest outside the laboratories. On one occasion, they entered adjacent phone booths in their hotel at the same time, and called each other. After spending their days separated, for the purposes of the testing, they would hurry back to each other in the evening. The normally quiet, reserved men would, in each other's company, become comics who, according to Stacey, "act like they've been practicing as a team for years."

Both had also started keeping a scrapbook since they had been reunited. These books contain news clippings about their reunion, their birth certificates, and snapshots of their first birthday spent together, on January 4, 1980. But the pair has also received a number of letters from strangers who seem moved by their story, showing the special feeling the bonds between twins evokes in many people. "I really don't have a special reason for writing," said one fifteen-year-old girl in her letter. "All I know is that, when I read about you finding your brother, I felt so happy inside that I cried."

CHECK FOR UNDERSTANDING

1. How long did Dr. Bouchard keep the twins for testing?
2. Why do you think the researchers asked the twins approximately 15,000 questions?
3. In what ways were Jake and Keith different?
4. Why do you think the normally reserved Jake and Keith "clowned around" when in each other's company?
5. Scientists have recently developed the theory that all humans have a "biological clock" within their genes that determines the approximate age at which an individual will die. How might the study of twins confirm this opinion as fact?
6. Why would seeing one's interests, likes and dislikes, and attitudes in another person help one to understand oneself better?

WRITE ABOUT *"A Study of Twins"*

What conclusions do *you* draw from the information that Dr. Bouchard reports? Write a paragraph stating your opinions and the reasons supporting them.

LITERATURE

Point of View

The way a story is told depends on the person telling the story. In literature, this is called the **point of view.** Every story has to have a point of view, a vantage point from which the story is told.

The following is a passage from *Little Looks*, a story told through the eyes of Little Little, a girl who never grows taller. The narrator telling this story refers to himself as "I." This is called a **first-person point of view.**

> Although in various ways and straight out I was told by my mother I would not grow to be as tall as other people, it did not sink in until my little sister grew bigger than I was.

When the author has a character tell a story, he allows the character's feelings and attitudes to affect the way the story is told.

Many stories are told from the point of view of the author who remains outside the story. These stories are called **third-person point of view,** and are told by someone who is not in the story. The following paragraph, taken from *The Red Pony,* is told from a third-person point of view.

> Billy Buck wasn't wrong about many things. He couldn't be. But he was wrong about the weather that day, for a little after noon the clouds pushed over the hills and the rain began to pour down. Jody heard it start on the schoolhouse roof.

In this passage, the narrator tells the reader that Billy Buck was wrong about the weather. The narrator is telling us things that the character in the story does not directly think or observe. The narrator is giving us additional information. Sometimes the narrator makes a judgment. This is known as **omniscient,** or **all-knowing.**

Sometimes the writer limits the third-person point of view so that the reader views the story through the eyes of one character only. This is called **limited third-person point of view.** The narrator does not tell the reader what the other characters are thinking or feeling.

The next selection, "Kilroy's New Act," is an example of a limited third-person point of view. Part of the humor of this lively tale is in the point of view from which the story is told. In the following paragraph, Kilroy, an orca or "killer whale," is being trained to perform in a water show.

"No, no, no!" the trainer shouted. "Hit it with your nose! Your nose!" Kilroy didn't understand the words but got the message, and he glumly circled the pool, shot in the air, and hit the ball with his nose as he was supposed to. "Marvelous!" the trainer cried. "Perfect! Bravo!" Kilroy sank to the bottom of the pool, and sulked. I'd like to teach this man a trick or two, he thought.

How would this scene be told from the viewpoint of the trainer?
Why do you think the author chose this particular point of view to tell his story?
As you read "Kilroy's New Act," notice the details that reveal this unusual point of view.

Just·A·Taste

KILROY AND THE GULL

Nathaniel Benchley

The selections in this unit have shown several ways in which "the human kind" view one another. This story raises the issue of how animals view human beings. The main character, Kilroy, meets human beings for the first time.

What puzzles Kilroy about his first trainer? Why does the author choose to create a whale's-eye view of the world?

Kilroy was an orca, an intelligent sea mammal that is sometimes called a "killer whale." Born and raised in the ocean, Kilroy was captured and transported to an amusement park, where he was trained to perform in aquatic shows. He befriended a seagull named Morris, who tried to help him understand the puzzling behavior of his human captors. Are humans intelligent? Before Kilroy could answer this question, he was transferred to another aquarium.

KILROY'S NEW ACT

After a long trip, by truck and airplane and then by truck again, Kilroy arrived at his new home. The aquarium was larger than the first one, and there were tiers of seats on both sides of the main pool, seats that he found out later were occupied by tourists who came to watch the show. His pool was off the main one, and had a large wall, or fence, separating it from the sea, so his water was constantly changed by the tides and was always fresh. His first thought was to see if he could jump over the fence, but it had been made too high for that, and, after exploring all the possibilities, he gave up and resigned himself to captivity.

It was tantalizing to be so close to the sea without being able to swim away, but at least it was better than being cooped up in one small pool. If Kilroy had learned anything in the last little while, it was to make the best of what was at hand and not try to do the impossible.

There was a sort of sluice gate leading from his pool into the main one, and this was opened when the people wanted him to go from one to the other. The first time he went into the main pool he saw, at the opposite end, three bottlenosed dolphins, who were regarding him in silence. "Oh, no," he said to himself. "Not *that* again!" He looked at the dolphins, and they looked at him, and he finally decided to see if he could start things off on a friendly basis. He went slowly toward them, and they clustered together and waited.

"My name is Kilroy," he said.

269

The dolphins didn't answer.

"If we're going to share the same pool we might as well try to get along," he went on. "As far as I'm concerned, we're all in one family."

There was a short silence, then one of the dolphins said, "I'm glad to hear it. Where'd you come from?"

"Another aquarium."

"Then you're not a dolphin eater?"

"No, and I never have been. Our pod never once touched a dolphin." This wasn't exactly the truth, but it was close enough, because he himself had never eaten one.

"I thought you said you came from an aquarium," the dolphin said.

"I did, but before that I lived in the ocean. I was born in the ocean."

"Then how come you've never eaten dolphin?"

"Look," said Kilroy. "If you'll just stop being suspicious, we can all have a good time. At this other aquarium there was a dolphin who made life miserable for both of us, just because he'd had an uncle who was eaten by orcas. Forget what other orcas have done, and listen to me when I say I want to be friendly. What have you got to lose?"

The dolphins looked at each other, and then the first one said, "Come to think of it, I guess you're right. If you want to be friendly, there's no reason we shouldn't be."

"All right then. My name is Kilroy. What are yours?"

"I'm called Groucho," said the first.

"I'm Harpo," said the one on his left.

"Chico," said the third.

"Glad to know you," said Kilroy.

"You sound Italian. Are you?"

"Don't ask me," Groucho replied. "The trainer gave us our names."

"What's he like?" Kilroy asked.

"He's all right. He doesn't work us too hard."

"Can you talk to him?"

Groucho thought for a moment, then said, "Not really. You know what he wants by the signals he gives you, but that isn't exactly talking."

"I think there's got to be some way to get through to people," Kilroy said. "I have a feeling they may be a lot more intelligent than we think they are."

"I'll tell you one thing about this man," Chico put in. "He gives you a fish only when you do the trick right. You can't cut corners with him."

"I don't care about the fish," Kilroy replied. "I'd like to know what he's thinking."

"That never occurred to me," said Groucho. "To me, he's just another way of getting food."

Harpo, who had drifted slightly away from the others, now started a series of leaps, going high in the air and then falling back, only to shoot straight

up again, like a bouncing ball. Each leap was more frenzied than the first, until it looked as though he were trying to fly.

"That means the trainer's coming," Groucho observed. "Harpo always goes a little crazy when training time begins."

"Why?" said Kilroy. "Doesn't he get enough exercise?"

"He likes to get the first fish. I think he's afraid the bucket'll be empty before he's had his share."

The trainer flipped a fish to Harpo, who swallowed it and, grinning, re-joined the others.

"All right," Groucho said.

"Places for ACT ONE." Chico and Harpo fell in line behind him, and all three waited for the signal from the trainer.

"Where do I go?" Kilroy asked.

"Wait till he tells you," Groucho replied. "I don't know where you fit into the act."

The trainer blew a whistle and the three dolphins started off, leaping in unison as they made a circuit of the pool. Then they gathered beneath him and put their heads out of water, and he tossed a fish to each one. Kilroy, who was afraid he was being left out of the act, also put his head out of water, smiling broadly to attract the trainer's attention.

271

"Oh, you want one, too?" said the trainer, and he tossed a fish to Kilroy, who held it in his teeth, then took it back and laid it at the trainer's feet. The man stared at him, then said, "What's the matter with it?" and picked up the fish and examined it.

"We haven't finished our act yet," Groucho said. "Why don't you wait until—" But Kilroy was off on a tour of the pool, leaping as the dolphins had done, and ending back in front of the trainer. Again the man gave him a fish, and again Kilroy gave it back. "Believe me, I don't mean to sound impatient," Groucho said, "but maybe if we finish our act first, then he'll know where to fit you in."

"I'm sorry," Kilroy said, backing away. "I just wanted to make a point." He retired across the pool and the dolphins waited for the signal for their next trick, but the trainer kept looking at Kilroy, trying to understand what was going on. Finally Harpo started leaping straight up in the air, and the trainer returned his attention to the dolphins. They went through a whole series of tricks, jumping through and over various obstacles, but the trainer was so distracted that at one point he forgot to give them their fish, and Harpo had to start leaping again to remind him.

When, finally, the training session was over, Groucho came to Kilroy and, trying as hard as he could to be tactful, said, "I hope you didn't think I was rude, asking you to wait for us to finish."

"Not in the least," Kilroy replied. "It was my fault entirely."

"This morning it didn't matter," Groucho went on, "because it was only a rehearsal, but if it had been show time it would have disrupted the act."

"When is the show?" Kilroy asked.

"We do two a day, in the afternoons," Groucho told him. "Then on weekends we do three, one morning and two afternoon. It comes out to sixteen shows a week."

"That's a lot of shows," Kilroy observed. "I should think you'd be good and sick of it by now."

Groucho looked at the other two, who were chasing each other around the perimeter of the pool. "I suppose if we thought about it, we would be," he replied. "But it's exercise, and we get food for it, so we can't complain."

"What I'd like to do is talk to the trainer," Kilroy said. "If I could just do that, I have a feeling life wouldn't be so dull."

"You don't want much, do you?" said Groucho.

"I don't know. It may be perfectly simple, once I find the key."

"Well, let me know how you make out," Groucho replied. "So long as he keeps the fish coming, I don't care what he has to say." And with that he swam off and joined the others.

Somewhat to the dolphins' annoyance, a new training schedule was started, in which Kilroy had a leading part. The trainer, seeing that Kilroy was doing the tricks for their own sake, rather than for food, reasoned there was nothing he wouldn't do if he just got the idea, and to this end he began to devise all sorts of elaborate routines. The trouble was that they were all variants of the same trick: Kilroy would butt a ball, or jump a hurdle, or smack the water so many times with his tail, and the only really tricky things were the props the trainer invented to go along with the basics. He made, for instance, a large fountain pen, which Kilroy grasped in his mouth in an act during which he was supposed to sign a contract; the same stick that was the core of the pen could also be made into a baseball bat, when the story accompanying the act was changed. Or a flag, for the Iwo Jima monument.* Or a toothbrush, for a domestic scene. And so on. In short, Kilroy was doing one basic trick, the extremely simple one of holding something in his mouth, while the trainer invented the frills that went with it.

* the famous statue of five Marines raising the flag on the Pacific island of Iwo Jima during the World War II battle there.

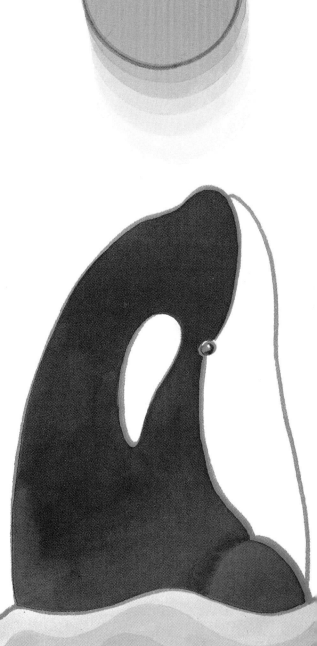

To Kilroy this was deeply discouraging, and he finally decided to invent a trick of his own, one that would show he was thinking, instead of merely obeying orders. He pondered the problem for a while, and then, during a training session, when he was supposed to leap high in the air and butt a ball with his nose, he made the leap, flipped over and slapped the ball with his tail, and returned to the water in a grotesque parody of a swan dive.

"No, no, no!" the trainer shouted. "Hit it with your nose! Your nose!" Kilroy didn't understand the words, but he got the message, and he glumly circled the pool, shot in the air, and hit the ball with his nose, as he was supposed to. "Marvelous!" the trainer cried. "Perfect! Bravo!" Kilroy sank to the bottom of the pool, and sulked. I'd like to teach this man a trick or two, he thought. I'd like to have him swallow a salmon in one bite, or find a squid down where the water's as black as midnight, or leap his full length out of the water. Or— or— I'd like to teach him to *think*. That would be something. I'd gladly put up with all this silliness, just to show that he was thinking. We might even have some thoughts in common, and we could exchange ideas, and teach one another things we hadn't known before. The thought of sharing ideas with a man was so exciting that Kilroy came up

from the bottom, opened his mouth wide, and wiggled his tongue at the trainer. The gesture reminded him of Morris, who had tweaked his tongue the first time they met, and he did it on the chance it might mean something to the trainer beyond the simple gesture. The man looked at him, laughed, then reached into a bucket, and threw him a fish. "Oh, all right," he said. "You've worked for it." Kilroy took the fish by the tail and then, with his head out of water, spun around faster and faster and finally let the fish go. It sailed out in a

bright, twinkling arc, and landed in the grandstand seats. The trainer watched it, then cast a baleful glance at Kilroy. "That's gratitude for you," he said. "Now I've got to clean it up." Kilroy made a honking noise through his blowhole, then started a series of fast laps around the pool, chasing an imaginary flying fish, until the trainer opened the sluice gate to his own pool and let him through.

Kilroy's first public show was a thundering success. The grandstand was filled with people in brightly col-

ored shirts and dresses, and from them rose a gabble of voices punctuated by the shouts and cries of children; soft-drink and hot-dog vendors hawked their wares, and over the loudspeaker came a program of canned music that under other circumstances would have been offensive to Kilroy's sense of hearing. As it was, it was part of the circus atmosphere, and, as such, exciting, and while Kilroy wasn't nervous, he was so stimulated that he couldn't resist doing a few small motions of his own. He was like a racehorse at the starting gate, waiting to be released to show what he could do.

The act started off with Kilroy and the three dolphins covering an obstacle course around the pool, and when the dolphins received their fish, Kilroy stood by and applauded. Then they swam in formation, with the dolphins rotating from one side to the other of their large companion, and finally tail-walking ahead of him, while he pretended to give chase. Then came Kilroy's solo act, in which he was rigged out in a Revolutionary War hat, and made to do a number of things that had an allegedly patriotic theme. All he was really doing was holding something in his mouth, and hitting the water with his tail, and all the simple, humdrum bits of routine, but the voice over the loudspeaker read all sorts of meaning

275

into his acts. The audience applauded wildly, but to Kilroy the whole act was frustrating, because he'd been drubbed into doing meaningless things, when all the time he'd wanted to do something better. He did his act exactly as he was supposed to, because every time he tried something a little different, he got a warning scowl from the trainer and he finally gave up, and went through the mindless routine as quickly and as professionally as he could.

When, finally, the sluice gate was opened and he returned to his pool, the audience cheered and whistled and clapped, but the noise meant nothing to Kilroy, other than a lot of people making sounds. He couldn't even hear them using a language, and he wondered briefly if he'd been performing for a group of subnormal specimens, incapable of thought or speech on their own. It was an explanation, but it was such a degrading one that he preferred not to think of it, telling himself instead that they were being taught a new language by watching him and the dolphins. If this were true, he thought, then perhaps he could have a hand at teaching them. . . . He stopped, as the beauty of the idea came over him. Suppose he were chosen to teach people something—anything he wanted—what would he do? He decided he'd teach them the things they seemed to be miss-ing, or misunderstanding, about life. He'd heard that people were cruel, but he'd never seen them in an act of cruelty, so he didn't know if they were or not. He'd heard they were wasteful of life, and if this was so there was a lot he could teach them, because orcas valued every life as worth something, to be surrendered only in the interest of food or the preservation of the group. No orca ever wasted a life, and no orca ever killed for the sheer fun of it, as he'd heard humans did. There was nothing more wasteful or obscene than killing for fun, and if he could stop just one human from doing that, he'd figure his time had been well spent.

He remembered the time, perhaps a year ago, when his pod had been in the Northwest, and an old bull orca had managed to run himself aground. He was past his prime, and it was time for another bull to assume leadership, and nobody could be exactly sure why this one had got himself in such a stupid situation. There was some thought he'd done it deliberately, to avoid the inevitable battle; others thought his eyesight was failing, or his sonar had begun to malfunction, and then he'd run aground accidentally while chasing a seal. Whatever the reason, there he was, left high and dry by the receding tide, while the weight of his body, unsupported by water, began to press heavily on his lungs. He might have survived until the next high tide, but he didn't seem to want to; he just gave up and lay there with his eyes closed, breathing heavily, and bleeding from the spots where his drying skin had begun to crack. The rest of the pod circled in deeper water, offering suggestions and advice, and conferring among themselves as to what to do, but nothing availed, and, at the turn of the tide, the old bull gasped three times and ceased breathing. Then a strange thing happened. A man, dressed in furs and skins, appeared in a skin-covered boat, took one look at the dead orca, and paddled away as fast as he could. Within a short time, people began to appear along the shore, and they gathered around and performed a dance, stamping their feet and making gull-like cries, and this went on for what seemed like to the other orcas, an unnecessarily long time. At last the people got down to the intelligent part of the routine, which was to take out their knives and dismember the carcass, and within a short while all that was left was a small pile of scraps for the dogs. The pod, under the leadership of the next senior bull, moved away, and when, in a few months' time, they revisited the spot, they saw a large wooden pole, covered with carved figures, rising from the beach where the orca had died. The figures were hard to make out, but the topmost one had large teeth and a gaping grin, and was clearly a representation of an orca. Kilroy had thought about this, on and off, and he couldn't make out its meaning beyond the fact that it seemed like some sort of compliment, or gesture of respect. It was one of those mysteries about people he wanted to unravel, if only he could find the key to their nature.

In the meantime, he did his tricks as the trainer wanted and tried to keep his mind from turning to jelly. People came from miles around to see the miraculous performing orca that could sign the Declaration of Independence and count the original colonies with slaps of his tail, and all the while Kilroy was saying to himself, "Grab the pen—give it back—slap the water—two-three-four-five—up in the air—hit the bell—I wish they'd get some fresh salmon for a change—six-seven-eight-nine—or a squid; I haven't had a decent piece of squid in months—around the tank—jump the hurdle—and the last time I ate an octopus—eleven-twelve, thirteen—is this the first show today, or the second? —salute the flag—I wonder what's gotten into Groucho; he hasn't spoken for three days—twice around the pool—once—twice—I guess he must be jealous—well, he's welcome to the act if he wants it—here comes the finale—up on the tail—smile nicely—

open up that sluice gate, will you?—there. At last. Peace and quiet."

One afternoon, at the conclusion of the last show, he charged through the sluice gate to the cheers and applause of the audience, and heard an odd, but somehow familiar, noise in all the tumult. It was the braying of a seagull, and Kilroy looked back and saw, atop one of the light poles, his old friend Morris, beating his wings together and screeching, "Encore! Encore!"

"Morris?" Kilroy said with delight. "What are you doing here?"

Morris glided down and lit at the edge of the pool. "I just thought I'd come and see how you're doing," he said.

"How did you find where I was?"

"If you ever want to know anything, ask the birds," Morris replied. "We don't do a lot of talking, but nothing escapes our attention. Given time, I could tell you what they had for dinner at the White House last night, or whose car was parked in the wrong driveway, or why there was a rash of seafood poisoning at the local luncheonette. I could tell you—"

"O.K., O.K., I believe you," Kilroy cut in. "I just didn't expect to see you, that's all."

"We gulls move in strange and mysterious ways," said Morris. "They seem to keep you busy around here."

"If you want to call it busy. It's about as stimulating as counting plankton."

Morris thought for a moment, then said, "You're awfully good at it."

"Big deal," Kilroy replied. "I'd rather be on my own."

"Did you ever wonder what would happen if you weren't quite so good?"

"What do you mean?"

"Suppose you were to flub a trick or two. What would happen?"

"The trainer'd make me do them over and over until I got them right."

"But suppose you didn't want to do them right. What then?"

"I don't know. They're so simple, it never occurred to me."

"Think about it. He can't *make* you do them. There's nothing in the world he can do to force you."

"He can withhold my food."

"Pooh. He's not going to starve you to death, just for a few tricks. The s.p.c.a.'d be on him like a ton of bricks."

"What's the s.p.c.a.?"

"Society for the Prevention of Cruelty to Animals. They got my grandfather out of a nasty jam once, when some kids caught him on a fishline and were flying him like a kite."

"You mean they have to have a society to keep people from being cruel?"

"They do, indeed. And even they can't stop it all. You'd be amazed at what some people think is fun.

"What I'm getting at is, you're not going to suffer if you botch up a few tricks. And the worse you get, the more likely they are to want to get rid of you. People can't stand trained animals with minds of their own."

"It's a thought, all right. And it might be fun, just to see how the trainer reacts. I get the feeling he's a lot more interested in these tricks than I am."

"All right, then. What are you waiting for?"

279

Kilroy beamed, showing all his teeth. "Morris," he said, "don't ever leave me again. You make my life worth living."

"You were the one who left, not I," Morris reminded him. "And while you've got your mouth open, just hold it. You haven't had a decent cleaning job in weeks."

At the next show, when he was supposed to take the pen and sign the Declaration of Independence, Kilroy instead flipped the pen over his back, smacked it with his tail, and sent it spinning toward the seats. The hot-dog vendor saw it coming and managed to catch it, but in so doing, spilled most of his hot dogs, and in a rage he flung the pen back at Kilroy, who took it in his teeth and raced once around the pool, while

the trainer danced about and screamed, "No! No! No! Come back! Come back and do it right!" Grinning, Kilroy presented the pen to him, and when he leaned down to take it Kilroy squirted a big mouth full of water straight in his face. The audience, thinking this was part of the act, cheered and applauded, but the trainer came close to having a stroke. He tried to continue with the prepared act, following the script read by the announcer over the loudspeaker, but Kilroy did whatever appealed at the

moment, adding new twists as they occurred to him. He found that no matter how many times he soaked the trainer, it was always good for a laugh, and this led him to see what would happen if he soaked a few of the people, as well. This brought screams along with the laughter, and there was a rush of people trying to get out of the front row seats. One or two of the slower-moving people were stepped on, and, although they had laughed the loudest when the trainer was drenched, they no longer saw anything funny, and they raised their voices in shrill wails of protest. Finally, when panic and confusion had reduced the whole show to a shambles, the sluice gate was belatedly opened, and Kilroy glided gleefully into his own pool. Morris was waiting for him by the gate.

"Well, you did it," said Morris. "There's no question about that."

"It was fun," Kilroy replied. "I haven't had so much fun since I've been here."

"And you may not have again."

"Do you think they'll let me go?"

Morris hesitated. "That's just the trouble," he said. "You did it too well. They can't let you go, because you're too much of an attraction—even misbehaving the way you did, you had a certain repulsive appeal. The crowds love that."

"This was your idea, you know," Kilroy told him. "You were the one who said it would make them let me go."

"I know. I wasn't counting on your going quite so far overboard."

"So now what do I do?"

"If you ask me, your best move is to dog it. Don't do anything, and see what happens. Pretend you're sick, pretend you've gone deaf, pretend anything, but just don't do any more tricks."

"That won't be as much fun."

"No, but it may work better. The way you're going now, people will come from all over the country just to watch you misbehave. You're an asset, instead of a liability."

Kilroy shook his head. "I wish I could figure people out," he said.

"The more unlikeable a thing is, the more they like it. They don't make sense."

"Don't try to figure them," Morris advised him. "That's a shortcut to insanity. Just do as I tell you, and maybe they'll let you go."

Kilroy sighed, emitting a large cloud of water vapor from his blowhole. "Things were never this complicated in the pod," he said. "All we had to worry about then was getting enough food."

"That's what happens when you get your food for free," Morris observed. "You buy a lot of other problems instead."

Slowly the sluice gate opened, and the trainer stood there, regarding Kilroy with hostile eyes. He'd changed his clothes since the show, but his hair was still wet. "All right, Mr. Smart Apple," he said. "Let's go back and start with the basics." Kilroy did nothing, and the trainer blew his whistle. "Move!" he commanded.

"Remember what I told you," Morris said, quietly. Pretend you don't hear him."

Kilroy grinned broadly and rolled on his back, as though luxuriating in the sun. The trainer blew his whistle again, and Kilroy filled his mouth, rose from the water, and soaked the man to his socks. Then he drifted to the bottom of the pool, making small squeaking noises that echoed through the water. The trainer blew his whistle until he felt his lungs would burst, but Kilroy remained at the bottom of the pool, pretending to be looking for something.

Finally, at the end of a long and frustrating day, the trainer stamped into the office of the aquarium administrator. He was wet all over, water squilched in his shoes, and his eyes were bloodshot from salt water and rage. "That

orca's had it," he announced. "I want nothing more to do with him."

The administrator, who'd been counting the day's gate receipts, looked up over his glasses. "What's the matter with him?" he asked, mildly.

"He's turned bad. There's no telling what he may do next. If you ask me,

the safest thing would be to shoot him."

"That seems a little drastic," the administrator replied. "What's he done that's so bad?"

"He won't do any of his tricks. He's developed a mean streak. I wouldn't be surprised to see him leap out of the pool and snap up a child."

"Oh, come, now," said the administrator. "Aren't you being a little dramatic?"

"He went after the whole first row of spectators today. He deliberately started a panic. All he had to do was reach and pluck up one of those squalling kids."

"But did he?"

"No. What I'm saying is, he could have. And with this personality change, I can't guarantee what may happen."

"What personality change?"

"I've just been telling you—he's turned mean! He used to be all friendliness, and now he spits in my eye every time he gets a chance! He's anti-people! The only thing he'll let near him is that silly seagull, and one of these days he's going to snap that bird right out of the air!"

"It seems to me," the administrator said slowly, "that you're dreaming up a lot of problems just because you can't make him do your tricks."

"*I'm* dreaming up the problems?" the trainer shouted. "*I* am? Were you out there today? Did you see what he did?"

"No. I've been busy counting the money he's made."

"Well, you're going to need every nickel of it, once he eats a child. There won't be enough money in the world to pay for the lawsuits."

"I think we'll worry about that when it happens. He's too valuable a property to let go."

The trainer rolled his eyes and slowly intoned, "Will you do me just one favor?"

"What's that?"

"Will you remember that I was the one who said he should be shot?"

"I'll remember."

"And will you let me bring a rifle, in case he goes after the crowd?"

"Oh, I don't know about that. I'd rather have him bite someone than have you shoot someone by mistake."

"I'm not going to shoot anyone," the trainer said, his voice heavy with sarcasm. "I simply want a deterrent, in case this orca does what I think he may do."

"All right, then. But be careful."

"Don't worry. My middle name is Caution." And with that the trainer left the room, trailing little puddles of water behind him.

Every seat was sold for the next show. At the administrator's direction, the public address system announced that the main act featured a wild killer whale, and the public was warned that their presence in the grandstands was at their own risk. Parents were advised to keep a firm hold on their children, and on no condition should anyone get close to the edge of the pool. As an added precaution, someone would be standing by with a high-powered rifle, but the public could rest assured he would use it only as a last resort. With that the music rose to a crescendo, the sluice gate opened, and the trainer blew his whistle. Everyone strained forward, staring at the gate through which the monster would come.

For several seconds nothing happened, and once more the trainer blew his whistle. Still nothing.

"Fake!" shouted a voice in the bleachers.

Then there was a gasp from the crowd as a high, black dorsal fin appeared in the sluice gate, and they could see the monstrous body beneath. Kilroy glided into main pool; the sluice gate

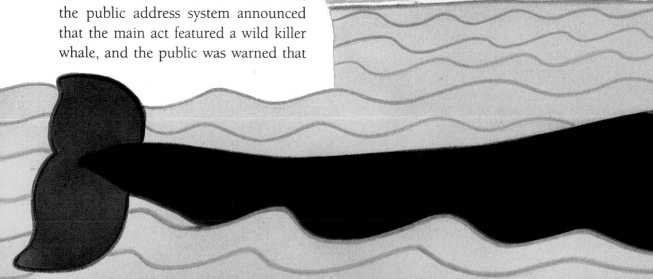

closed behind him, and the trainer blew his whistle a third time. Kilroy sank to the bottom of the pool and stayed there, every now and then emitting tiny bubbles.

"He's resting now, ladies and gentlemen," the loudspeaker announced. "Gathering his strength for an assault. Any living thing that comes near him will be torn to shreds." As though making an offering to a god, the trainer threw a large salmon into the pool; it settled slowly to the bottom near Kilroy, but he ignored it. "Of course, that fish was not alive," the speaker went on. "The killer whale prefers the blood to be fresh. There's been a problem keeping him supplied with, ah, fresh meat, because his appetite is such that he

could eat a whole flock of sheep, or one whole grain-fed steer, or the like, in a very short time. He's known as the wolf of the sea, and with good reason. He's moving now! He's coming to the surface! Everyone stand back, please!"

Slowly, Kilroy put his head above water, grinned, and rolled over on his back. Morris flew down from a light post, lit on Kilroy's chin, and began to clean his teeth.

"Keep it up," Morris said, in a low voice. "You're doing great."

"Fake!" shouted the same voice as before. "He's been drugged!"

"Ladies and gentlemen, this animal has not been drugged," the announcer said, a frantic tone creeping into his voice. "He's merely resting. There's no

telling when he may—" The sentence trailed off, as Kilroy sank quietly to the bottom of the pool, leaving Morris swimming on the surface. Morris paddled about in a circle, rose, and flapped his wings, then extended his neck and gave his imitation of a braying donkey. The audience applauded.

"Let's hear it for the trained seagull!" someone called. "At last we get some of the action!" There was laughter and applause, and the announcer, forgetting to cover his microphone, said, "Someone get that bird outa there!" This brought more laughter, and cheers for Morris as he nimbly avoided the long-handled net the trainer stabbed at him. The trainer was in such a rage that he kept flailing away with the net, and he didn't return to his senses until a voice shouted, "Three strikes and you're out! Bring on the next batter!" Then he subsided, panting and glowering, while Morris cruised serenely about the center of the pool. For a moment the trainer was tempted to use his rifle, but he couldn't shoot at Morris without risking a ricochet into the crowd, so he could do nothing but accept defeat, while the spectators cheered and stamped and whistled.

Finally, in desperation, another gate was opened, and the three dolphins were let into the pool. They performed their tricks with neat precision, aware that they were regaining some of the prestige they'd lost to Kilroy, and while they presented a pretty picture, they didn't satisfy the crowd, which had come to see the mad killer whale. The dolphins leaped and pirouetted and tail-walked, and all the while the spectators stamped and clapped and chanted, "We want the killer whale! We want the killer whale!" At the conclusion of one leap, Groucho went down past Kilroy and said "What's the matter? You sick or something?"

"Just resting," Kilroy replied cheerfully, and closed his eyes.

"I don't suppose you ever heard the saying that the show must go on?"

"Never. What's it mean?"

"Let it pass." Groucho shot to the surface, tail-walked across the pool, and leaped through a hoop, while the audience continued its chant.

Finally, at the end of the day, the trainer went into the office of the administrator. "I've had it," he announced. "Either that orca goes, or I do. You can take your choice."

"Let's not go overboard about this," the administrator replied. "He didn't hurt anyone, did he?"

"That depends on what you mean by hurt. I can tell you, my nerves won't take another day like this. I'll be a raving maniac by sundown."

"He made a lot of money."

286

"And I wind up fanning a seagull with a fishnet. No, thank you. I know when I've had enough."

The administrator turned his chair, and looked out the window. "I'll be sorry to see you go," he said.

There was a long silence, while the trainer opened and closed his mouth like a fish out of water. Then he snapped his mouth shut, and stamped out of the room.

Kilroy's popularity lasted just about a week. A new trainer was brought in, but she had no better luck than the first, and after a while the word got around that the orca was sick, possibly having been starved in an attempt to make him fierce. The S.P.C.A. sent an agent around to investigate, but he found nothing wrong; the orca was simply lethargic, and that was all there was to it. Attendance began to drop off, and the administrator found he was paying a great deal more to feed Kilroy than he was taking in at the gate, and the longer Kilroy stayed around, the bigger he grew, and the more he ate. Finally, after a week during which almost nobody came to the show, the administrator put through a call to the aquarium from which Kilroy had originally come.

"That orca you sold me," he announced to the man at the other end of the line. "He's a dud. I want my money back."

"What do you mean, he's a dud?" came the reply. "There was nothing the matter with him when he left here."

"Well, there's something the matter with him now. He just lies at the bottom of the pool and sulks."

"I'm sorry, pal, but that's your problem. You must be doing something wrong."

"I'm not doing anything wrong! I even got a new trainer!"

"Well, that's show biz for you. You win a few, you lose a few."

"Will you refund half of what I paid?"

"I won't refund a nickel. He was A-1 when he left here, and that's the end of my responsibility. Now, if you'll excuse me, I have work to do." The line went dead, and the administrator slowly replaced the instrument in its cradle. He looked out the window for a while, then went outside, where the new trainer was putting the dolphins through their paces.

"How's the orca?" the administrator asked.

"About the same," replied the trainer. "I think he's sick."

"The last thing we need is a lot of vet's bills," the administrator said. "Maybe you'd better turn him loose."

"Whatever you say. He's certainly no good to us the way he is."

"O.K., then, let him go." The administrator returned to his office, and the trainer went to Kilroy's pool and unlocked a section of the barrier that led to the sea. Morris, who was perched at the side of the pool, saw what was happening.

"Hey!" he squawked. "Kilroy! Look here!"

Kilroy had been prowling around the bottom of the pool, and he came to the surface and looked around. "What?" he said. "Where?"

"There! He's opening the gate!"

They both watched, hardly daring to believe their eyes, while the trainer swung the gate open. Then the trainer turned to Kilroy.

"O.K., sport," he said. "You're on your own. Good luck."

Kilroy cleared the gate in one giant leap and headed out to sea, leaping like a kangaroo, while Morris flew noisily overhead. The trainer watched them go, then swung the gate closed.

"For a sick orca, he sure recovered fast," he remarked, and bolted the gate and returned to the dolphins.

●

Kilroy seems to have left those baffling humans behind, but he goes on to learn more about human beings. To find out what else Kilroy learns, read the rest of the novel Kilroy and the Gull *by Nathaniel Benchley.*

CHECK FOR UNDERSTANDING

1. What puzzled Kilroy about the first trainer's behavior?
2. Why was the trainer puzzled when Kilroy tossed the fish back to him?
3. What was Kilroy's first reaction to the routines he needed to learn for the show? Did his feelings change? If so, how?
4. How did Morris's first plan backfire? What was his second plan?
5. Why did the author choose to create a whale's-eye view of the world?

WRITE ABOUT *"Kilroy's New Act"*

Imagine that a translating machine existed that would allow Kilroy to speak directly to his trainer. What would Kilroy have asked him? Write at least three questions that he might have asked. What answers would the trainer give?

THINK ABOUT IT

The Human Kind was a unit about people—characters who were special to the authors because of their special qualities. In "Portrait Gallery," for example, the authors have written poems about particular people that have meant much to them. We enjoy these poems because the poets, with their skills, have been able to express the kind of appreciation we have felt but could not quite say.

"Rembrandt's Late Self-Portraits" is the poet's thoughts on Rembrandt, the painter, and what he may have thought as he grew older. "Portrait by a Neighbour" is a description of a neighbor woman observed by the author. "My Cousin Agatha" tells about the magic Agatha brings to the author. "The Old Charcoal Seller" shows a day in the life of an old man who peddles coal.

In the short stories in this unit we also learn how circumstances sometime shape the character himself. Little Little was born a dwarf, which affected her personality, for example.

- How do Harriet Tubman's circumstances influence her attributes?
- How would being a twin shape someone's personality?
- Was the character in "Charles" shaped by circumstances?

WRITE ABOUT IT

Choose one of the characters that you've read about in this unit. Pretend that you have just met him or her—at a party, on the street, in school, or at a certain time in history. Then write a letter to a friend, describing this person. Show why this person is special and why you think your friend would like him or her. Choose a time and place and activity where the three of you can meet.

READ ABOUT IT

Paul B. Janeczko, editor. *Strings: A Gathering of Family Poems.* Bradbury Press, 1984.

This collection of poems is like a family reunion—time for an appreciation of the personalities of people we may sometimes take for granted.

M. E. Kerr. *Me Me Me Me Me: Not a Novel.* Harper & Row, Publishers, 1983.

This book is the autobiography that every reader wishes his or her favorite author would write. M. E. Kerr describes incidents that happened to her as a teenager. Then she explains how these real-life events sparked ideas for her novels.

Joseph Krumgold. *Onion John.* Harper & Row, Publishers, 1959.

Onion John is a strange character in town, harmless but unintelligible to everyone except the narrator. The other people in the community, including the narrator's father, want to "do something" for Onion John. Only the narrator appreciates Onion John for what he is.

Ursula K. Le Guin. *Very Far Away from Anywhere Else.* Atheneum Publishers, 1976.

Owen Thomas Griffiths begins his story by announcing, "If you'd like a story about how I won my basketball letter and achieved fame, love, and fortune, don't read this." Instead, Owen describes how his new friend Natalie helps him to come to terms with his exceptional abilities in science.

Cynthia Rylant. *Waiting to Waltz: A Childhood.* Bradbury Press, 1984.

This wonderfully subtle collection of poetry describes growing up in Appalachia.

CROSSROADS

Whenever you reach a crossroads, you must make a decision. Should you turn left, turn right, go straight ahead, or even turn back? The only choice you cannot make is—not to choose. The characters in this unit reach important points in their lives. They must determine new directions for themselves.

4

GROWING UP WITH GUMPTION

by RUSSELL BAKER

Certain jobs, like selling and entertaining, require a lot of energy and initiative. A person with gumption is usually very successful at those jobs. In this excerpt from his autobiographical book *Growing Up,* Russell Baker reveals that, as a boy, he did not believe he had gumption.

How does Russell feel when he tries to sell magazines door-to-door? How are Doris's and Russell's approach to selling different?

I began working in journalism when I was eight years old. It was my mother's idea. She wanted me to "make something" of myself and, after a level-headed appraisal of my strengths, decided I had better start young if I was to have any chance of keeping up with the competition.

The flaw in my character which she had already spotted was lack of "gumption." My idea of a perfect afternoon was lying in front of the radio rereading my favorite Big Little Book, *Dick Tracy Meets Stooge Viller.** My mother despised inactivity.

* **Dick Tracy and Stooge Viller,** two characters from the *Dick Tracy* comic strip.

Seeing me having a good time in repose, she was powerless to hide her disgust. "You've got no more gumption than a bump on a log," she said. "Get out in the kitchen and help Doris do those dirty dishes."

My sister Doris, though two years younger than I, had enough gumption for a dozen people. She positively enjoyed washing dishes, making beds, and cleaning the house. When she was only seven, she could carry a piece of short-weighted cheese back to the grocery store, threaten the manager with legal action, and come back triumphantly with the full quarter-pound we'd paid for and a few ounces extra thrown in for forgiveness. Doris could have made something of herself if she hadn't been a girl. Because of this defect, however, the best she could hope for was a career as a nurse or schoolteacher, the only work that capable women were considered up to in those days.

This must have saddened my mother, this twist of fate that had allocated all the gumption to the daughter and left her with a son who was contented with Dick Tracy and Stooge Viller. If disappointed, though, she wasted no energy on self-pity. She would make me make something of myself, whether I wanted to or not. "The Lord helps those who help themselves," she said. That was the way her mind worked.

She was realistic about the difficulty. Having sized up the material the Lord have given her to mold, she didn't overestimate what she could do with it. She didn't insist that I grow up to be President of the United States.

Fifty years ago parents still asked boys if they wanted to grow up to be President, and asked it not jokingly, but seriously. Many parents who were hardly more than paupers still believed their sons could do it. Abraham Lincoln had done it. We were only sixty-five years from Lincoln. Many a grandfather who walked among us could remember Lincoln's time. Men of grandfatherly age were the worst for asking if you wanted to grow up to be President. A surprising number of little boys said yes and meant it.

I was asked many times myself. No, I would say, I didn't want to grow up to be President. My mother was present during one of these interrogations. An elderly uncle, having posed the usual question and exposed my lack of interest in the Presidency, asked, "Well, what *do* you want to be when you grow up?"

I loved to pick through trash piles and collect empty bottles, tin cans with pretty labels, and discarded magazines. The most desirable job on earth sprang instantly to mind. "I want to be a garbage man," I said.

My uncle smiled, but my mother had seen the first distressing evidence of a bump budding on a log. "Have a little gumption, Russell," she said. Her calling me Russell was a signal of unhappiness. When she approved of me, I was always "Buddy."

When I turned eight years old, she decided that the job of starting me on the road toward making something of myself could no longer be safely delayed. "Buddy," she said one day, "I want you to come home right after school this afternoon. Somebody's coming and I want you to meet him."

When I burst in that afternoon, she was in conference in the parlor with an executive of the Curtis Publishing Company. She introduced me. He bent low from the waist and shook my hand. Was it true, as my mother had told him, he asked, that I longed for the opportunity to conquer the world of business?

My mother replied that I was blessed with a rare determination to make something of myself.

"That's right," I whispered.

296

"But have you got the grit, the character, the never-say-quit spirit it takes to succeed in business?"

My mother said I certainly did.

"That's right," I said.

He eyed me silently for a long pause, as though weighing whether I could be trusted to keep his confidence, then spoke man-to-man. Before taking a crucial step, he said, he wanted to advise me that working for the Curtis Publishing Company placed enormous responsibility on a young man. It was one of the great companies of America. Perhaps the greatest publishing house in the world. I had heard, no doubt, of the *Saturday Evening Post*?

Heard of it? My mother said that everyone in our house had heard of the *Saturday Post* and that I, in fact, read it with religious devotion.

Then doubtless, he said, we were also familiar with those two monthly pillars of the magazine world, the *Ladies Home Journal* and the *Country Gentleman*.

Indeed we were familiar with them, said my mother.

Representing the *Saturday Evening Post* was one of the weightiest honors that could be bestowed in the world of business, he said. He was personally proud of being a part of that great corporation.

My mother said he had every right to be.

Again he studied me as though debating whether I was worthy of a knighthood. Finally, "Are you trustworthy?"

My mother said I was the soul of honesty.

"That's right," I said.

The caller smiled for the first time. He told me I was a lucky young man. He admired my spunk. Too many men thought life was all play. Those young men would not go far in this world. Only a young man willing to work and save and keep his face washed and his hair neatly combed could hope to come out on top in a world such as ours. Did I truly and sincerely believe that I was such a young man?

"He certainly does," said my mother.

"That's right," I said.

He said he was so impressed by what he had seen of me that he was going to make me a representative of the Curtis Publishing Company. On the following Tuesday, he said, thirty freshly printed copies of the *Saturday Evening Post* would be delivered at our door. I would place these magazines, still damp with the ink of the presses, in a handsome canvas bag, sling it over my shoulder, and set

forth through the streets to bring the best in journalism, fiction, and cartoons to the American public.

He had brought the canvas bag with him. He showed me how to drape the sling over my left shoulder and across the chest so that the pouch lay easily accessible to my right hand, allowing the best in journalism, fiction, and cartoons to be swiftly extracted and sold to a citizenry whose happiness and security depended upon us soldiers of the free press.

The following Tuesday I raced home from school, put the canvas bag over my shoulder, dumped the magazines in, and, tilting to the left to balance their weight on my right hip, embarked on the highway of journalism.

We lived in Belleville, New Jersey, a commuter town at the northern fringe of Newark. It was 1932, the bleakest year of the Depression. My father had died two years before, leaving us with a few pieces of furniture and not much else, and my mother had taken Doris and me to live with one of her younger brothers. This was my Uncle Allen. Uncle Allen had made something of himself by 1932. As salesman for a soft-drink bottler in Newark, he had an income of thirty dollars a week, wore pearl gray spats, detachable collars, and a three-piece suit, was happily married, and took in threadbare relatives.

With my load of magazines I headed toward Belleville Avenue. That's where the people were. There were two filling stations at the intersection with Union Avenue, as well as a grocery store, a fruit stand, a bakery, a barber shop, Zuccarelli's drugstore, and a diner shaped like a railroad car. For several hours I made myself highly visible, shifting position now and then from corner to corner, from shop window to shop window, to make sure everyone could see the heavy black lettering on the canvas bag that said THE SATURDAY EVENING POST. When the angle of the light indicated it was suppertime, I walked back to the house.

"How many did you sell, Buddy?" my mother asked.

"None."

"Where did you go?"

"The corner of Belleville and Union avenues."

"What did you do?"

"Stood on the corner waiting for somebody to buy a *Saturday Evening Post*."

"You just stood there?"

"Didn't sell a single one."

"Russell!"

Uncle Allen intervened. "I've been thinking about it for some time," he said, "and I've about decided to take the *Post* regularly. Put me down as a regular customer." I handed him a magazine and he paid me a nickel. It was the first nickel I earned.

Afterward, my mother instructed me in salesmanship. I would have to ring doorbells, address adults with charming self-confidence, and break down resistance with a sales talk pointing out that no one, no matter how poor, could afford to be without

the *Saturday Evening Post* in the home.

I told my mother I'd changed my mind about wanting to succeed in the magazine business.

"If you think I'm going to raise a good-for-nothing," she replied, "you've got another think coming." She told me to hit the streets with the canvas bag and start ringing doorbells the instant school was out next day. When I objected that I didn't feel any aptitude for salesmanship, she asked how I'd like to lend her my leather belt so she could whack some sense into me. I bowed to superior will and entered journalism with a heavy heart.

And so I set forth with my sack of magazines. I was afraid of the dogs that snarled behind the doors of potential buyers. I was timid about ringing the doorbells of strangers, relieved when no one came to the door, and scared when someone did. Despite my mother's instructions, I could not deliver an engaging sales pitch. When a door opened I simply asked, "Want to buy a *Saturday Evening Post*?" In Belleville few persons did. It was a town of 30,000 people, and most weeks I rang a fair majority of its doorbells. But I rarely sold my thirty copies. Some weeks I canvassed the entire town for six days and still had four or five unsold magazines on Monday evening; then I dreaded the coming of Tuesday morning, when a batch of thirty fresh *Saturday Evening Post*s was due at the front door.

"Better get out there and sell the rest of those magazines tonight," my mother would say.

I usually posted myself then at a busy intersection where a traffic light controlled commuter flow from Newark. When the light turned red, I stood on the curb and shouted my sales pitch at the motorists.

"Want to buy a *Saturday Evening Post*?"

One rainy night when car windows were sealed against me I came back soaked and with not a single sale to report. My mother beckoned to Doris.

"Go back down there with Buddy and show him how to sell these magazines," she said.

Brimming with zest, Doris, who was then seven years old, returned with me to the corner. She took a magazine from the bag, and when the light turned red she strode to the nearest car and banged her small fist against the closed window. The driver, probably startled at what he took to be a midget assaulting his car, lowered the window to stare, and

Doris thrust a *Saturday Evening Post* at him.

"You need this magazine," she piped, "and it only costs a nickel."

Her salesmanship was irresistible. Before the light changed half a dozen times she disposed of the entire batch. I didn't feel humiliated. To the contrary, I was so happy I decided to give her a treat. Leading her to the vegetable store on Belleville Avenue, I bought three apples, which cost a nickel, and gave her one.

"You shouldn't waste money," she said.

"Eat your apple." I bit into mine.

"You shouldn't eat before supper," she said. "It'll spoil your appetite."

Back at the house that evening, she dutifully reported me for wasting a nickel. Instead of a scolding, I was rewarded with a pat on the back for having the good sense to buy fruit instead of candy. My mother reached into her bottomless supply of maxims and told Doris, "An apple a day keeps the doctor away."

By the time I was ten I had learned all my mother's maxims by heart. Asking to stay up past normal bedtime, I knew that a refusal would be explained with, "Early to bed and early to rise, makes a man healthy, wealthy, and wise." If I whimpered about having to get up early in the morning, I could depend on her to say, "The early bird gets the worm."

The one I most despised was, "If at first you don't succeed, try, try again." This was the battle cry with which she constantly sent me back into the hopeless struggle whenever I moaned that I had rung every doorbell in town, and knew there wasn't a single potential buyer left in Belleville that week. After listening to my explanation, she handed me the canvas bag and said, "If at first you don't succeed . . ."

Three years in that job, which I would gladly have quit after the first day except for her insistence, produced at least one valuable result. My mother finally concluded that I would never make something of myself by pursuing a life in business, and started considering careers that demanded less competitive zeal.

One evening when I was eleven I brought home a short "composition" on my summer vacation which the teacher had graded with an A. Reading it with her own schoolteacher's eye, my mother agreed that it was top-drawer seventh grade prose and complimented me. Nothing more was said about it immediately, but a new idea had taken life in her mind. Halfway through supper she suddenly interrupted the conversation.

"Buddy," she said, "maybe you could be a writer."

I clasped the idea to my heart. I had never met a writer, had shown no previous urge to write, and hadn't a notion how to become a writer, but I loved stories and thought that making up stories must surely be almost as much fun as reading them. Best of all, though, and what really gladdened my heart, was the ease of the writer's life. Writers did not have to trudge through the town peddling from canvas bags, defending themselves against angry dogs, being rejected by surly strangers. Writers did not have to ring doorbells. So far as I could make out, what writers did couldn't even be classified as work.

I was enchanted. Writers didn't have to have any gumption at all. I did not dare tell anybody for fear of being laughed at in the schoolyard, but secretly I decided that what I'd like to be when I grew up was a writer.

CHECK FOR UNDERSTANDING
1. What did Doris's actions reveal about her character?
2. What effect do you think Uncle Allen's situation had on the goals Russell's mother set for her son?
3. How did Russell feel when he tried to sell magazines door-to-door?
4. How were Doris's and Russell's approach to selling different?
5. Do you think that writers really do not need to have any gumption? Explain.

WRITE ABOUT *"Growing Up with Gumption"*
Russell Baker is now a very successful writer and newspaper columnist. What traits and interests did Russell have as a boy that were important for his real choice of career? Write a paragraph giving at least three examples.

THE ROAD NOT TAKEN

by ROBERT FROST

Two roads diverged in a yellow wood,
And sorry I could not travel both
And be one traveler, long I stood
And looked down one as far as I could
To where it bent in the undergrowth;

Then took the other, as just as fair,
And having perhaps the better claim,
Because it was grassy and wanted wear;
Though as for that, the passing there
Had worn them really about the same,

And both that morning equally lay
In leaves no step had trodden black.
Oh, I kept the first for another day!
Yet knowing how way leads on to way,
I doubted if I should ever come back.

I shall be telling this with a sigh
Somewhere ages and ages hence:
Two roads diverged in a wood, and I—
I took the one less traveled by,
And that has made all the difference.

COMPREHENSION

Fact and Opinion

REPORTER: My paper got a call downtown about a moose at this address. Could you give me the facts, ma'am?

WOMAN: Well, this is the worst thing that ever happened!

REPORTER: That's not a fact, ma'am. That's an opinion.

WOMAN: No one will ever want to visit my house again!

REPORTER: That's another opinion, ma'am.

WOMAN: Oh, dear! The moose is eating my roses!

REPORTER: Now *that's* a fact, ma'am!

A **fact** is something that can be proved—or disproved—by first-hand observation. If the woman had said that the moose was sitting in her car, it would also have been a fact. The fact would have been proved false when the reporter checked it out.

Opinion, on the other hand, is someone's personal judgment about something. It cannot be proved.

Read this excerpt from "Growing Up with Gumption," and decide whether it is fact or opinion.

My sister Doris, though two years younger than I, had enough gumption for a dozen people. . . . Doris could have made something of herself if she hadn't been a girl. Because of this defect, however, the best she could hope for was a career as a nurse or schoolteacher, the only work that capable women were considered up to in those days.

Does this excerpt contain any information that can be observed first-hand? Could you measure the amount of gumption that would be needed for "a dozen people"? Of course not. Since gumption is not a measurable commodity, any statement about it has to be an opinion.

Read the following passage. Does it contain facts or opinions?

With my load of magazines I headed toward Belleville Avenue. That's where the people were. There were two filling stations at the intersection with Union Avenue, as well as a grocery store, a fruit stand, a bakery, a barber shop, Zuccarelli's drugstore, and a diner shaped like a railroad car. For several hours I made myself highly visible, shifting position now and then from corner to corner, from shop window to shop window, to make sure everyone could see the heavy black lettering on the canvas bag that said *THE SATURDAY EVENING POST.*

These are facts. If you had gone to Belleville, New Jersey, in 1932, you would have been able to confirm whether or not Russell Baker was selling magazines on those particular street corners.

Often you will find that facts are used to support opinions. Which of these sentences is fact, and which is opinion?

Her salesmanship was irresistible. Before the light changed half a dozen times, she disposed of the whole batch.

The first sentence is, of course, an opinion. The second sentence is the fact that the author gives to support his opinion. In spite of the fact that the opinion is supported by evidence, however, it is *still* an opinion.

As you read about Leonor Villegas de Magnon and Katherine Davalos Ortega, look for statements of opinion and see if they are supported by facts.

Trailblazers

Only through hard work and determination can the impossible be turned into reality. In the following biographies, two women achieve their independence and pioneer in fields that seem all but closed to them as they are growing up.

Why is Leonor Villegas de Magnon an unlikely person to organize medical relief during the battles of the Mexican Revolution? How does Katherine Davalos Ortega view the work men and women are assigned to in the family's café?

LEONOR VILLEGAS DE MAGNON

by MARY BETH ROGERS and JANELLE D. SCOTT

When Leonor Villegas de Magnon was a little girl, her father called her *La Rebelde*, "the rebel." The name stayed with her throughout her life.

Leonor Villegas de Magnon was a lively, intelligent child. When she made up her mind to do something, no one could stop her.

Some fathers in the 1870s in Mexico might not have wanted their little girls to be so independent or willful. Back then girls and women were supposed to be passive and obedient. But Leonor's father admired her spirit, and he encouraged Leonor to develop her independence. He wanted her to have every advantage that men had, and so he sent Leonor to the United States so that she could receive a good education. When Leonor grew up, she married a United States citizen, Adolpho Magnon. Leonor and Adolpho had three children and for a time lived in Mexico City. Leonor's father, who had moved across the Mexico-Texas border to Laredo, died there in 1910. Leonor was heartbroken. She and her children went to Laredo to attend her father's funeral.

While Leonor attended the funeral, revolutionary fighting erupted in Mexico. It was too dangerous to try to return home to her husband in Mexico City. Adolpho wrote to tell her to remain in Laredo. She did so, reluctantly.

Leonor was not the only Mexican exiled in Laredo when the fighting began. Though away from their homeland, Leonor and the others did not ignore the events in Mexico. They debated the ideas of the revolution and tried to think of ways to get involved. Like many of the exiles, Leonor's sympathies were with the revolutionaries who were trying to establish a new system of justice for Mexico. They were fighting for equality, economic opportunity, and religious freedom.

If Leonor had been a politician, she could have participated in the planning.

If she had been a commander, she could have led troops into battle.

But in 1910 women were not politicians or commanders, and Leonor could not lead the revolutionary action.

Leonor followed the news of the revolution avidly and began to formulate her own opinions about the revolution. Leonor found that her interests in the revolution were shared by many Laredo citizens, including the influential Idar family, who published the Spanish-language newspaper, *La Crónica*. Leonor began writing for *La Crónica*, outlining the issues of the revolt in Mexico. She defended the revolutionary cause against the Mexican government.

Early on the morning of March 17, 1913, Leonor got her chance to become actively involved in the revolution.

The people of Laredo awakened to the sound of rifle shots and cannon fire. Nuevo Laredo, across the Río Grande from Laredo, was under attack.

Leonor immediately realized a battle had erupted. This was it! She rushed outside to find the streets filled with screaming people fleeing the gunfire. Leonor fought her way through the crowd, bumping into those running away from the battle scene. But Leonor did not want to run away. She wanted to help the revolutionaries.

As she ran along, she persuaded women to follow her.

Upon reaching the battle-torn town, the women immediately went to work.

They dragged soldiers and civilians from the streets to safety. They took others to Nuevo Laredo's general hospital. They assisted physicians and nursed gunshot victims. They worked tirelessly and heroically. Soldiers would have bled to death in the street if Leonor and the other women had not been there.

Leonor decided to form the women into a permanent organization designed to provide medical relief during the revolution. She named her organization *La Cruz Blanca* ("The White Cross"), hoping it would be similar to the Red Cross that Clara Barton had started in 1881 in America. The women began to organize, gathering medical supplies and bandages.

Nuevo Laredo came under attack again on New Year's day in 1914. Leonor and the other women of *La Cruz Blanca* were ready to help. But this time they were unable to cross the Rio Grande into Nuevo Laredo.

The fight lasted for hours, leaving many revolutionaries wounded and dying. To give treatment to the soldiers who managed to cross the river, Leonor turned her home into a hospital. Nearly a hundred men made it to Leonor's home. Her living room became an operating room. Local doctors and the women of *La Cruz Blanca* cared for the men day and night. Eventually, Leonor set up three emergency hospitals in Laredo.

At the end of January, the United States Army ordered that the men be released from the hospital and sent to military prison. After all, they reasoned, these were Mexican revolutionaries on American soil.

Leonor refused to release them.

The army stationed soldiers outside Leonor's home.

She developed a plan. She dressed the wounded soldiers in American clothes and discarded their bloody and dirty soldier's garb. When the revolutionary soldiers walked away from her house, the army did not recognize the revolutionaries.

Leonor was able to get about fifteen men safely past the army. But the most seriously wounded were unable to take advantage of Leonor's cleverness.

The U. S. Army finally took thirty-seven of Leonor's patients into custody and put them into prison.

Leonor believed that the men were innocent, that they had not committed any crime, and that they should not be in prison. She hired a lawyer to argue the case for the soldiers' innocence. Leonor did not stop there. She wrote letters pleading the soldiers' case to the governor of Texas, a Texas senator, the U. S. War Department and the U. S. secretary of state.

She finally won. Secretary of State William Jennings Bryan ordered the prisoners' release.

Word of the courageous efforts of Leonor and *La Cruz Blanca* spread across the border deep into Mexico. When the revolutionary leader Venustiano Carranza heard about them, he urged the group to help him in Mexico. Leonor immediately telegraphed that she and twenty-five nurses were ready to join him.

Throughout the year of 1914, Leonor's group braved wartime conditions to nurse the wounded in battle after battle. They risked their lives daily to provide support for the revolution. When Carranza's forces finally took over the capital of Mexico City, Leonor and *La Cruz Blanca* shared in the victory.

Later, Mexico awarded Leonor five medals for her work in 1914. One proclaimed her a veteran of the 1910–1914 campaign. Others honored her for "national merit."

Leonor was a heroine of the war.

After the revolution, Leonor settled down to write about her beloved Mexico and her work in *La Cruz Blanca*. She died in 1955, at the age of seventy-nine.

Her father's affectionate nickname for Leonor—*La Rebelde*—was truly accurate.

She had been a rebel, as well as a writer, a teacher, and a nurse. It was her independent and adventurous spirit that led her to be involved in dangerous situations when most people would have sought safety. Her personal courage and daring inspired others to act in the same manner. And the revolutionary effort benefited from her dedication and determination to do what she believed to be right.

KATHERINE DAVALOS ORTEGA

When she was eight years old, Katherine clutched the day's earnings from the family restaurant, walked more than a block, and proudly deposited the money in the bank. This was one of Katherine's favorite jobs. Today, she is Treasurer of the United States.

Born July 16, 1934, in Tularosa, New Mexico, Katherine Davalos Ortega was the youngest of Donaciano and Catarina Davalos Ortega's eight children. As soon as Katherine learned to walk, she was expected to join her brothers and sisters at work.

During the Depression the family was very poor. Every family member had to work hard for everything they had.

Katherine's sister remembers the times when they had to wait until the end of the day when their father got paid for his work.

311

Only then would they have money to buy as much flour as they could.

Katherine's father spent his early years working in the copper, gold, and tungsten mines of New Mexico. Then he opened a blacksmith shop near Mescalero, New Mexico. In the 1930s her father opened a Mexican-American café and later a furniture business.

The café was a family business and everyone pitched in, including Katherine, who began to wait on tables at age seven. The family even lived behind the café in a large room that was partitioned off into smaller areas.

When Katherine was growing up, there was certain work women did and certain work men did. But Katherine questioned this division of labor, and her father changed things in the household. From then on, the boys started to do more of the dishes.

Katherine was a negotiator. If she wanted something, she was bound and determined to get what she wanted.

She wanted to go to Eastern New Mexico University, but she knew the family could not afford to send her. This situation did not stop her, however. Katherine got a job and worked her way through college.

Katherine was very eager to learn and loved challenges. She was also very adept at handling money. While attending Eastern New Mexico University, Katherine and her roommate decided to move off campus. They moved to a small, one-bedroom apartment. Though they had little money, they managed to live on ten dollars a week—all because of Katherine's ability to handle money.

Katherine has achieved much in her life. She was an accountant, vice president of a bank, the first woman president of a California bank, a member of the President's Advisory Committee on Small and Minority Business, and a commissioner on the Copyright Royalty Tribunal.

Then, on September 22, 1983, Katherine Davalos Ortega was nominated by President Reagan to become the thirty-eighth Treasurer of the United States. The Treasurer's job is to oversee the Bureau of Engraving and Printing, the U. S. Mint, and the U. S. Savings Bond Division. Her name will be seen often, because her signature appears on all new U. S. currency. This $63,000-a-year job is a long way from Katherine's childhood. She grew up believing in strong family devotion, a commitment to earning a living by hard work, patience, determination, and perseverance.

CHECK FOR UNDERSTANDING

1. What did Leonor Villegas de Magnon think of the Mexican Revolution while she wrote for the newspaper, *La Crónica*?

2. Why was Leonor an unlikely person to organize medical relief during the battles of the Mexican Revolution?

3. How did Katherine Davalos Ortega view the work men and women were assigned to do in the family's café?

4. What similar conditions did both Leonor and Katherine overcome?

5. Why is the term "trailblazers" applied to Leonor and Katherine?

WRITE ABOUT *"Trailblazers"*

What would Leonor Villegas de Magnon and Katherine Davalos Ortega talk about if they could meet? Write an imaginary conversation between them.

VOCABULARY · LANGUAGE

Literal and Figurative Meanings

Read the two brief scenes that follow. One word is used in both scenes but has a different meaning in each.

SCENE 1

A car with a DRIVER and a PASSENGER slows to a stop at the intersection of three roads. The DRIVER suddenly turns to the PASSENGER.

DRIVER (in a worried tone): These crossroads confuse me. I never know which road to take.

PASSENGER (reassuringly): According to the map, we turn left here onto the main road.

SCENE 2

It is the morning of MIGUEL'S thirteenth birthday. As MIGUEL enters the kitchen, his DAD gets up from the breakfast table and shakes his hand.

DAD (with a big smile): Well, MIGUEL, today you're a teenager. Whether or not you know it, you are at one of life's many crossroads.

MIGUEL (grinning): Thanks, Dad. I thought I'd never make it!

Which scene illustrates the most common meaning of the word *crossroads?* Which illustrates a more imaginative meaning? The usual, or more common, meaning of a word is its *literal* meaning. Many word meanings are created or given added meaning when a word that generally means one thing is used in a different sense, or context. The newly created meaning is the **figurative** meaning.

In scene 1, for example, the driver uses *crossroads* in its literal, or most common, sense: "the place of intersection of two or more roads." In scene 2, Miguel's father uses *crossroads* in a figurative, or more imaginative, sense: "a point where one must choose a course of action." Why do you suppose Miguel's father considers becoming a teenager a crossroad in one's life? What crossroads lie ahead for Miguel?

Think for a moment about the name of this unit. When you first read the title, did you picture intersecting roads, or did you picture someone at a critical point in life? Now that you have read part of the unit, do you suppose the authors wanted you to think of the literal or the figurative meaning of the word *crossroads?*

In the next selection you are going to read, "A Contest of Wills," a young woman, Annie Sullivan, has been hired to teach Helen Keller, a girl who has been left blind, deaf, and mute by a serious illness. Annie becomes involved in a power struggle with the strong-willed Helen. In the following passage, Annie pleads for the right to continue teaching her student. Annie says:

> *I'm* interested. Of course she's testing me. Let me keep her to what she's learned, and she'll go on learning from me. Take her out of my hands, and it all comes apart.

In this play, the playwright uses the word *hands* in a figurative manner. Explain why the expression "Take her out of my hands" is an example of a figurative rather than a literal meaning. What other words might Annie have used to express herself?

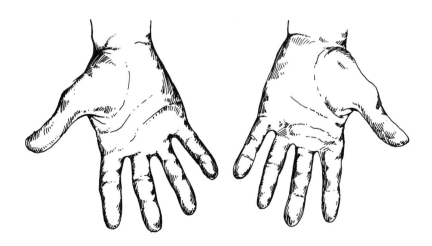

A CONTEST OF WILLS

by WILLIAM GIBSON

Mathematical problems are impossible to solve if you do not know what the symbols mean. Even simple addition and subtraction would be impossible to complete if you did not know the plus and minus signs. For Helen Keller, language was meaningless until Annie Sullivan taught her the code of the alphabet.

What makes Annie's promise to Captain Keller difficult to keep? Why does Kate feel that she has simultaneously found and lost a child when Helen spells "teacher" into her hand?

The characters in The Miracle Worker, *the stage play from which this excerpt was taken, were based on real people. Helen Keller was an intelligent baby—she had already learned to say the word* water*—when a serious illness left her blind, deaf, and mute. A young woman named Annie Sullivan entered her life as a teacher. Upon her arrival, Annie found an unmanageable child who was spoiled by her parents. As the weeks progressed, Annie taught Helen many symbols in the manual alphabet, but she was forced to battle with Helen's strong will and temper tantrums. Annie took Helen away from the family for a time, and Helen learned to be more disciplined. Now, in the last section of the play, Annie and Helen return to the family.*

CHARACTERS

KELLER, *Helen's father*   AUNT EV, *Helen's aunt*
ANNIE SULLIVAN, *Helen's teacher*   KATE, *Helen's mother*
HELEN, *a blind and deaf girl*   JAMES, *Helen's brother*

Time: *The 1880s*
Place: *In and around the Keller house in Tuscumbia, Alabama*

The stage is divided into two areas. One area represents a dining room in the Keller house. In the other area, representing the yard, there is a water pump. As the curtain opens, ANNIE SULLIVAN and CAPTAIN KELLER stand in the doorway.

KELLER: Miss—Annie.

(*He has an envelope in his fingers.*)

I've been waiting to give you this.

ANNIE: (*after a breath*) What?

KELLER: Your first month's salary.

(*He puts it in her hand.*)

With many more to come, I trust. It doesn't express what we feel. It doesn't pay our debt for what you've done.

ANNIE: What have I done?

KELLER: Taken a wild thing, and given us back a child.

ANNIE: (*presently*) I taught her one thing, no. Don't do this, don't do that—

KELLER: It's more than all of us could, in all the years we—

ANNIE: I wanted to teach her what language is. I wanted to teach her yes.

KELLER: You will have time.

ANNIE: I don't know how. I know that without it to do nothing but obey is—no gift, obedience without understanding is a—blindness, too. Is that all I've wished on her?

KELLER: (*gently*) No, no—

ANNIE: Maybe. I don't know what else to do. Simply go on, keep doing what I've done, and have faith that inside she's—that inside it's waiting. Like water, underground. All I can do is keep on.

KELLER: It's enough. For us.

ANNIE: You can help, Captain Keller.

KELLER: How?

ANNIE: Even learning no has been at a cost. Of much trouble and pain. Don't undo it.

KELLER: Why should we wish to—

ANNIE: (*abruptly*) The world isn't an easy place for anyone. I don't want her just to obey, but to let her have her way in everything is a lie, to *her*, I can't—

(*Her eyes fill, it takes her by surprise, and she laughs through it.*)

And I don't even love her, she's not my child! Well. You've got to stand between that lie and her.

KELLER: We'll try.

ANNIE: Because *I* will. As long as you let me stay, that's one promise I'll keep.

KELLER: Agreed. We've learned something too, I hope.

(*a pause*)

Won't you come now, to supper?

ANNIE: Yes. I used to wonder how I could—earn a living.

KELLER: Oh, you do.

ANNIE: I really do. Now the question is, can I survive it!

(*Now in the dining room the rear door opens, and HELEN steps in. She stands a moment, then sniffs in one deep, grateful breath, and her hands go out vigorously to familiar things, over the door panels, and to the chairs around the table, and over the silverware on the table. HELEN hurries, groping, to the front door, opens and closes it again to be sure it is unlocked, gropes back to the rear door and repeats the procedure, removing its key and hugging herself gleefully. AUNT EV is next in by the rear door, with a relish tray; she bends to kiss HELEN's cheek. HELEN finds KATE behind her, and thrusts the keys at her.*)

KATE: What? Oh.

(*to Ev*)

Keys.

(*She pockets them, lets HELEN feel them.*)

Yes, I'll keep the keys. I think we've had enough of locked doors, too.

(*JAMES now appears and takes his place at the table.*)

JAMES: Evening, general.

(KATE, *surveying the table, breaks the silence.*)

KATE: Will you say grace, Jimmie?

(*They bow their heads, except for* HELEN, *who palms her empty place and then reaches to be sure her mother is there.*)

JAMES *considers a moment, glances across at* ANNIE, *lowers his head again, and obliges.*

JAMES: (*lightly*) And Jacob was left alone, and wrestled with an angel until the breaking of the day; and the hollow of Jacob's thigh was out of joint, as he wrestled with him; and the angel said, Let me go, for the day breaketh. And Jacob said, I will not let thee go, except thou bless me. Amen.

(ANNIE *has lifted her eyes suspiciously at* JAMES, *who winks expressionlessly and inclines his head to* HELEN.)

Oh, you angel.

(*The others lift their faces;* ANNIE *puts a napkin around* HELEN.)

AUNT EV: That's a very strange grace, James.

KELLER: Will you start the muffins, Ev?

JAMES: It's from the Good Book, isn't it?

AUNT EV: (*passing a plate*) Well, of course it is. Didn't you know?

JAMES: Yes, I knew.

KELLER: (*serving*) Ham, Miss Annie?

ANNIE: Please.

AUNT EV: Then why ask?

JAMES: I meant it *is* from the Good Book, and therefore a fitting grace.

AUNT EV: Well. I don't know about *that*.

KATE: (*with the pitcher*) Miss Annie?

ANNIE: Thank you.

(*When* ANNIE *reaches for the pitcher,* HELEN *removes her napkin and drops it to the floor.* ANNIE *is filling* HELEN'S *glass when she notices it; she considers* HELEN'S *bland expression a moment, then bends, retrieves it, and tucks it around* HELEN'S *neck again.*)

JAMES: Well, fitting in the sense that Jacob's thigh was out of joint, and so is this piggie's.

AUNT EV: I declare, James—

(*She interrupts herself, seeing* HELEN *deliberately lift off her napkin and drop it again to the floor. She bends to retrieve it, but* ANNIE *stops her arm.* ANNIE *picks up the napkin.*)

AUNT EV: James, now you're pulling my—lower extremity, the first thing you know we'll be—

(*She stops, hearing herself in the silence.* ANNIE, *with everyone now watching, for the third time puts the napkin on* HELEN. HELEN *yanks it off, and throws it down.* ANNIE *rises, lifts* HELEN'S *plate, and bears it away.* HELEN, *feeling it gone, slides down and commences to kick up under the table; the dishes jump.* ANNIE *contemplates this for a moment, then coming back takes* HELEN'S *wrists firmly and swings her off the chair.* HELEN, *struggling, gets one hand free, and catches at her mother's skirt; when* KATE *takes her by the shoulders,* HELEN *hangs quiet.*)

KATE: Miss Annie.

ANNIE: No.

KATE: (*a pause*) It's a very special day.

ANNIE: (*grimly*) It will be, when I give in to that.

(*She tries to disengage* HELEN'S *hand;* KATE *lays hers on* ANNIE'S.)

KATE: Please. I've hardly had a chance to welcome her home—

ANNIE: Captain Keller.

KELLER: (*embarrassed*) Oh, Kate, we—had a little talk, Miss
    Annie feels that if we indulge Helen in these—
AUNT EV: But what's the child done?
ANNIE: She's learned not to throw things on the floor and
    kick. It took us the best part of two weeks and—
AUNT EV: But only a napkin, it's not as if it were breakable!
ANNIE: And everything she's learned *is*? Mrs. Keller, I don't
    think we should—play tug-of-war for her. Either give her
    to me or you keep her from kicking.
KATE: What do you wish to do?
ANNIE: Let me take her from the table.
AUNT EV: Oh, let her stay, my goodness, she's only a child,
    she doesn't have to wear a napkin if she doesn't want to
    her first evening—
ANNIE: (*level*) And ask outsiders not to interfere.
AUNT EV: (*astonished*) Out—outsi—I'm the child's *aunt*!
KATE: (*distressed*) Will once hurt so much, Miss Annie?
    I've—made all Helen's favorite foods, tonight. (*a pause*)
KELLER: (*gently*) It's a homecoming party, Miss Annie.
    (ANNIE *after a moment releases* HELEN. *But she cannot
    accept it, at her own chair she shakes her head and turns
    back, intent on* KATE.)
ANNIE: She's testing you. You realize?
JAMES: (*to Annie*) She's testing you.
KELLER: Jimmie, be quiet.
    (JAMES *sits, tense.*)
    Now she's home, naturally she—
ANNIE: And wants to see what will happen. At your hands. I
    said it was my main worry. Is this what you promised me
    not half an hour ago?
KELLER: (*reasonably*) But she's not kicking, now—
ANNIE: And not learning not to. Mrs. Keller, teaching her is
    bound to be painful, to everyone. I know it hurts to

watch, but she'll live up to just what you demand of her,
and no more.

JAMES: (*palely*) She's testing *you*.

KELLER: (*testily*) Jimmie.

JAMES: I have an opinion, I think I should—

KELLER: No one's interested in hearing your opinion.

ANNIE: *I'm* interested. Of course she's testing me. Let me
keep her to what she's learned, and she'll go on learning
from me. Take her out of my hands, and it all comes
apart.

(*She turns to* JAMES, *flatly.*)

Please pass me more of—her favorite foods.

(*Then* KATE *lifts* HELEN's *hand, and turning her toward*
ANNIE, *surrenders her;* HELEN *makes for her own chair.*)

KATE: (*low*) Take her, Miss Annie.

ANNIE: (*then*) Thank you.

(*But the moment* ANNIE, *rising, reaches for her hand,* HELEN *begins to fight and kick, clutching the tablecloth, and uttering laments.* ANNIE *again tries to loosen her hand, and* KELLER *rises.*)

KELLER: (*tolerant*) I'm afraid you're the difficulty, Miss Annie. Now, I'll keep her to what she's learned, you're quite right there—

(*He takes* HELEN's *hands from* ANNIE, *pats them;* HELEN *quiets down.*)

—but I don't see that we need send her from the table, after all, she's the guest of honor. Bring her plate back.

ANNIE: If she was a seeing child, none of you would tolerate one—

KELLER: Well, she's not. Bring her plate, please.

(ANNIE's *jaw sets, but she restores the plate, while* KELLER *fastens the napkin around* HELEN's *neck; she permits it.*)

There. It's not unnatural, most of us take some aversion to our teachers, and occasionally another hand can smooth things out.

(*He puts a fork in* HELEN's *hand;* HELEN *takes it. Genially.*)

Now. Shall we start all over?

(*He goes back around the table, and sits.* ANNIE *stands watching.* HELEN *is motionless, thinking things through, until, with a wicked glee, she deliberately flings the fork to the floor. After another moment she plunges her hand into her food, and crams a fistful into her mouth.*)

JAMES: (*wearily*) I think we've started all over—

(KELLER *shoots a glare at him, as* HELEN *plunges her other hand into* ANNIE's *plate.* ANNIE *at once moves in, to grasp her wrist, and* HELEN, *flinging out a hand, encounters the pitcher; she swings with it at* ANNIE; ANNIE, *falling back blocks it with an elbow, but the water flies over her dress.* ANNIE *gets her breath, then snatches the pitcher away in one hand, hoists* HELEN *up bodily under the other arm, and starts to carry her out, kicking.* KELLER *stands.*)

ANNIE: (*savagely polite*) Don't get up!

KELLER: Where are you going?

ANNIE: Don't interfere in any way! I treat her like a seeing child because I ask her to see, I expect her to see. Don't undo what I do!

KELLER: Where are you taking her?

ANNIE: To make her fill this pitcher again!

(*She thrusts out with* HELEN *under her arm, but* HELEN *escapes up the stairs and* ANNIE *runs after her.* KELLER *stands, rigid.* AUNT EV *is astounded.*)

AUNT EV: You let her speak to you like that, Arthur? A creature who works for you?

KELLER: (*angrily*) No. I don't.

(*He is starting after* ANNIE *when* JAMES, *on his feet with shaky resolve, interposes his chair between them in* KELLER's *path.*)

JAMES: Let her go.

KELLER: What!

JAMES: (*a swallow*) I said—let her go. She's right.

(KELLER *glares at the chair and him.* JAMES *takes a deep breath, then, headlong.*)

She's right! Kate's right, I'm right, and you're wrong! If you drive her away from here it will be over my dead—chair. Has it never occurred to you that on one occasion you might be wrong?

(KELLER's *stare is unbelieving, even a little fascinated.*

KATE *rises in trepidation, to mediate.*)

KATE: Captain.

(KELLER *stops her with his raised hand; his eyes stay on* JAMES' *pale face, for a long hold. When he finally finds his voice, it is gruff.*)

KELLER: Sit down, everyone.

(*He sits.* KATE *sits.* JAMES *holds onto his chair.* KELLER *speaks mildly.*)

Please sit down, Jimmie.

(JAMES *sits, and a moveless silence prevails;* KELLER'S *eyes do not leave him.* ANNIE *has pulled* HELEN *downstairs again by one hand, the pitcher in her other hand, down the porch steps, and across the yard to the pump. She puts* HELEN'S *hand on the pump handle, grimly.*)

ANNIE: All right. Pump.

(HELEN *touches her cheek, waits uncertainly.*)

No, she's not here. Pump!

(*She forces* HELEN'S *hand to work the handle, then lets go. And* HELEN *obeys. She pumps till the water comes, then* ANNIE *puts the pitcher in her other hand and guides it under the spout, and the water tumbling half into and half around the pitcher douses* HELEN'S *hand.* ANNIE *takes over the handle to keep water coming, and does automatically what she has done so many times before. Using the manual alphabet, she spells into* HELEN'S *free palm:*)

Water. W-a-t-e-r. Water. It has a name—

(*And now the miracle happens.* HELEN *drops the pitcher on the slab under the spout; it shatters. She stands, transfixed.* ANNIE *freezes on the pump handle. There is a change in the sundown light, and with it a change in* HELEN'S *face, some light coming into it we have never seen there, some struggle in the depths behind it; and her*

lips tremble, trying to remember something the muscles around them once knew, till at last it finds its way out, painfully.)

HELEN: Wah. Wah.

(*and again, with great effort*)

Wah. Wah.

(HELEN *plunges her hand into the dwindling water, spells into her own palm. Then she gropes frantically,* ANNIE *reaches for her hand, and* HELEN *spells into* ANNIE's *hand.*)

ANNIE: (*whispering*) Yes.

(HELEN *spells into it again.*)

Yes!

(HELEN *grabs at the handle, pumps for more water, plunges her hand into its spurt, and grabs* ANNIE's *to spell it again.*)

Yes! Oh, my dear—

(*She falls to her knees to clasp* HELEN's *hand, but* HELEN *pulls it free, stands almost bewildered, then drops to the ground, pats it swiftly, and holds up her palm, imperious.* ANNIE *spells into it.*)

G-r-o-u-n-d.

(HELEN *spells it back.*)

Yes!

(HELEN *whirls to the pump, pats it, holds up her palm, and* ANNIE *spells into it.*)

P-u-m-p.

(HELEN *spells it back.*)

Yes! Yes!

(*Now* HELEN *is in such an excitement she is possessed, wild, trembling, cannot be still, turns, runs, falls on the porch steps, claps it, reaches out her palm, and* ANNIE *is at it instantly to spell.*)

S-t-e-p.

(HELEN *has no time to spell back now. She whirls, groping, to touch anything, encounters the trellis, shakes it, thrusts out her palm, and* ANNIE, *while spelling to her, cries wildly at the house.*)

T-r-e-l-l-i-s. Mrs. Keller! Mrs. Keller!

(*Inside,* KATE *starts to her feet.* HELEN *scrambles back onto the porch, groping, and finds the bell string, tugs it, the bell rings, the distant chimes begins tolling the hour, all the bells in town seem to break into speech while* HELEN *reaches out and* ANNIE *spells feverishly into her hand.* KATE *hurries out, with* KELLER *after her;* AUNT EV *is on her feet, to peer out the window; only* JAMES *remains at the table, and, with a napkin, wipes his damp brow.* HELEN, *ringing the bell, with her other hand encounters her mother's skirt; when she throws a hand out,*

ANNIE *spells into it.*)
M-o-t-h-e-r.
(KELLER *now seizes* HELEN's *hand. She touches him, gestures a hand, and* ANNIE *again spells.*)
P-a-p-a—She knows!

(KATE *and* KELLER *go to their knees, stammering, clutching* HELEN *to them, and* ANNIE *steps unsteadily back to watch the threesome:* HELEN *spelling wildly into* KATE's *hand, then into* KELLER's, KATE *spelling back into* HELEN's; *they cannot keep their hands off her, and rock her in their clasp. Then* HELEN *gropes, feels nothing, turns all around, pulls free, and comes with both hands groping to find* ANNIE. *She encounters* ANNIE's *thighs,* ANNIE *kneels to her.* HELEN's *hand pats* ANNIE's *cheek impatiently, points a finger, and waits; and* ANNIE *spells into it.*)
T-e-a-c-h-e-r.
(HELEN *spells it back, slowly;* ANNIE *nods.*)
Teacher.
(*She holds* HELEN's *hand to her cheek. Presently* HELEN *withdraws it, not jerkily, only with reserve, and retreats a*

step. She stands, thinking it over, then turns again, and stumbles back to her parents. They try to embrace her, but she has something else in mind, it is to get the keys, and she hits KATE's *pocket until* KATE *digs them out for her.* ANNIE, *with her own load of emotion, has retreated, her back turned, toward the pump, to sit;* KATE *moves to* HELEN, *touches her hand questioningly and* HELEN *spells a word to her.* KATE *comprehends it, their first act of verbal communication, and she can hardly utter the word aloud, in wonder, gratitude, and deprivation. It is a moment in which she simultaneously finds and loses a child.)*

KATE: Teacher?

(ANNIE *turns, and* KATE, *facing* HELEN *in her direction by the shoulders, holds her back, holds her back, and then relinquishes her.* HELEN *feels her way across the yard, rather shyly, and when her moving hands touch* ANNIE's *skirt, she stops. Then she holds out the keys and places them in* ANNIE's *hand. For a moment neither of them moves. Then* HELEN *slides into* ANNIE's *arms, and, lifting away her smoked glasses, kisses her on the cheek.* ANNIE *gathers her in.* KATE, *torn both ways, turns from this, and makes her way into the house on* KELLER's *arm. The lights are half down now, except over the pump.*
ANNIE *and* HELEN *are here, alone in the yard.* ANNIE *has found* HELEN's *hand, almost without knowing it, and she spells slowly into it, her voice unsteady, whispering.)*

ANNIE: I, l-o-v-e, H-e-l-e-n.
(*She clutches the child to her, tight this time, not spelling, whispering into her hair.*)
Forever, and—
(*She stops.*)
—ever.

(In the dining room KATE *has stood over the table, staring at* HELEN's *plate, with* KELLER *at her shoulder; now* JAMES *takes a step to move her chair in, and* KATE *sits, with head erect, and* KELLER *inclines his head to* JAMES; *so it is* AUNT EV, *hesitant, and rather humble, who, moves to the door. Outside* HELEN *tugs at* ANNIE's *hand, and* ANNIE *comes with it.* HELEN *pulls her toward the house; and, hand in hand, they cross the yard, and ascend the porch steps, to where* AUNT EV *is holding the door open for them. The curtain ends the play.)*

CHECK FOR UNDERSTANDING

1. What was the promise Annie said she would keep as long as she stayed in the Keller house?
2. What made Annie's promise to Captain Keller so difficult to keep?
3. Why did Annie's treatment of Helen seem a bit harsh from the viewpoint of Captain Keller and Kate?
4. How did James help Annie?
5. Why was the word *water* so significant to Helen?
6. Why did Kate feel that she had simultaneously found and lost a child when Helen spelled "teacher" into her hand?

WRITE ABOUT *"A Contest of Wills"*

There are several "contests of wills" going on in the play. Write a paragraph describing at least two of them, and explain how the contests were resolved.

Remembering the Moment

Did the play tell the real story? Helen Keller and Annie Sullivan both wrote about the moment dramatized in "A Contest of Wills," when Helen realized that "everything has a name."

Helen Keller recalled...

One day, while I was playing with my new doll, Miss Sullivan put my big rag doll into my lap also, spelled "d-o-l-l," and tried to make me understand that "d-o-l-l" applied to both. Earlier in the day we had had a tussle over the words "m-u-g" and "w-a-t-e-r." Miss Sullivan had tried to impress it upon me that "m-u-g" is *mug* and that "w-a-t-e-r" is *water*, but I persisted in confounding the two. . . .

We walked down the path to the well-house, attracted by the fragrance of the honeysuckle with which it was covered. Someone was drawing water, and my teacher placed my hand under the spout. As the cool stream gushed over one hand she spelled into the other the word *water*, first slowly, then rapidly. I stood still, my whole attention fixed upon the motions of her fingers. Suddenly I felt a misty consciousness as of something forgotten—a thrill of returning thought—and somehow the mystery of language was revealed to me. I knew then that "w-a-t-e-r" meant the wonderful cool something that was flowing over my hand. That living word awakened my soul, gave it light, hope, joy, set it free! There were barriers still, it is true, but barriers that could, in time, be swept away.

I left the well-house eager to learn. Everything had a name, and each name gave birth to a new thought. As we returned to the house every object which I touched seemed to quiver with life. That was because I saw everything with the strange, new sight that had come to me. . . .

I learned a great many new words that day. I do not remember what they all were; but I do know that *mother*, *father*, *sister*, *teacher* were among them—words that were to make the world blossom for me. . . .

Annie Sullivan wrote to a friend...

April 5, 1887

I must write you a line this morning because something very important has happened. Helen . . . has learned that everything has a name, and that the manual alphabet is the key to everything she wants to know.

In a previous letter I think I wrote you that "mug" and "milk" had given Helen more trouble than all the rest. She confused the nouns with the verb "drink." She didn't know the word for "drink," but went through the pantomime of drinking whenever she spelled "mug" or "milk." This morning, while she was washing, she wanted to know the name for "water." When she wants to know the name of anything, she points to it and pats my hand. I spelled "w-a-t-e-r," and thought no more about it until after breakfast. Then it occurred to me that with the help of this new word I might succeed in straightening out the "mug-milk" difficulty. We went out to the pump-house, and I made Helen hold her mug under the spout while I pumped. As the cold water gushed forth, filling the mug, I spelled "w-a-t-e-r" in Helen's free hand. The word coming so close upon the sensation of cold water rushing over her hand seemed to startle her. She dropped the mug and stood as one transfixed. A new light came into her face. She spelled "water" several times. Then she dropped on the ground, asked for its name, pointed to the pump and the trellis, and, suddenly turning round, she asked for my name. I spelled "Teacher." Just then the nurse brought Helen's little sister into the pump-house, and Helen spelled "baby" and pointed to the nurse. All the way back to the house she was highly excited, and learned the name of every object she touched, so that in a few hours she had added thirty new words to her vocabulary. Here are some of them: *door, open, shut, give, go, come,* and a great many more.

P.S. I didn't finish my letter in time to get it posted last night; so I shall add a line. Helen got up this morning like a radiant fairy. She has flitted from object to object, asking the name of everything and kissing me for very gladness.

Have you ever heard the expression "the best of both worlds"? Jim Yoshida wants to play football. His father believes that the skills Jim would learn in judo are far more valuable. Father and son agree to compromise by including both sports in their lives.

How does learning judo affect Jim Yoshida's skill as a football player? How are Jim and his father both benefited by the compromise they make?

FOOTBALL VS. JUDO

by JIM YOSHIDA   with BILL HOSOKAWA

My father was a sturdily built man, and he became heavier as he grew older. He sported a bristly Charlie Chaplin mustache. He never learned much English, so he always spoke to us in Japanese. I could understand him, but I couldn't express myself in Japanese, so I replied in English. This is the way most Japanese-American families communicated, and we got along quite well.

I could never seem to penetrate my father's gruff exterior, and I feared him as much as I loved him. I can't ever remember hearing him praise me. Whenever I did anything well, he simply said he expected me to do better the next time, and eventually I came to understand that this was his way. When I was sixteen years old I picked a hundred pound sack of rice off the floor and held it up over my head, the way a weight lifter lifts barbells. This was a feat of strength recognized among Japanese families as a sign that a lad had reached manhood. If Dad was proud, he didn't show any sign. But later Mother told me how really happy he was. About the same time, I defeated my father for the first time at arm wrestling. We sat at the kitchen table facing each other. With elbows down on the table, we locked right hands and each tried to force the other's

arm down. I was surprised at how easily I defeated him, for Dad had a reputation for physical strength. He was proud that I was growing strong, and I felt sad that he was getting old, but neither of us said anything. Our relationship was such that we seldom voiced our thoughts to each other, and I suppose that's the way he was brought up.

With my mother, the relationship was altogether different. She was a tiny woman, no more than five feet two inches tall, but she was blessed with enormous vitality. She had a beautiful, heart-shaped face. She was gentle; not once did she ever strike me, although I deserved punishment frequently, and I don't recall that she ever raised her voice to me. But she had a way of talking to me when I did wrong; these talks usually left me weeping in remorse.

Mother had an understanding of young people that was extremely unusual in the Japanese immigrant generation. Dad was strict and stern. He wanted to rear his children the way he had been brought up. Mother was wise enough to know that American children could not be reared like Japanese children, that we were products of the new world and we required freedom. Eventually I came to realize

she was a mellowing, liberalizing influence on my father. This does not mean she was entirely permissive. In her own way she kept a tight rein on her children. When I became old enough to go out at night, she insisted that I let her know when I came home. I would walk by her bedroom door and knock, *tum-ta-ta-tum-tum*. And she would knock back, *tum-tum*. If she slept while I was out, it was only lightly.

We lived an oddly mixed and pleasant life. We celebrated the Fourth of July and Thanksgiving, as well as the Japanese festivals like Boys' Day and Girls' Day and the Festival of the Dead in late summer. As children we went to public schools and learned about George Washington at Valley Forge, and the grand heritage of a people who were willing to revolt for liberty and freedom. And after school was dismissed at 3 P.M., we trudged on to the Japanese Language School to learn a little about that very difficult language of our parents. Although some resented the double dose of schooling, we did not think it strange, because many of our Jewish friends in Seattle attended Hebrew school.

Somehow this life must have agreed with me, for by the time I was fifteen years old and a freshman at

Broadway High School, I stood five feet seven inches tall and weighed 168 pounds. Many of the other fellows signed up to try out for the freshman football team. I couldn't, because I had to go to Japanese school.

Still, it wouldn't hurt to watch for a little while. I sat on the sidelines, glancing at my watch frequently to make sure I would leave in time to get to Japanese school before the bell rang. About the third day the freshmen engaged in a scrimmage, and I couldn't tear myself away. I had played some sandlot football, and I figured I could do just as well as the boys in uniform. Before I knew it, it was too late to get to Japanese school on time. It didn't take me long to rationalize—being absent was only a little worse than being tardy. I was going to get a scolding if I showed up late without a good excuse, so I might just as well play hookey for the day. Before long, nothing seemed to be more important than playing football with the Broadway High School freshman team. I found myself walking over to the coach—his name was Bob Heaman—and telling him I wanted to turn out.

Heaman looked up and down my stocky frame. "What's your name?" he asked.

"Katsumi Yoshida," I replied.

"That's no name for a kid who wants to play football," he said. "I'm going to call you Jim." He reached into a pocket and pulled out a mimeographed form. "You have to get your father to sign it. Come down to the locker room after school tomorrow and check out a uniform."

My heart sank. Here I was being invited to try out for the team and parental permission—an impossible obstacle—blocked the way.

Full of apprehension, I went home at the normal time. Apparently my mother was unaware of my absence from Japanese school, and if my sister Betty had noticed, she hadn't said anything. I knew that my mother could sense when I had something on my mind. Besides, I wanted to talk to her before Dad came home, so I came straight to the point.

"Mom," I said, "I want to turn out for the football team at school."

She scarcely looked up from her cooking. "Isn't it a very rough game?"

"Not really," I said.

After a moment she replied: "You are our only son, Katsumi, and I don't know what we would do if you were injured permanently playing football. Besides, what would you do about Japanese school? I think we had better forget about football."

I knew it was useless to try to change her mind, and even more useless to talk to Dad.

Next day, during a study period, I gave myself permission to play football. I carefully forged my father's

signature on the slip. My hands were clammy when I gave the slip to Coach Heaman. I was sure he could hear the pounding of my heart, and see the look of guilt that I knew was written on my face. But he failed to notice, and routinely filed the permission form, and issued me an ancient, hand-me-down uniform and a pair of ill-fitting shoes.

I made the team as a running guard. This meant I pulled out of the line and ran interference for the ball-carrier. If I did what I was supposed to do and threw a good block, the ball-carrier had a chance of making a good gain. The position required speed, agility, size, and the willingness to play the part of a human battering ram. I loved the body contact. At the end of the freshman season I was one of several boys invited to suit up with the varsity. In the season finale the varsity coach, Jerry Robinson, let me play half the game.

Meanwhile, for some reason I have never understood, my absence from Japanese school went unnoticed. Perhaps I had dropped out before anyone became aware that I should have been attending classes. At any rate three months had slipped by without my ever setting foot in Japanese school, and I all but forgot that I was really supposed to be studying the intricacies of the ancestral language rather than learning to block and tackle.

I was finally tripped up when Betty brought home her report card from Japanese school right after the football season ended. As usual she

had done very well in her studies, and Dad nodded his approval as he examined her record. I knew what was coming next. He turned to me and asked to see my report card.

"Sir," I said, "I don't have one."

His eyebrows shot up. "Why not? Did you lose it?"

"No sir, I haven't been attending Japanese school."

He fixed me with a stare that bored right through me. We were at the dinner table and Mother had served all of us with hot boiled rice to eat with the cooked meat and vegetables. Steam rose from the bowl in front of my father, and I could see his temper rising, too. Ordinarily, I was famished by mealtime and made quick work of my dinner, but now I had lost all interest in food.

"Explain yourself," Dad ordered.

So I told him the whole story, including the way I had forged his signature, and his frown grew darker and darker.

"Bakatare!" he finally shouted in fury. There is no precise English equivalent for that word. It means fool, or imbecile, but there is much more scorn, vitriol, and invective in the word than is indicated by direct translation.

Good old Mom. She averted a very explosive situation by suggesting that the dinner table was not the place for a scolding. She suggested we finish our dinner and then talk about the problem. I picked at my food while all the others seemed to eat with the usual relish. I wasn't too worried about what had happened— that was over the dam. My real concern was whether Dad would let me play football next season.

Sometime during the meal Dad must have seen the humor of my transgression. Perhaps he remembered pranks he had pulled as a boy. I was relieved to see his anger had given way to simply a serious mood when finally the dishes were cleared away.

First, he lectured me about how wrong it was to deceive one's parents, and I had to agree with him. Eventually he got around to football. "I can understand why you would want to play the game," he said. "It is a rough game and it is natural for boys to want to engage in rough sports. But you must remember you are the son of Japanese parents, and therefore you should take an interest in Japanese sports, like *kendo* and judo."

Kendo is a form of fencing. The participants wear masks, helmets, and armor, and whale away at each other with split bamboo staves which simulate the long, curved steel swords used by the samurai warriors of old. Judo is like wrestling, hand-to-hand combat in which a smaller and weaker man learns to use his opponent's strength to defeat him. I wanted nothing to do with *kendo*; the prospect of fighting with sticks was too much. And I didn't have much enthusiasm for judo either, for I had heard that clever little fellows could whip big ones, and I was one of the "big" guys.

"Either sport is good," Dad was saying. "Either one will give you the discipline you need because they are Japanese sports. American life is too soft. You must learn to grow tougher, physically, mentally, and morally."

Football isn't tough? He had never played football. He didn't know what it was to get your brains jarred loose in a hard tackle and then come back for more.

Just then I saw an out. I apologized for what I had done. I was truly sorry. I agreed to go back to Japanese school and try my best to make up

for what I had missed. And I said I would go to judo class—and here was the hooker—if I could play football again next year.

The smile that had started to take shape on Dad's face vanished.

"All right," he said with resignation. "Play football if you must, if it's that important to you. But remember, there are things that are important to me, too. So go to Japanese school and try to learn a little about the language. And go to judo classes and learn a little about discipline." We shook hands and I think I gained a deeper understanding of Dad that night than ever before.

Several nights later, when I came home from Japanese school, Dad introduced me to a handsome, curly-haired fellow who was about eight or ten years older than I. His name was Kuniyuki; he was an instructor at the

Tentokukwan Judo School, and the son of one of Dad's best friends. Dad told me Kenny would be my judo teacher. Kenny was a little taller than I, and powerfully built, with broad, square shoulders that tapered down to slim hips and the muscular legs of an athlete. I liked him immediately. We had dinner together, and then he drove me to the judo school.

There were perhaps two dozen boys, many of whom I knew, fooling around on the judo mats. All were wearing padded jackets and short trousers. When Kenny entered, their yelling and laughing stopped abruptly, and they snapped to attention. Apparently he was a very important person at the school. Kenny led me to the framed portrait of a little, half-bald old man which hung on one wall, and told me to bow before it each time I entered the hall. Later I learned he was Jigoro Kano, the father of modern Judo.

For the next three weeks, every Monday, Wednesday, and Friday, I went to the school and learned to sit Japanese-style, with my legs folded under me, and to fall. Falling without hurting yourself is an art in itself. Gradually I learned to roll to absorb the impact as I hit the mat, to break the momentum with my arms and legs and shoulders before I crashed

to the floor. Then Kenny—I was supposed to call him Kuniyuki Sensei (Instructor Kuniyuki)—began on the holds and throws. He seemed to think the best way to teach was to demonstrate. From 7 to 9:30 P.M. I would practice with the other boys, throwing and being thrown almost without a break. Then the others were told to shower and change, but my evening was just starting.

"Come on, Yoshida," Kenny would say. He would let me throw him a few times . . . then *wham*, I would find myself thrown flat on the mat. "Get up," he would say. "We don't have time to sit around." *Wham*, I would go down again. Or he would say something like, "How would you like to see Tokyo?" I would drop my guard for the barest instant to reply, and *wham*, I would crash into the wall. He would pick me up, sweep my legs from under me, and slam me to the mat, scolding me all the time for not taking the offensive.

Some of my friends felt that Kenny was picking on me unfairly. "Jim," one of them asked, "how come you take all that punishment? I'd quit if I were in your place." I must admit that I thought about quitting, especially on mornings after a particularly strenuous workout, when I was so sore I could hardly crawl out of bed. But I knew that if I dropped judo I could forget about playing football. I also suspected that Dad had given Kenny orders to make it as rough as he could for me, and that only firmed up my determination to stick it out. Then one day it occurred to me that Kenny wouldn't be spending all that time with me if he didn't think a lot of me. And after that I vowed to take all the punishment he dealt out, and come back for more. When Mom asked how I was getting along, I assured her that Kuniyuki Sensei was being extra nice to me.

About six months after I began judo lessons, everything began to fall into place. I was tough physically. I had learned, finally, to take the hardest falls without hurting myself, and now I was able to coordinate my skill together with my strength and dish it out as well as take it. I found a new exhilaration in the combat of judo, and excitement in the smell of the judo mats. Judo was as much fun as football.

Once a month we would have an intra-club tournament. The boys at the Tentokukwan School would be divided into two teams; then we would engage in elimination matches, starting with the youngest and newest students. If you threw an opponent, or won a decision over him, you took on the next man and remained in the ring until you were defeated. Although I was bigger than most of the fellows, I still wore the white belt of the novice and was about in the middle of our lineup. In my first tournament I threw seven boys in a row, including two wearing the black belts of experts. I was having the time of my life. A black-belter must throw a white-belter, or lose face. I had nothing to lose, and could go all out. Kuniyuki Sensei gave me an approving look. Not long afterward I was jumped over all the intermediate steps—yellow, green, brown, and purple—and given a black belt. It usually takes a student three or four years of hard work to win black-belt rating. I had done it

in a fraction of that time. Dad beamed approval.

He raised no objection when I turned out for football in the fall of my sophomore year. I had kept my end of the bargain, and he kept his. I made the team as running guard, and was lucky enough to be an all-city selection even though we didn't win a single game. This was a busy time, for I continued with judo after the daily football workouts. Still, I managed to keep my grades up. After football season I returned to Japanese school, and made a valiant, but futile, effort to catch up with the other students trying to master an almost incomprehensible language.

These were happy times. As a football star, I was a "big man" in school. My teammates were of many ethnic origins, but it never occurred to me that we were different. We were all Americans, held together by a common love for football and loyalty to our school.

By the time my senior year rolled around, both my parents had become ardent football fans. Since someone had to stay at the barbershop, they alternated in coming out to watch me play. We had still another new coach, Al Lindquist. He figured that since I was fast enough to run in front of the ball-carrier, why couldn't I play

in the backfield where my size would be useful? He shifted me to fullback, and I guess the experiment was a success because, even though we still didn't win a game, we scored a touchdown—the first in three years. I took it over again against Garfield High, and this is what I kept dreaming about when everything else in my life had turned to ashes. We eventually lost the game, twenty-seven to seven. The crowd had overflowed from the stands onto the field, and, as I picked myself up after scoring, I saw Dad standing just outside the end zone in his big brown overcoat, a big grin on his face. I think the sight of that grin made me happier than scoring the touchdown.

CHECK FOR UNDERSTANDING

1. What was the conflict between Jim Yoshida and his father?
2. How does learning judo affect Jim's skill as a football player?
3. Were the Broadway High Tigers a successful team? Did this matter to Jim Yoshida? Explain your answer.
4. How were Jim and his father both benefited by the compromise they made?
5. Compare Jim's view of football to that of his father.

WRITE ABOUT *"Football vs. Judo"*

What was Jim's father thinking when he saw his son score a touchdown against Garfield High? Write two or three paragraphs from his point of view, describing his thoughts and feelings.

Choosing Appropriate Reference Source

Imagine that you were born in 2085, the first child in the Martian space colony. Your teacher has asked you to write a paper on American clothing. You go to your computer and ask its "Library" to give you the listings on "Clothing in America." This is what it has in its files:

Clothing, American, history of
   pre-European
   Colonial styles
   Revolutionary War
   Early Republic
   mid-eighteenth century
   nineteenth century
   twentieth century

You read some books and articles under each category and get copies of photographs to add to the report. When you finish writing and editing, you electronically send the report to your teacher. Two days later you get it back with this note, "Fine as far as it goes, but what about current fashion?"

That paper was incomplete because you used information only about the past. To answer the question "What are current fashions like today?" you would have had to use another source of information.

Getting General Information. Most researchers start with a general encyclopedia to give them an overview of their subject. An **encyclopedia** is an alphabetically arranged series of volumes that contains articles, called **entries**, about people, places, and things. Some of the articles are very long; some are just one paragraph. The last volume of the encyclopedia is usually the index.

To get the most out of an encyclopedia, you may have to look at more than one entry. For example, for a report on modern Japan, you would first look at the article "Japan" in the "J" volume. This major article would be divided into sections that might begin with the physical description of the country, followed by a long history of the country. After that, there might be separate sections on Japanese art, literature, technology, education, sports. Be sure to preview any major article you read in an encyclopedia so that you won't overlook any part that might prove interesting. At the end of a major article, there are often references to other articles that refer to Japanese culture or to the Japanese people. For example, you might find a reference to a separate article entitled "Judo" (also in the "J" volume), or to a major article entitled "Immigration," which would contain a subsection called "Japanese Immigration."

Getting Current Information. For recent facts about a country, nothing is better than an **almanac.** For example, in the section of the almanac that lists the countries of the world, you can find out who the country's leaders are and when they were elected. You will also find statistics on agriculture, population, health, and education; and you will probably get some information on any big events—such as disasters—of the previous year. For even more up-to-date information, use one of the weekly newsmagazines or the weekly review in a major Sunday newspaper.

Getting Information about Places. An **atlas** is a collection of maps. General atlases, often called **world** atlases, show all the continents, bodies of water, and countries of the world, along with any major cities, important rivers, and mountain ranges. In addition to these kinds of maps—which show the way humans have divided the land and the distances between places—an atlas might contain maps that show different land forms over a large region. For example, a map could show the desert that extends over much of northern Africa or it could show the plateau that forms Tibet and part of China. Atlases contain other kinds of geographical information—often in list or chart form. A chart may show how much rainfall there is in a particular area or how much wheat is grown. A list may compare the length of all the rivers in Asia.

Getting Special Information. In addition to general atlases, almanacs, and encyclopedias, the reference section of your school or local library will contain all kinds of books devoted to special subjects. There are historical atlases that show maps of what the Roman Empire looked like in the first century A.D., and there are collections of literature from all countries of the world. There are foreign-language dictionaries, and there are encyclopedias that concentrate on music, sports, art, or science and technology. Some special dictionaries give the histories of words, and some focus on antonyms and synonyms. There are also biographies of people in public life. All of these books can be very useful when you are writing research papers.

Using What You Have Learned

Write the letter of the reference work listed below that would give you the most information to answer each question that follows.

Reference Works
a. an atlas of the world
b. a sports dictionary
c. a world almanac
d. an historical atlas of Asia
e. a book of Japanese poetry in translation
f. a weekly newsmagazine
g. a dictionary of synonyms
h. a Japanese-English dictionary
i. an encyclopedia
j. an encyclopedia of world literature

1. Which reference work gives an overview of Japanese history and culture?
2. What is the Japanese word for *athlete?*
3. What are the current major exports of Japan?
4. How far is Shanghai, China, from Tokyo, Japan?
5. What were the trade routes to Japan used by the Europeans in the sixteenth century?
6. Where would you find a Japanese poem to memorize?
7. Who wrote the great Japanese work of literature known as the *Tale of Genji?*
8. When was judo invented?
9. What is a good synonym for *goal?*
10. What happened last week in Japan?

Expanding Your Skills

When you finish reading the next selections, go to the library. List the reference works you would use to write a report on migrant workers.

The Circuit

by FRANCISCO JIMÉNEZ

Some situations seem impossible to change. Panchito, the main character in "The Circuit," is trying to change things in his life. In an interview after the story, Mr. Jiménez explains how the real-life Panchito overcame his difficulties.

What does the list of family possessions tell you about the life of the migrant farm worker? What will happen to the trumpet lessons that Mr. Lema has promised to give Panchito?

It was that time of year again; Ito, the strawberry share-cropper, did not smile; it was natural. The peak of the strawberry season was over, and the last few days the workers, most of them braceros,[1] were not picking as many boxes as they had during the months of June and July.

As the last days of August disappeared, so did the number of braceros. Sunday, only one—the best picker—came to work; I liked him. Sometimes we talked during our half-hour lunch

[1] (bra ser'ō) a Mexican farm worker

break; that is how I found out he was from Jalisco, the same state in Mexico my family was from. That Sunday was the last time I saw him.

When the sun had tired and sunk behind the mountains, Ito signaled us that it was time to go home. *"Ya esora,[2]"* he yelled in his broken Spanish. Those were words I waited for twelve hours a day, every day, seven days a week, week after week; and the thought of not hearing them again saddened me.

As we drove home Papa did not say a word. With both hands on the wheel, he stared at the dirt road; my older brother, Roberto, was also silent. He leaned his head back and closed his eyes; once in a while he cleared from his throat the dust that blew in from the outside.

Yes, it was that time of year. When I opened the front door of our *casita*,[3] I stopped; everything we owned was neatly packed in cardboard boxes. Suddenly I felt even more the weight of hours, days, weeks, and months of work. I sat down on a box; the thought of having to move to Fresno, and knowing what was in store for me there, brought tears to my eyes.

That night I could not sleep; I lay in bed, thinking about how much I hated this move.

A little before five o'clock in the morning, Papa woke everyone up. A few minutes later, the yelling and screaming of my little brothers and sisters, for whom the move was a great adventure, broke the silence of dawn. Shortly, the barking of the dogs accompanied them.

While we packed the breakfast dishes, Papa went outside to start the *Carcanchita*; that was the name Papa gave his old '38 black Plymouth. He bought it in a used car lot in Santa Rosa in the winter of 1949. Papa was very proud of his car; *Mi Carcanchita*, my little jalopy, he called it; he had a right to be proud of it. He spent a lot of time looking at other cars before buying this one. When he finally chose the *Carcanchita*, he checked it thoroughly before driving it out of the car lot; he examined every inch of the car. He listened to the motor, tilting

[2] *Ya es hora,* "It's time to go."
[3] little house

his head from side to side like a parrot, trying to detect any noises that spelled car trouble. After being satisfied with the looks and sounds of the car, Papa insisted on knowing who the original owner was. He never did find out from the car dealer, but he bought the car anyway. Papa figured the original owner must have been an important man, because behind the rear seat of the car he found a blue necktie.

Papa parked the car out in front and left the motor running; "*Listo*,[4]" he yelled. Without saying a word, Roberto and I began to carry the boxes out to the car. Roberto carried the two big boxes and I carried the two smaller ones; Papa threw the mattress on the top of the car roof and tied it with ropes to the front and rear bumpers.

Everything was packed except Mama's pot; it was an old, large, galvanized pot she had picked up at the army surplus store in Santa María the year I was born. The pot was full of dents and nicks, and the more dents and nicks it had, the more Mama liked it. "*Mi olla*,[5]" she used to say proudly.

I held the front door open as Mama carefully carried out her pot by both handles, making sure not to spill the cooked beans. When she got to the car, Papa reached out to help her with it. Roberto opened the rear car door and Papa gently placed it on the floor behind the front seat. All of us climbed in; Papa sighed, wiped the sweat off his forehead with his sleeve, and said wearily, "*Es todo*.[6]"

As we drove away, I felt a lump in my throat; I turned around and looked at our *casita* for the last time.

At sunset we drove into a vineyard near Fresno. Since Papa did not speak English, Mama asked the boss if he needed any

[4] ready
[5] my kettle
[6] That's everything.

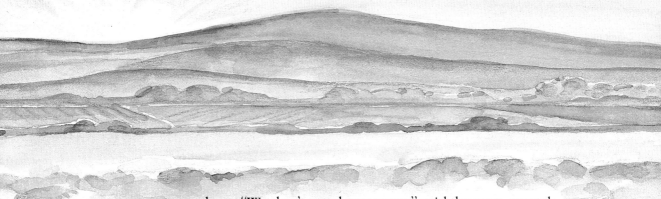

more workers; "We don't need any more," said the man, scratching his head. "Check with Sullivan, down the road; can't miss him; he lives in a big white house with a fence around it."

When we got there, Mama walked up to the house. She went through the white gate, past a row of rose bushes, up the stairs to the front door; she rang the doorbell. The porch light went on and a tall, husky man came out; they exchanged a few words. After the man went in, Mama clasped her hands and hurried back to the car. "We have work! Mr. Sullivan said we can stay there the whole season," she said, gasping and pointing to an old garage near the stables.

The garage was worn out by the years. It had no windows; the walls, eaten by termites, strained to support the roof; the loose dirt floor looked like a gray road map.

That night, by the light of a kerosene lamp, we unpacked and cleaned our new home. Roberto swept away the loose dirt, leaving the hard ground; Papa plugged the holes in the walls; Mama fed my little brothers and sisters. Papa and Roberto then brought in the mattress and placed it in the far corner of the garage. "Mama, you and the little ones sleep on the mattress; Roberto, Panchito, and I will sleep outside, under the trees," Papa said.

Early next morning Mr. Sullivan showed us where his crop was, and, after breakfast, Papa, Roberto, and I headed for the vineyard to pick.

Around 9 A.M. the temperature had risen to almost one hundred degrees; I was completely soaked in sweat, and my mouth felt as if I had been chewing on a handkerchief. I walked over to the end of the row, picked up the jug of water we had

brought, and began drinking. "Don't drink too much; you'll get sick," Roberto shouted. No sooner had he said that than I felt sick to my stomach; I dropped to my knees and let the jug roll off my hands; I remained motionless, with my eyes glued on the hot, sandy ground. All I could hear was the drone of insects. Slowly I began to recover; I poured water over my face and neck, and watched the black mud run down my arms and hit the ground.

I still felt a little dizzy when we took a break to eat lunch; it was past 2 P.M. and we sat underneath a large walnut tree that was on the side of the road. While we ate, Papa jotted down the number of boxes we had picked; Roberto drew designs on the ground with a stick. Suddenly I noticed Papa's face turn pale as he looked down the road; "Here comes the school bus," he whispered loudly in alarm. Instinctively, Roberto and I ran and hid in the vineyards. We did not want to get in trouble for not going to school. The yellow bus stopped in front of Mr. Sullivan's house; two neatly dressed boys my age got off. They carried books under their arms. After they crossed the street, the bus drove away. Roberto and I came out from hiding and joined Papa; "*Tienen que tener cuidado,*[7]" he warned us.

After lunch, we went back to work; the sun kept beating down; the buzzing insects, the wet sweat, and the hot, dry dust made the afternoon seem to last forever. Finally, the mountains around the valley reached out and swallowed the sun; within an hour, it was too dark to continue picking. The vines blanketed the grapes, making it difficult to see the bunches; "*Vámonos,*[8]" said Papa, signaling to us that it was time to quit work. Papa

[7] You have to be careful.
[8] Let's go.

then took out a pencil and began to figure out how much we had earned our first day. He wrote down numbers, crossed some out, wrote down some more; "*Quince*,[9]" he murmured.

When we arrived home, we took a cold shower underneath a waterhose. We then sat down to eat dinner around some wooden crates that served as a table. Mama had cooked a special meal for us. We had rice and tortillas with *carne con chile*,[10] my favorite dish.

The next morning I could hardly move; my body ached all over. I felt little control over my arms and legs. This feeling went on every morning until my muscles got used to the work.

It was Monday, the first week of November; the grape season was over, and I could now go to school. I woke up early that morning and lay in bed, looking at the stars and savoring the thought of not going to work and of starting school for the first time that year. Since I could not sleep, I decided to get up and join Papa and Roberto at breakfast. I sat at the table across from Roberto, but I kept my head down. I did not want to look up and face him. I knew he was sad; he was not going to school today; he was not going tomorrow, or the next week, or next month. He would not go until the cotton season was over, and that was some time in February. I rubbed my hands together and watched the dry, acid-stained skin fall to the floor in little rolls.

When Papa and Roberto left for work, I felt relief. I walked to the top of a small grade next to the garage and watched the *Carcanchita* disappear in the distance in a cloud of dust.

[9] fifteen
[10] meat with chile peppers

355

Two hours later, around 8 A.M., I stood by the side of the road waiting for school bus number twenty. When it arrived, I climbed in. No one noticed me; everyone was busy either talking or yelling. I sat in an empty seat in the back.

When the bus stopped in front of the school, I felt very nervous; I looked out the bus window and saw students carrying books under their arms. I felt empty; I put my hands in my pants pockets and walked to the principal's office. When I entered I heard a woman's voice say, "May I help you?" I was startled; I had not heard English for months. For a few seconds I remained speechless; I looked at the woman who waited for an answer. My first instinct was to answer in Spanish, but I held back. Finally, after struggling for English words, I managed to tell her that I wanted to enroll in school. After answering many questions, I was led to the classroom.

Mr. Lema, the teacher, greeted me and assigned me a desk; he then introduced me to the class. I was so nervous and scared at that moment when everyone's eyes were on me that I wished I were with Papa and Roberto picking cotton. After taking roll, Mr. Lema gave the class the assignment for the first hour; "The first thing we have to do this morning is finish reading the story we began yesterday," he said enthusiastically. He walked up to me, handed me an English book, and asked me to read; "We are on page 125," he said politely. When I heard this, I felt my blood rush to my head; I felt dizzy. "Would you like to read?"

he asked hesitantly. I opened the book to page 125. My mouth was dry; my eyes began to water; I could not begin. "You can read later," Mr. Lema said understandingly.

For the rest of the reading period I kept getting angrier and angrier with myself. I should have read, I thought to myself.

Between classes I went to the restroom and opened my English book to page 125. I began to read in a low voice, pretending I was in class. There were many words I did not know; I closed the book and headed back to the classroom.

Mr. Lema was sitting at his desk correcting papers. When I entered he looked up at me and smiled; I felt better. I walked up to him and asked if he could help me with the new words; "Gladly," he said.

The rest of the month I spent my lunch hours working on English with Mr. Lema, my best friend at school.

One Friday during lunch hour, Mr. Lema asked me to take a walk with him to the music room. "Do you like music?" he asked me as we entered the building.

"Yes, I like Mexican *corridos*,[11]" I answered. He then picked up a trumpet, blew on it, and handed it to me; the sound gave me goose bumps. I knew that sound; I had heard it in many Mexican *corridos*. "How would you like to learn to play it?" he asked. He must have read my face because before I could answer, he added: "I'll teach you how to play it during our lunch hours."

[11] ballads; popular songs

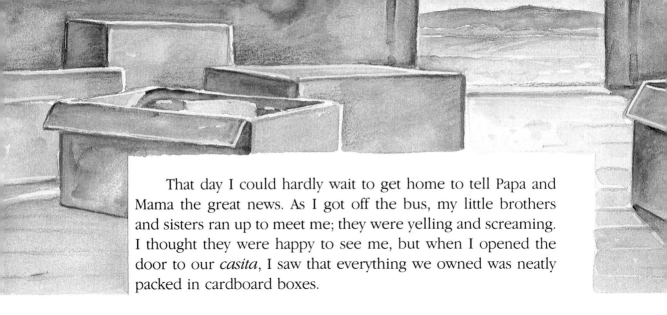

That day I could hardly wait to get home to tell Papa and Mama the great news. As I got off the bus, my little brothers and sisters ran up to meet me; they were yelling and screaming. I thought they were happy to see me, but when I opened the door to our *casita*, I saw that everything we owned was neatly packed in cardboard boxes.

CHECK FOR UNDERSTANDING

1. What possessions did the family have?
2. What does the list of family possessions tell you about the life of the migrant worker?
3. What was Panchito's reaction when Mr. Lema asked him if he wanted to read? Why was Panchito unable to begin reading at once?
4. What happened to the trumpet lessons that Mr. Lema promised to give Panchito?
5. Do you think that Panchito will ever be able to escape from his life of poverty? Explain you answer.

WRITE ABOUT *"The Circuit"*

Why is the story called "The Circuit"? Write an explanation of why this title is appropriate for the story. Be sure to consider figurative as well as literal meanings of the word *circuit*.

AN INTERVIEW
WITH FRANCISCO
JIMENEZ

Francisco Jiménez based "The Circuit" on some of
experiences growing up. The story was first published
in Spanish. Why does the fact that Spanish is the
primary language of his childhood cause Francisco
Jiménez to write about these experiences in Spanish?
Why does Francisco Jiménez need his high school counselor's
encouragement and guidance?

Francisco Jiménez won The Arizona Quarterly Annual Award
*in 1973 for his short story "The Circuit." Since his youth as a mi-
grant worker, Mr. Jiménez has gone far both professionally and aca-
demically. He first studied at the University of Santa Clara, where
he now teaches Spanish language and literature. Later he earned a
doctorate from Columbia University in New York.*

*In the following interview, Mr. Jiménez talks about "The Cir-
cuit." He describes the journey from Santa María's strawberry fields
to some of the nation's most scholarly circles.*

What parts of "The Circuit" are autobiographical?

All of the events are autobiographical. But the sequence of events has been rearranged to tell the story. For example, in the second paragraph I mention the strawberry picker from Jalisco. I actually met him in the summer of my eighth grade. The garage that I mention was the place in which we lived in the seventh grade. Hiding from the school bus was something my brother and I did maybe three or four times in different years, so I decided to include it in the story.

Some of the details were mere inventions. For example, I could not remember the number of the school bus, so I made one up. I also invented page 125, the number of the page I was asked to read in Mr. Lema's class.

One of the things I embellished was the pot, *la olla.* I wanted to bring out its significance. Traditionally, the kitchen is the place where families spend most of the time sitting around discussing the day's events. We did not have a kitchen per se.* So the pot came to represent or symbolize that family unity which is tied to the kitchen.

Your teacher Mr. Lema had a big impact on you. What other persons strongly influenced you?

Besides Mr. Lema, two of them stand out: Miss Bell and Mr. Penney. Miss Bell was my English teacher during my first

* (pər sā') in the strictest sense of the word

year in high school. In her class I wrote about my personal experiences. The remarks she made about my writing were very encouraging. For example, in one of my essays she commented that the experiences I wrote about were very moving, and that I should continue to write. She also told me not to be discouraged by hardships; that I had the strength and the talent to overcome them. I believed her and tried to live up to her expectations. I am glad I did.

The other person who influenced me tremendously was Mr. Penney. He was my high school counselor. During my senior year he encouraged me to apply to college and for financial aid. Thanks to his guidance I was able to attend Santa Clara University.

It sounds as though Miss Bell got you started in writing. Did she recommend a specific approach?

Miss Bell encouraged the class to write detailed narrative accounts of personal experiences. Even though I had difficulty expressing myself in English, I enjoyed the assignments. And with much effort I wrote about what I knew best. Long after I left her class I continued to reflect upon my experiences and often thought of expressing them in writing. Whenever I could, I would jot down recollections hoping to write about them in the future.

How old were you when you wrote "The Circuit"? Why did you focus on that episode in your life?

The idea for the story goes back many years when I was in Miss Bell's English class. I was 15 years old at the time. I actually wrote the story in graduate school at Columbia University in 1972. That year I shared two autobiographical narrative accounts with my teacher. He looked at them and urged me to publish my work. Encouraged by his remarks, I decided to write the short story, describing in detail the joys and disappointments I encountered as I grew up in a migrant setting.

What were the biggest obstacles you encountered in trying to complete school and finally going on to college?

As I relate in the story, the biggest obstacles in finishing school were the constant moving from place to place, starting school late in the year, usually after Thanksgiving, and not knowing English very well.

A very important reason why I was able to do well in school is that I enjoyed learning. I was fascinated with knowledge. I wanted to know about everything. I also discovered that whatever I learned was mine to keep, no matter what happened. Wherever we moved, the knowledge I had would go with me. This gave me a sense of stability, of permanence. In my life as a migrant child, this was very important to me.

How did you eventually master English?

English was my most difficult subject. The only opportunity I had to learn it and to practice it was in school because at home we only spoke Spanish. My father did not speak English. My mother spoke it very little. This was true of most of the families with whom we had any contact. I was held back in the first grade because of my difficulties with English. This was painful for me, and I felt embarrassed, especially when some of the children made fun of me. Fortunately I did very well in subjects that did not require a lot of English, such as art and mathematics.

This gave me encouragement to work hard in English, and I did. I kept a note pad where I wrote spelling words and definitions. Every day I would add a word to my note pad. As I worked in the fields I memorized them.

However, I did not learn to appreciate the value and power of language until I read *The Grapes of Wrath*. I could identify with the suffering of the migrant families described in the novel. My family and I shared with them the same hopes for a better life. The more I read, the more I was convinced of the power of language. This gave me the impetus to become proficient in English and to continue the study of Spanish.

As a native of Mexico, you grew up speaking Spanish. Do you usually write in Spanish or in English? What determines what language you use?

I write in both English and Spanish. However, I have written more in Spanish than in English. The language I use is determined by what period in my life I write about. Since Spanish was the dominant language during my childhood, I generally write about those experiences in Spanish. In fact, I first wrote ''The Circuit'' in Spanish, and then translated it into English.

You originally titled the story "Cajas de Cartón" or "Cardboard Boxes." Who renamed the story and why?

I gave the story the title. I didn't want to use the same title because "Cardboard Boxes" didn't sound right to me. "The Circuit" seemed to be a more appropriate English title. It is a term that is readily understood in English, but if translated into Spanish, it would not convey the same meaning.

What were the difficulties of translating your own work?

As you know, language, especially the spoken word, carries with it an emotion or a feeling. When I began to translate the story, it was very difficult to find the exact words, because the events were not originally experienced in the English language. That explains why I kept some of the Spanish words. For example, *la olla,* the term itself is very important; *la Carcanchita;* the words that Ito would say *ya esora.* All of those elicited a lot of emotions that were impossible to translate.

What have been the benefits of being bilingual?

I am able to participate in and enjoy two cultures. As I travel to Spain and Mexico, I communicate easily with the people of these two countries. When I return to the United States, I have been able to appreciate more fully the people of both cultures. Because I am bicultural, I can move in and out of both cultures with ease. This is extremely helpful to me as a professor of Spanish language and literature. On a more personal level, being bilingual has helped me fulfill one of my goals: to fill the need for cultural understanding, between the United States and Mexico in particular. Furthermore, I have been able to write stories in both English and Spanish. I consider this a privilege.

You mention one of your goals is "to fill the need for cultural understanding." What steps can be taken to fill that need?

The most important step would be to become educated. The greatest obstacle to cultural understanding, it seems to me, is ignorance: the fear of what we don't know or understand. In the process of becoming educated we destroy those barriers or that ignorance which separates us. This is why I became an educator. My hope has always been to establish bridges of cultural understanding.

CHECK FOR UNDERSTANDING

1. What kinds of stories did Francisco Jiménez first write?
2. What made the teacher at Columbia University urge Francisco Jiménez to publish his work?
3. Who were the most influential people in Francisco Jiménez's education?
4. Why did Francisco Jiménez need Mr. Penney's encouragement and guidance?
5. Francisco Jiménez feels that he can establish a bridge of cultural understanding through his writing. In what way can he do this?
6. Why did the fact that Spanish was the primary language of his childhood cause Francisco Jiménez to write about those experiences in Spanish?

WRITE ABOUT *"An Interview with Francisco Jiménez"*

If you could talk with Mr. Jiménez, what would you ask him? Write at least three questions that are not included in the interview. Explain why you chose to ask those questions.

LITERATURE

Hyperbole

She moved faster than lightning.
His face turned as red as a beet.
It was raining buckets.

The statements above are exaggerations. Exaggeration is saying that something is much greater than it actually is. Exaggeration for the purpose of emphasis and without any intention of being taken literally is know as **hyperbole.**

In some stories, an author may exaggerate his character's actions or words. For example, instead of a character saying, "I'm very hungry," he may say, "I'm starving to death!"

Using hyperbole is a common way of creating humor. An author will use hyperbole to make the characters funny to the reader.

In "Growing Up with Gumption," Russell Baker relates the events of his childhood and his first job selling newspapers. Look for the examples of hyperbole used to make us laugh in these passages.

> Heard of it? My mother said that everyone in our house had heard of the *Saturday Post* and that I, in fact, read it with religious devotion.
> Again he studied me as though debating whether I was worthy of a knighthood.
> Finally: "Are you trustworthy?"

A phrase like "worthy of a knighthood" makes us smile because the images Russell Baker creates are so unbelievable, they are funny. We often laugh at these exaggerations because we know they cannot be true.

The next selection, "Cut Down to Size" has many examples of hyperbole. Bobby Marks has just begun his summer job: mowing the lawn for Dr. Kahn. But Bobby, embarrassed because he is over-weight, finds it difficult to survive his first day on the job.

I was sweating all over, even my knees and elbows were sweating. Each scorching drop of sweat rolled slowly down my chest and back like a scorching drop of acid burning out a furrow in my skin.

The author has managed to make cutting the grass amusing by using hyperbole to compare drops of sweat to drops of acid. Bobby exaggerates everyday situations. In this way he makes us see ourselves and everyday life in a new and comic light.

As you read "Cut Down to Size," identify other examples of hyperbole.

One Fat Summer

by Robert Lipsyte

Just·A·Taste

Making a decision to change is easy. Sticking to the resolution can become very difficult, as Bobby discovers on his first day at a new job.

Why is the job so important to Bobby? Who is "Captain Marks," and how does he help?

Cut Down to Size

For Bobby Marks, this help-wanted ad on the community bulletin board represented a crossroads. Embarrassed because he was overweight, Bobby usually hated the summer season. He wanted this summer to be different, however. Encouraged by his friend Joanie, Bobby answered the help-wanted ad and was hired by Dr. Kahn. "Cut Down to Size" describes his first day on the job.

I reached Dr. Kahn's lawn at exactly 8:47 A.M. by my wristwatch. It was probably 8:48. My watch always runs a minute slow because of my metabolism. That's the speed at which your body burns up energy. Once I took a test called a Basal Metabolism. I lay in a doctor's office for an hour, breathing into a rubber mouthpiece connected by a tube to a machine. My nose was clipped shut. Afterward, the doctor said I had a low normal Basal Metabolism, which means my body burns up food a little slower than most bodies. That's why I put on weight easily. The doctor made a joke about it. He said I could walk into a bakery, and if I took too deep a breath, I'd gain a pound. My father and Michelle have high Basal Metabolisms, which means they could eat a pound of cake and burn it right off. That's why they're always bothering me about my weight, they don't understand the problem. My mother is a normal

Basal Metabolism, so she sort of understands. The doctor told her that I'd probably start losing weight sometime in my teens, so she doesn't make such a big fuss about it. She's had a few arguments with my father about my weight. She thinks he needles me about it too much. I think my father's sort of ashamed of having a fat son. He wants me to be lean and athletic like he is.

I made it up Dr. Kahn's gravel driveway in under nine minutes: 8:57 A.M.

He was waiting for me on the porch steps, and looking at his watch.

"Two minutes late," he said. He must be a high Basal. "I don't like tardiness in a boy. See that it doesn't happen again. You'll work until 3:02 P.M."

"Yes, sir." No point in making a federal case on my first day.

"Follow me."

We walked around the back of the house, past a swimming pool. The place was deserted. We walked into a toolshed that was as big as some of the cottages around the lake. It was dark and cool in the shed. Hanging from the walls, in neat rows, were rakes, shovels, hoes, and pitchforks, clean and shining in the dim light. I couldn't wait to get my hands on them. My father never let me use his garden tools, he thought I would break them or leave them out in the rain to get rusty. Just give me a good shovel and I'll make the dirt fly. I felt excited. Dr. Kahn pointed toward a green, motorized lawn mower. I had never worked a power mower before. At home we had a hand mower. It was rusty from all the nights I left it out.

"You know how to operate this?"

"Sure."

"Pull it out."

I dragged the mower out of the shed. It was much heavier than it looked.

"Each morning, before you begin, you'll clean the blade, and check the gas and oil." He untied a length of rope from the handle, wrapped it around a cylinder on the top of the motor, and yanked. The motor roared to life, and the spinning blade sprayed grit.

"Watch for stones, they'll chip the blade. You'll be responsible for damage." He walked away.

I pushed the mower to the front of the house. He hadn't told me the direction in which I was supposed to mow—up and down the hill, the long way, or from side to side. My decision. My father was very fussy about my cutting in long rows. He hated it when I made designs or cut in squares, which he said wasted energy. I decided to cut from side to side, it made more sense than pushing the heavy mower all the way up the hill from the county road, then running down the hill after it.

Cutting the first few rows was uncomfortable until I got my fingers just right around the handlebar grips, and figured out the best distance between me and the mower. If I was too close my belly banged against the handlebars, which hurt, and I couldn't use my shoulders to push. If I was too far away I'd have to bend so far forward with my arms outstretched that my back ached.

And then I got the right grip and the right position, and it was easy. What a job! A piece of cake. Ho, boy, I can do this in my sleep. If I could swim the way I cut lawns, I thought, I'd be the city champ. This lawn will win prizes. Just back and forth, nice and easy, follow the lines of the last cut, straight as an arrow, watch for stones. You old lawn, you don't have a chance against me and my green machine. I'm gonna cut you down to size, lawn.

Power surged out of my chest and shoulders, through my arms, out my fingers into the green machine. Scraps of grass flew out from under the mower. My nostrils twitched with the beautiful stinging smell of fresh-cut grass. I felt like singing. So I made up a song, and sang it.

> Listen to the birds,
> The eagles and the larks,
> Saying good-by, grass,
> Here comes Big Bob Marks.

I felt terrific. What a great summer this is going to be. I've reached a decision, I've got a plan, don't worry about me hanging around all summer feeling sorry for myself. I've got a job. I got it all by myself, nobody helped me. Well, almost all by myself. Wait till they find out about it. They'll be proud. And they should be. Nobody ever cut a lawn like I'm cutting this lawn. By the time I'm finished with this lawn it'll look like wall-to-wall carpet. Smooooth.

I've got a job. My own money. Seventy-five cents an hour, six hours a day, that's four dollars and fifty cents. Five days. That's twenty-two dollars and fifty cents a week. My own money. I'm rich. I won't tell anybody for a while. One day I'll go into town, buy some earrings for Mom, a belt for Dad; I might even get Michelle some perfume. I'll write a note with that: For a sister who smells.

And then I'll tell them. That'll get a smile out of my father. He'll be proud of me.

I'll get Joanie a book of poems. Emily Dickinson. She loves Emily Dickinson. I can't wait to tell her about my job. She'll have a lot to say about it.

Ouch. A small stone shot out from under the mower and bounced off my ankle. Watch those stones. I was just about to stop and rub my ankle, it really hurt, when I noticed that Dr. Kahn was watching me from the porch. Wouldn't want him to know I ran over a stone.

The sun was prickling the little hairs on the back of my neck. I could use one of those big white cavalry hats John Wayne wears in the movies. Captain Marks of the U.S. Cavalry, the only man who understands the Apaches. He grew up with them after his parents were killed in a wagon-train massacre. A renegade band has broken loose from the reservation. They're on the warpath, raiding settlements; nobody's safe. And the colonel's daughter is coming in on the next stagecoach to visit our desolate desert outpost. Captain Marks and his rough-and-tumble troopers, the dregs of the cavalry who'll take orders only from him, will ride out and save her.

Once I had a U.S. cavalry hat. I had a complete U.S. cavalry uniform with a holster belt that went around your waist and over your shoulder, and a metal cap pistol shaped like a six-shooter. My grandparents sent it to me for my birthday. The pants were blue with a yellow stripe down the leg. The jacket was blue, too, and had captain's bars on the shoulders, and ribbons and shiny gold buttons. It was beautiful. But it didn't fit. Not even the hat.

I couldn't button the jacket or zipper the pants or even get the belt around my waist. I never even got to play with the gun because my mother wanted to keep the set new so she could exchange the uniform for a larger size. But it was the largest size they made. I guess I was around eight or nine years old then. My father wanted me to keep it, he said it would give me an incentive to lose weight so I could fit into it. I wish they had given it away. Just looking at that uniform in its box

made me feel so bad I ate more. One day when I was alone in the house I opened a box of cookies and jammed them into my mouth, fast as I could, not caring about the brown crumbs spilling out of the corners of my mouth; just jammed in those cookies faster than I could chew them, swallowing lumps of cookies big as Ping-Pong balls that got stuck in my throat and chest until I choked and had to wash them down with cold milk. They still hurt going down; I felt every Ping-Pong ball push through my throat and chest until it fell with a thump into my stomach. And still I couldn't stop until I'd finished every cookie in the box, and then I had to lie down. My stomach had turned to concrete. I couldn't move for hours until it was digested.

I felt hungry. I looked at my watch. 9:42 A.M. That's all it was. I'd been cutting only a little more than a half hour. How could time move so slowly? The world must have a low Basal Metabolism today.

Keep cutting. Can't stop. He's watching me from the porch. My mouth got dry and my nose filled with fumes from the gasoline engine, and every time I turned to start a new row, pain exploded in my wrists and shot up my arms into my shoulders. My fingers were numb; I'd never be able to pry them off the handlebar grips. My back hurt. My head hurt.

My feet were very hot. I was sweating all over; even my knees and elbows were sweating. Each scorching drop of sweat rolled slowly down my chest and back like a scorching drop of acid burning out a furrow in my skin. If only I could take off my shirt, like everybody else who cuts grass. But my pants weren't buttoned, and, anyway, I never take off my shirt when people are watching.

Everything was getting hazy. Trees swayed, and there wasn't even a breeze. The lawn began to move. It rippled. Everything was wavy; it was like looking at the world through a fish tank. The lawn began to roll like the ocean. I was getting lawn sick.

And then the motor stopped. Just stopped dead. I hadn't realized how loud the mower was, how its roar banged against my ears and clogged my brain, until it was suddenly silent, and I heard birds tweet again, and crickets chirp, and the whoosh of traffic on the county road. Far away, a dog barked.

Why did it stop? Did I break it? The sweat turned cold on my skin. I have to start it again. The rope was still on the handlebars. I tried to remember how Dr. Kahn had started the engine. Wind the rope around the cylinder, and pull. I had trouble opening my hands; they were locked into hooks around the grips.

Out of the corner of my eye I saw Dr. Kahn step off the porch and start down the lawn toward me. My hands slowly opened. They were red and swollen. I wrapped the rope around the cylinder, and pulled. The motor whined, and died. I tried again. This time, nothing.

I heard his slippers slapping against his heels. I pulled with all my might, lost my balance, and tripped over the mower. I could have just stayed there, sprawled out on the lawn, my face in the sweet grass. But he was coming and I jumped up.

"You're out of gas," he said. The shotgun eyes blasted right through me. He unscrewed a little cap on the side of the motor and stuck his finger in the gas tank. It came out dry. "A gas mower runs on gas. Did you know that?"

"Yek."

"The gas is in the shed. And don't forget the funnel."

The hill seemed steeper now, it was like climbing a mountain. A very steep, short mountain. I was much closer to the porch than I thought. I hadn't cut all that much grass.

I felt better in the shed, soothed by the coolness and the darkness. I found a gallon can of gasoline and a funnel. Outside again, the heat slammed into me like a wall of hot wet cotton. My tongue stuck to the roof of my mouth, and I could hardly breathe.

"Is this job too tough for you?" Dr. Kahn had followed me up.

"Nnnnnn . . ." It was the best my tongue could do.

"What was that?"

"Wa'er. Nee' a glath wa'er."

"There's a spigot on the side of the house. You're not to go inside."

I stumbled toward it. A water hole in the desert. Or a mirage. Until I touched the rusty handle, I was sure it would disappear. The water wasn't cold and it tasted like metal, but I drank it out of my hands until I thought my belly would burst.

I staggered back down the hill, burping. Even with the funnel, I spilled some gas on the lawn. It took four hard yanks, but the green machine roared back to life.

Cut on, and on. And on. Back and forth, side to side, watch for stones, keep a neat row.

I wanted to stop. Just leave the machine and go home. Nobody at home knew I had a job, so nobody would know I quit. This is torture. Who needs it? I'm walking on burning needles. My blisters have blisters. Hammers banging on my shoulders. Electric jolts in my wrists. I can feel every inch of me, and every inch of me hurts. Just stop and walk away.

A long black car swept down the driveway, stopped, and honked. Dr. Kahn stuck his head out the window, yelled something at me, then drove down to the county road and out of sight.

I could leave now.

You've got to do it, Captain Marks. You're the only one who can make it through the renegades to Fort Desolation and bring back the Regiment. We're counting on you.

And then suddenly I didn't hurt anymore, and I couldn't have stopped if I had wanted to. All I could do was go back and forth, back and forth; sometimes I ran into the bushes along the side of the lawn, the sharp thorns snagging on my sleeves and whipping at my chest and scratching the back of my hands until blood bubbled up in the thin red lines, and twice I stepped into holes and fell down, and stones clattered against the whirling blade and bounced off my legs, and when the mower ran out of gas again I filled it and yanked it back to life and pushed on, and on.

"You call this mowing a lawn?"

I was halfway between the porch and the county road. I had cut half the front lawn; what was he talking about? I followed his long, quivering finger up the hill. The lawn was a mess. I had missed hundreds of tufts of grass. Most of the rows were squiggly light-green snakes lying among darker green patches of uncut grass.

"I call this a disgrace."

He lifted the mower and examined the blade. "You must have gone out of your way to find every stone on the lawn. Look at the chips on the blade. I'll have to get another one. Cost at least four fifty." He shook his head. "That'll come from your wages, of course."

He looked at his watch. "Well, it's after three o'clock. Tomorrow you'll do it all over again. What did you say?"

I hadn't said a word. I turned away so he couldn't see me cry, and I stumbled down to the county road.

Bobby lost this battle with the lawn, but "Captain Marks" comes back to fight another day. Read about his efforts, described in the novel One Fat Summer *by Robert Lipsyte.*

CHECK FOR UNDERSTANDING

1. At first, how did Bobby feel as he began to mow the lawn?
2. How and why did his feelings change?
3. Why was the job so important to Bobby?
4. Who was "Captain Marks," and how did he help?
5. Compare Bobby with Walter Mitty. How were they alike? How was Bobby different from Walter?

WRITE ABOUT *"Cut Down to Size"*

Did the help-wanted ad that Bobby answered really give enough information? Or should it have included more facts about the skills required for the job? Write a more complete ad, based on the work that Bobby had to do. Then write the kind of ad that Bobby himself might write. Include examples of hyperbole, such as: Must be able to mow entire continent in one afternoon.

THINK ABOUT IT

The characters in this unit found themselves at a point in life in which they had to make a definite decision that would ultimately affect the rest of their lives. The characters had reached an important crossroad. Whose crossroad could you identify with the most? Who learns the most from his crossroad?

Both "Growing Up with Gumption" and "Cut Down to Size" present boys undergoing problems as they mature.

- In what way is Russell Baker's conflict similar to that of Bobby Marks?
- How is Russell Baker's mother's influence on her son similar to Dr. Kahn's influence on Bobby?
- Which boy displays the greater courage and maturity in settling his problem?
- How does each boy's decision ultimately affect his life?

An important crossroad in Helen Keller's life is described in two different points of view.

- How is Annie Sullivan's letter different from Helen Keller's recollection of the same "moment"?
- Both Helen Keller and Annie Sullivan come to a crossroad when Helen finally learns that everything has a name. How do their crossroads differ?

WRITE ABOUT IT

Choose one of the characters in a selection in this unit. Pretend you are that character writing in your diary or journal. It is ten years after you faced your crisis, or crossroad. Write a one-page journal entry which describes how that crossroad has affected your life since that time. Has it caused you to change your thinking toward a certain person? Has the crossroad made you stronger, wiser, happier? Be sure to give examples to illustrate your feelings.

READ ABOUT IT

Nathaniel Benchley. *Only Earth and Sky Last Forever*. Harper & Row, 1972.

This historical novel describes a crossroads in American history: the battle of Little Big Horn. The author tells the story from the point of view of the winners of that battle.

Vera and Bill Cleaver. *Dust of the Earth*. J. B. Lippincott, 1975.

Fern moves with her migrant family to a farm in South Dakota. When they decide to sell some land left to them by their grandfather, Fern finds that living in one place is not the answer to all her problems.

Gloria Skurzynski. *The Tempering*. Clarion Books, 1983.

Set early in this century, this book describes the decisions that Karl faces about his future career. Life in a steel mill town is realistically and sympathetically described.

Mildred D. Taylor. *Roll of Thunder, Hear My Cry*. Dial Press, 1977.

Cassie Logan and her closely-knit family face difficult times during the Great Depression.

Malcolm E. Weiss. *Seeing through the Dark: Blind and Sighted— A Vision Shared*. Harcourt Brace Jovanovich, 1976.

The author offers insights into the processes by which we can be said to "see through the dark": the vibrations of sound waves, the sense of touch, and memory.

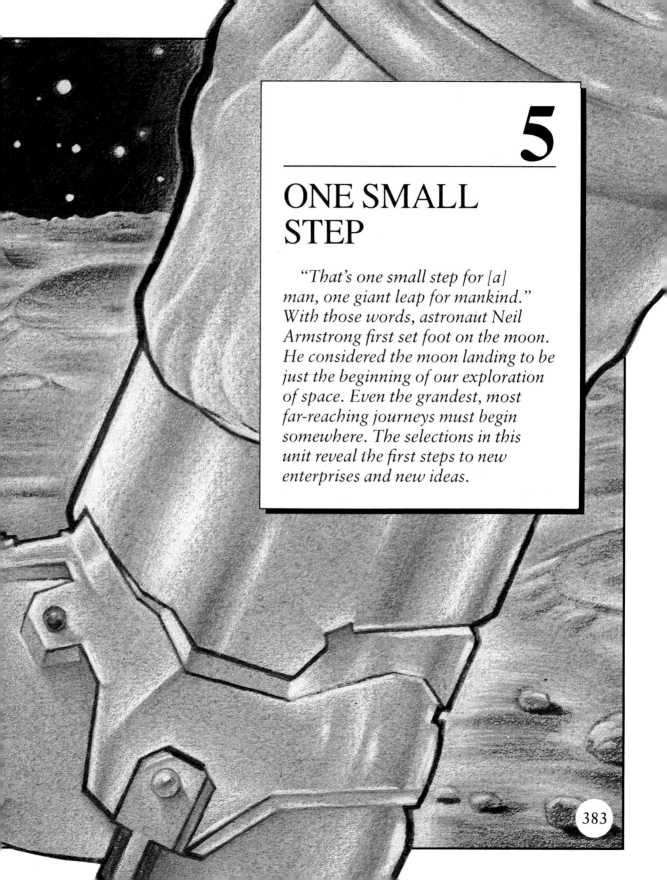

5

ONE SMALL STEP

"That's one small step for [a] man, one giant leap for mankind." *With those words, astronaut Neil Armstrong first set foot on the moon. He considered the moon landing to be just the beginning of our exploration of space. Even the grandest, most far-reaching journeys must begin somewhere. The selections in this unit reveal the first steps to new enterprises and new ideas.*

NO ORDINARY SEAGULL

by RICHARD BACH

Why should falcons soar while seagulls only flap along? Jonathan Livingston Seagull refuses to accept limitations on his flying ability.

Why does Jonathan Livingston Seagull's kind of thinking make him unpopular with other birds? What negative advice from his inner voice provides Jonathan with the clue that leads to his ultimate success?

It was morning, and the new sun sparkled gold across the ripples of a gentle sea.

A mile from shore a fishing boat chummed the water, and the word for Breakfast Flock flashed through the air, till a crowd of a thousand seagulls came to dodge and fight for bits of food. It was another busy day beginning.

But way off alone, out by himself beyond boat and shore, Jonathan Livingston Seagull was practicing. A hundred feet in the sky he lowered his webbed feet, lifted his beak, and strained to hold a painful hard twisting curve through his wings. The curve meant that he would fly slowly, and now he slowed until the wind was a whisper in his face, until the ocean stood still beneath him. He narrowed his eyes in fierce concentration, held his breath, forced one . . . single . . . more . . . inch . . . of . . . curve. . . . Then his feathers ruffled, he stalled and fell.

Seagulls, as you know, never falter, never stall. To stall in the air is for them disgrace and it is dishonor.

But Jonathan Livingston Seagull, unashamed, stretching his wings again in that trembling hard curve—slowing, slowing, and stalling once more—was no ordinary bird.

Most gulls don't bother to learn more than the simplest facts of flight—how to get from shore to food and back again. For most gulls, it is not flying that matters, but eating. For this gull, though, it was not eating that mattered, but flight. More than anything else, Jonathan Livingston Seagull loved to fly.

This kind of thinking, he found, is not the way to make one's self popular with other birds. Even his parents were dismayed as Jonathan spent whole days alone, making hundreds of low-level glides, experimenting.

He didn't know why, for instance, but when he flew at altitudes less than half his wingspan above the water, he could stay in the air longer, with less effort. His glides ended not with the usual feet-down splash into the sea, but with a long flat wake as he touched the surface with his feet tightly streamlined against his body. When he began sliding in to feet-up landings on the beach, then pacing the length of his slide in the sand, his parents were very much dismayed indeed.

"Why, Jon, *why?*" his mother asked. "Why is it so hard to be like the rest of the flock, Jon? Why can't you leave low flying to the pelicans, the albatross? Why don't you eat? Son, you're bone and feathers!"

"I don't mind being bone and feathers, mom. I just want to know what I can do in the air and what I can't, that's all. I just want to know."

"See here, Jonathan," said his father, not unkindly. "Winter isn't far away. Boats will be few, and the surface fish will be swimming deep. If you must study, then study food, and how to get it. This flying business is all very well, but you can't eat a glide, you know. Don't you forget that the reason you fly is to eat."

Jonathan nodded obediently. For the next few days he tried to behave like the other gulls; he really tried, screeching and fighting with the flock around the piers and fishing boats, diving on scraps of fish and bread. But he couldn't make it work.

It's all so pointless, he thought, deliberately dropping a hard-won anchovy to a hungry old gull chasing him. I could be spending all this time learning to fly. There's so much to learn! It wasn't long before Jonathan Gull was off by himself again, far out at sea, hungry, happy, learning.

The subject was speed, and in a week's practice he learned more about speed than the fastest gull alive.

From a thousand feet, flapping his wings as hard as he could, he pushed over into a blazing steep dive toward the waves, and learned why seagulls don't make blazing steep power-dives. In just six seconds he was moving seventy miles per hour, the speed at which one's wing goes unstable on the upstroke.

Time after time it happened. Careful as he was, working at the very peak of his ability, he lost control at high speed.

Climb to a thousand feet. Full power straight ahead first, then push over, flapping, to a vertical dive. Then, every time, his left wing stalled on an upstroke, he'd roll violently left, stall his right wing recovering, and flick like fire into a wild tumbling spin to the right.

He couldn't be careful enough on that upstroke. Ten times he tried, and all ten times, as he passed through seventy miles per hour, he burst into a churning mass of feathers, out of control, crashing down into the water.

The key, he thought at last, dripping wet, must be to hold the wings still at high speeds—to flap up to fifty and then hold the wings still.

From two thousand feet he tried again, rolling into his dive, beak straight down, wings full out and stable from the moment he passed fifty miles per hour. It took tremendous strength, but it worked. In ten seconds he had blurred through ninety miles per hour. Jonathan had set a world speed record for seagulls!

But victory was short-lived. The instant he began his pullout, the instant he changed the angle of his wings, he snapped into the same terrible uncontrolled disaster, and at ninety miles per hour it hit him like dynamite. Jonathan Seagull exploded in midair and smashed down into a brick-hard sea.

When he came to, it was well after dark, and he floated in moonlight on the surface of the ocean. His wings were ragged bars of lead, but the weight of failure was even heavier on his back. He wished, feebly, that the weight could be just enough to drag him gently down to the bottom, and end it all.

As he sank low in the water, a strange hollow voice sounded within him. There's no way around it. I am a seagull. I am limited by my nature. If I were meant to learn so much about flying, I'd have charts for brains. If I were meant to fly at speed, I'd have a falcon's short wings, and live on mice instead of fish. My father was right. I must forget this foolishness. I must fly home to the Flock and be content as I am, as a poor limited seagull.

The voice faded, and Jonathan agreed. The place for a seagull at night is on shore, and from this moment forth, he vowed, he would be a normal gull. It would make everyone happier.

He pushed wearily away from the dark water and flew toward the land, grateful for what he had learned about work-saving low-altitude flying.

But no, he thought. I am done with the way I was, I am done with everything I learned. I am a seagull like every other seagull, and I will fly like one. So he climbed painfully to a hundred feet and flapped his wings harder, pressing for shore.

He felt better for his decision to be just another one of the flock. There would be no ties now to the force that had driven him to learn, there would be no more challenge and no more failure. And it was pretty, just to stop thinking, and fly through the dark, toward the lights above the beach.

Dark! The hollow voice cracked in alarm. *Seagulls never fly in the dark!*

Jonathan was not alert to listen. It's pretty, he thought. The moon and the lights twinkling on the water, throwing out little beacon-trails through the night, and all so peaceful and still. . . .

Get down! Seagulls never fly in the dark! If you were meant to fly in the dark, you'd have the eyes of an owl! You'd have charts for brains! You'd have a falcon's short wings!

There in the night, a hundred feet in the air, Jonathan Livingston Seagull—blinked. His pain, his resolutions, vanished.

Short wings. *A falcon's short wings!*

That's the answer! What a fool I've been! All I need is a tiny little wing, all I need is to fold most of my wings and fly on just the tips alone! *Short wings!*

He climbed two thousand feet above the black sea, and without a moment for thought of failure and death, he brought his forewings tightly in to his body, left only the narrow swept daggers of his wingtips extended into the wind, and fell into a vertical dive.

The wind was a monster roar at his head. Seventy miles per hour, ninety, a hundred and twenty and faster still. The wing-strain now at a hundred and forty miles per hour wasn't nearly as hard as it had been before at seventy, and with the faintest twist of his wingtips he eased out of the dive and shot above the waves, a gray cannonball under the moon.

He closed his eyes to slits against the wind and rejoiced. A hundred forty miles per hour! And under control! If I dive from five thousand feet instead of two thousand, I wonder how fast . . .

His vows of a moment before were forgotten, swept away in that great swift wind. Yet he felt guiltless, breaking the promises he had made himself. Such promises are only for the gulls that accept the ordinary. One who has touched excellence in his learning has no need of that kind of promise.

By sunup, Jonathan Gull was practicing again. From five thousand feet the fishing boats were specks in the flat blue water, Breakfast Flock was a faint cloud of dust motes, circling.

He was alive, trembling ever so slightly with delight, proud that his fear was under control. Then without ceremony he hugged in his forewings, extended his short, angled wingtips, and plunged directly toward the sea. By the time he passed four thousand feet he had reached terminal velocity, the wind was a solid beating wall of sound against which he could move no faster. He was flying now straight down, at two hundred fourteen miles per hour. He swallowed, knowing that if his wings unfolded at that speed he'd be blown into a million tiny shreds of seagull. But the speed was power, and the speed was joy, and the speed was pure beauty.

He began his pullout at a thousand feet, wingtips thudding and blurring in that gigantic wind, the boat and the crowd of gulls tilting and growing meteor-fast, directly in his path.

He couldn't stop; he didn't know yet even how to turn at that speed.

Collision would be instant death.

And so he shut his eyes.

It happened that morning, then, just after sunrise, that Jonathan Livingston Seagull fired directly through the center of Breakfast Flock, ticking off two hundred twelve miles per hour, eyes closed, in a great roaring shriek of wind and feathers. The Gull of Fortune smiled upon him this once, and no one was killed. By the time he had pulled his beak straight up into the sky he was still scorching along at a hundred and sixty miles per hour. When he had slowed to twenty and stretched his wings again at last, the boat was a crumb on the sea, four thousand feet below.

His thought was triumph. Terminal velocity! A seagull at *two hundred fourteen miles per hour!* It was a breakthrough, the greatest single moment in the history of the Flock, and in that moment a new age opened for Jonathan Gull. Flying out to his lonely practice area, folding his wings for a dive from eight thousand feet, he set himself at once to discover how to turn.

A single wingtip feather, he found, moved a fraction of an inch, gives a smooth sweeping curve at tremendous speed. Before he learned this, however, he found that moving more than one feather at that speed will spin you like a rifle ball . . . and Jonathan had flown the first aerobatics of any seagull on earth.

He spared no time that day for talk with other gulls, but flew on past sunset. He discovered the loop, the slow roll, the point roll, the inverted spin, the gull bunt, the pinwheel.

When Jonathan Seagull joined the Flock on the beach, it was full night. He was dizzy and terribly tired. Yet in delight he flew a loop to landing, with a snap roll just before touchdown. When they hear of it, he thought, of the Breakthrough, they'll be wild with joy. How much more there is now to living! Instead of our drab slogging forth and back to the fishing boats, there's a reason to life! We can lift ourselves out of ignorance, we can find ourselves as creatures of excellence and intelligence and skill. We can be free! *We can learn to fly!*

CHECK FOR UNDERSTANDING

1. What did Jonathan Livingston Seagull do when all the other gulls were feeding?

2. Why did Jonathan's parents urge him to stop experimenting?

3. What did the hollow voice within Jonathan warn him about as he flew back home in the dark after making his decision?

4. What negative advice from his inner voice provided Jonathan with the clue that led to his ultimate success?

5. What is the main idea of this story? What do you think of the way that Jonathan applied this idea in his life?

6. Why did Jonathan's kind of thinking make him unpopular with the other birds?

WRITE ABOUT *"No Ordinary Seagull"*

What do you think happens when Jonathan reports his discovery to the Breakfast Flock? Write a short radio play describing the conversation that might have taken place. Include appropriate sound effects.

THE EAGLE

by ALFRED, LORD TENNYSON

He clasps the crag with crooked hands:
Close to the sun in lonely lands,
Ringed with the azure world, he stands.

The wrinkled sea beneath him crawls;
He watches from his mountain walls,
And like a thunderbolt he falls.

Advice from an Innovator

by ROSALYN YALOW

Every day students discover new ways of solving problems at home and school. Often a friend, a book, or a film gives great ideas to them. Scientist Rosalyn Yalow searches for new solutions and works hard to prove them. Why does Rosalyn Yalow find the film *Marie Curie* so memorable? What accounts for the difference between the interpretations the two groups of scientists place on their observations?

Airplanes, vaccinations, eyeglasses, even paper clips, all came into existence because someone applied imagination and skill to find a new way to outwit an old problem. For example, one creative man disliked carrying out his family's trash on cold winter nights; as a result, he invented the trash compactor. However, no matter how useful an idea seems after it has been tried and tested over a number of years, most people tend to view every new idea with suspicion. Scientific innovator Rosalyn Yalow knows all about the patient waiting necessary before an idea becomes accepted.

She thought of a new idea over twenty years ago. Together with her co-worker Solomon Berson, she developed a way of measuring substances that were so tiny no one had ever been able to measure them before. They called this new technique radioimmunoassay. Other scientists quickly realized how important this technique was, yet it wasn't until 1977 that Dr. Yalow and Dr. Berson were awarded the Nobel Prize for Medicine, proof at last that radioimmunoassay had gained acceptance as a great innovation.

If you ever have a new idea, and it's really new, you have to expect that it won't be widely accepted immediately. It is a long hard process. Till my dying day I will remember Greer Garson and Walter Pidgeon, in the film *Marie Curie,* coming back to the laboratory at night and seeing the glowing that meant they had discovered radioactivity. That was exciting!

They knew they had it, but it was the culmination of a long process of blood, sweat, and tears. It was followed by a good deal more blood, sweat, and tears. You don't suddenly come out of your bath and say "Eureka*!" Science is only in part like that.

I'm a morning person. When I'm stewing about something I'm working on in the laboratory, I'll wake up at two or three in the morning and by daybreak everything will fall into place and I know the experiment that has to be done the next day. Usually there are a lot of experiments that have to be done. You try the critical experiment the next day, and somebody drops the tube or it's broken in the centrifuge or the refrigerators stop working. You know you have a great idea but until you've built in the many controls or verified and reverified the results, you're not completely certain. Perhaps theoretical physicists say "Eureka!" but we experimental physicists need a lot of hard work and luck. It isn't blind luck. Part of it is being in the right place at the right time, but recognition is important.

For instance, another group of scientists made the same observation as we did at the time . . . that the labeled insulin disappeared more slowly from diabetics than nondiabetics. The other investigators made the same observation but we discovered radioimmunoassay. Now would you call it luck that we made the discovery? If so, they had the same luck, but we knew what to do with it. We thought the slower disappearance of the insulin was due to antibodies. They thought it was due to something wrong with diabetics. They simply made the wrong interpretation. . . .

* (yoo rē'kə) Greek for "I have found it."

Now it was luck for both sets of investigators to discover that insulin disappears more slowly from one group of patients than from another. The rest was science. That's what you mean by discovering something by accident. You make an observation. But it isn't by accident that you interpret the observation correctly. That's creativity. Thirty-three years later, I still think discovery is the most exciting thing in the world.

CHECK FOR UNDERSTANDING
1. What did Rosalyn Yalow say happens to new ideas?
2. Why did Rosalyn Yalow find the film *Marie Curie* memorable?
3. What observation did another group of scientists make at the same time as Dr. Yalow and Dr. Berson?
4. What accounted for the difference between the interpretations the two groups of scientists placed on their observations?
5. What is the main idea that Rosalyn Yalow presents in this essay?

WRITE ABOUT *"Advice from an Innovator"*
What character traits do Rosalyn Yalow and Jonathan Livingston Seagull have in common? Write a description of an innovator, based on your comparison of the real-life scientist and the fictional character.

from
Star-gazing

by KEITH DEUTSCH

Writers of science fiction often imagine improbable settings and wildly complicated machines. At the time their stories are written, the writers' work seems fantastic, even ridiculous. But sometimes science fiction becomes science fact.

Why did writing about space travel become more scientific in the nineteenth century? Why is it significant that Jules Verne's hero was a scientist?

On July 20, 1969, Commander Neil Armstrong from the United States became the first person to step on the moon. His walk brought to a successful completion thousands of years of dreaming about space travel. On earth, a strange black and white pattern appeared on tens of millions of television screens. It was a picture of a boot. The boot grew into a leg. The leg moved, and a man came into view. He was climbing down a ladder from his space vehicle, the landing module, or LM as he called it. He was dressed in a familiar spacesuit.

to
Star Trekking

"I'm at the foot of the ladder," he said. "I'm going to step off the LM now. That's one small step for a man. One giant leap for mankind."

A giant leap indeed.

The earliest astronauts watched and studied the stars thousands of years ago from the great pyramids in Egypt and the Americas. But until the ancient Greeks, few people even realized that the moon and planets were reachable places, or that they might support life. When these important ideas took root, both space science and the science fiction of space travel were born.

The greatest astronomer of the ancient world lived in Greece about 2100 years ago. This scientist of the heavens, Hipparchus, made maps of the stars, and invented ways to measure the movements of the moon, the earth, and the sun. He measured the moon's size to within a few hundred miles, and its distance from earth to within a few thousand miles, all without using a telescope or calculator!

The Greeks followed this beginning in space science with the world's first story about space travel. About the year A.D. 160, a Greek named Lucian wrote *A True History,* describing a trip to the moon. The main character of the story flies to the moon on the wings of a vulture and an eagle. Of course Lucian was writing in fun. But the dream of space travel was born. It would grow until we reached the moon—and perhaps the stars.

Despite the billions of stars we see above us at night, the universe is mostly empty space, cold, dark, and hostile. Even at the speed of light (which travels at 186,000 miles, or 299,000 km per second), it would take a spaceship more than four years to reach the nearest star. And of course our spaceships cannot yet achieve even close to the speed of light.

But why should we want to go into space at all? And if we have good reasons for going, is it really worth the cost? The United States spent over $24 million on just that part of the *Apollo* mission that sent the first person to the moon.

Great space pioneers and dreamers feel it is worth the cost. They say we should want to travel in space for the same reason that explorers in the fifteenth and sixteenth centuries ventured out onto unknown seas, in order to explore new frontiers.

Many scientists want us to go into space so we can see the stars and other planets more clearly, and thereby increase our understanding of the universe. New knowledge is one important result of space travel.

So are the new technologies developed from space science.

For example, artificial space satellites have resulted in tremendous advances in weather forecasting, communications, and our understanding of the rays that bombard the earth from deep space and the sun. The development of a space science has also aided in the development of miniature electronics and computers, new methods of forming metals, and new medical practices that benefit us all on earth.

There are many reasons why America pushed so hard in the 1960s to go into space, and why that push continues today. But perhaps the most important reason is the one mentioned at the outset—because we have been dreaming about it for so long.

Our dreams about space travel were greatly influenced by the invention of the telescope in 1608. A Dutch spectacle-maker, Hans Lippershey, was the man who invented it. But it was the Italian scientist Galilei Galileo who made the telescope famous. He built his own, and studied the heavens with the eye of an astronomer. In 1610 he published a book that described the moon as it actually was, rather than as storytellers had imagined it to be. He wrote,

"We could perceive . . . that it is uneven, rough . . . [like] the earth, which is also characterized by mountains and valleys."

With the telescope and Galileo's descriptions of the moon, there followed a flood of stories about space travel. In the following years, new planets were discovered where the naked eye had seen nothing. And, under the influence of new theories about space put forth by the four great founders of space science—Nicolaus Copernicus, Johannes Kepler, Galileo, and Sir Isaac Newton—the foundations for space travel were laid.

Newton's great work, *The Principia*, was published in 1687. It explored and compared the findings of Galileo, Copernicus, and Kepler. His theories and mathematical laws made it possible for later scientists to predict how moving rocket ships and orbiting planets will act in space at any given time. Newton's work also made it possible for others to estimate how much fuel rockets need to escape earth's gravity, how to determine proper launch angles for rendezvous with planets or other celestial bodies in their moving orbits, and much, much more.

In the eighty years or so between the invention of the telescope and Sir Isaac Newton's great work, fiction writers had not sat idle. A popular idea of fiction was to do away with the need for power entirely. An "antigravity" (gravity is defined as the force which keeps us grounded on earth, rather than floating through the air) substance was all that Professor George Tucker of Virginia needed for his space travel novel, *A Voyage to the Moon*. This was one of the first space travel novels written by an American. Published in 1827 under the pen name of Joseph Atterlay, this book was the first to describe space as a bitterly cold void where unprotected life could not exist.

Cyrano de Bergerac, a playwright who wrote a series of stories published in 1657 called *Voyage to the Moon and the Sun*, suggested many methods for flying to the moon, such as bottles of dew that would rise like balloons, giant springs, and even rockets. In a story published in 1835, Edgar Allan Poe told of a balloon that carried a man to the moon. That same year, Richard Locke, in an article in *The New York Sun*, reported that a runaway balloon had sighted strange beings on the moon.

Newspaper readers believed this story, and the paper's sales skyrocketed until the hoax was found out. The nineteenth century was a period of great faith in science and progress. People believed that space travel was just around the corner, and were easily fooled by stories that confirmed that belief.

Space travel was not just around the corner. But rocket science was. Writings about space travel became more "scientific."

In 1865, Jules Verne, the famous French science fiction author, wrote his great novel, *From the Earth to the Moon*. This space novel is important because the hero is a *scientist,* for the first time. Verne tried very hard to base all his writings on science as he understood it.

Jules Verne, together with H. G. Wells, an Englishman, are the founders of the modern space travel novel. Wells wrote *The First Men on the Moon* in 1901. His book is important because of its descriptions of the moon's surface, and of the earth as seen from space. Some critics think his descriptions of space are the finest ever written.

CHECK FOR UNDERSTANDING

1. What was the difference between early writing about space travel and the writing of the nineteenth century?
2. Why did writing about space travel become more scientific in the nineteenth century?
3. Why was Jules Verne's *From the Earth to the Moon* an important space novel?
4. Why was it significant that Jules Verne's hero was a scientist?
5. Do you think that science fiction writers of the twenty-first century will be writing about the moon? Explain your answer.

WRITE ABOUT *"From Star-gazing to Star Trekking"*

If you could tell a writer how well he or she had succeeded in predicting the future, what would you say? Choose one of the writers mentioned in the article. Write a letter to the writer explaining how something he or she had only imagined had become a reality.

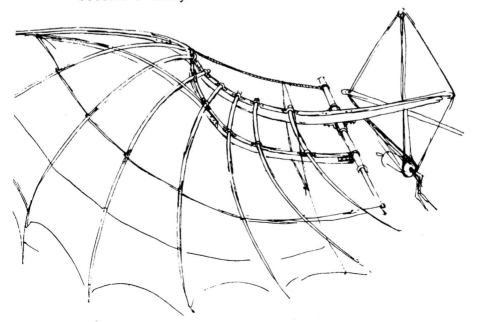

BY THE LIGHT

by ISAAC ASIMOV

Can you describe what it feels like to sail through space or to walk on the moon? Since you have never done these things, you must imagine the sensations, using what you have heard about space. Isaac Asimov takes what he knows about space to make predictions about the future of the moon.

What assumptions does Isaac Asimov make about the future of the moon? How are the nighttime skies different as seen from the earth and the moon?

Someday, when the moon is a busy world, with miners, electrical engineers, metallurgists, and astronomers all doing their work upon it, will tourists go there too? What would there be to do on the moon? What would there be to see?

I suppose there will be tours through the lunar mining operations. People will watch the mass-drivers operate and will visit the great lunar telescopes on the far side. There might even be considerable fun in experiencing the low gravity.

My own feeling, however, is that the chief tourist attraction on the moon will be the sky, for the fact is that the moon has a much more magnificent sky than we have, when it can be watched.

You see, the moon rotates very slowly with respect to the sun, once every 29.5 earth-days. That means it is two weeks between sunrise and sunset on the moon and another two weeks between sunset and sunrise.

During the two-week-long period of daytime, tourists will have to stay in underground accommodations. The temperatures get too high, and the sun's radiation, with no atmosphere to absorb any of it, is too dangerous. The two-week-long period of nighttime will represent the height of the tourists season for any given spot on the moon.

For one thing, the stars will all be brighter and sharper than on earth, since there will be no atmosphere to absorb any of the light, or to make what light gets through waver and "twinkle." Many stars too dim to see from earth will be visible from the moon, and there will never be any

OF THE EARTH

clouds. You will be in a planetarium that never turns off, provided there are nothing *but* stars in the sky.

You see, the moon doesn't rotate at all with respect to the earth. One side (the near side, as seen from earth) always faces the earth; the other (the far side) always faces away from the earth.

On the far side, the earth is never in the sky, and the stars are the objects to watch. On the near side, however, the earth is always in the sky, and no one is going to be watching the stars.

The earth, as seen in the moon's sky, goes through the same phases in the same time as the moon does in our sky, but in reverse order. In other words, when we see the full moon on earth, tourists on the moon will be seeing "new earth." On the other hand, when it is new moon on earth, tourists on the moon will be seeing "full earth."

During the two-week nighttime (if we are standing at the center of the near side) earth is at the zenith, and stays there, except for a small wobble called "libration."

The earth is in the first quarter at sunset, and looks like a bright semi-circle of light. The semicircle expands until, after a week, we see the full earth as a perfect circle of light.

Then the lighted portion of the earth begins to contract in the opposite direction until it is the last quarter (a semicircle facing the other way), at sunrise.

If you change your position on the near side, the earth will shift its position lower in the sky. Once you

have chosen your new position, the earth will also stay put in the sky. Depending on your new position, full earth may come earlier or later in the course of the lunar night, but at some time, during the course of that night, earth *will* be full.

And what an earth it will then be. The earth is larger in the moon's sky than the moon is in ours; the earth reflects a greater fraction of the light that reaches it from the sun than the moon does, and there is no atmosphere on the moon to absorb the earthlight. Taking all these factors together, it turns out that the full earth that shines on the moon does so with no less than seventy times (!) as much light as the full moon that shines on the earth.

Imagine standing on the lunar surface in the bright earthlight. There would be enough light to read by, without uncomfortable heat or dangerous radiation. If you stand in the center of the near side with full earth at zenith, earth's soft white light would cast virtually no shadow around you. If you stand elsewhere and the full earth is lower in the sky, pitch-black shadows are cast, within which you can stand to gaze at the stars, if you wish.

Then, too, the earth won't have the unchanging face of the moon. It will be a blue and white circle of light, and through the curling banks of clouds you will see glimpses of brownish desert areas (especially if you use binoculars). What's more, the cloud layers will be forever changing as the earth rotates and as its winds blow.

CHECK FOR UNDERSTANDING

1. What did Isaac Asimov say people will do when they visit the Moon?
2. What assumptions did Isaac Asimov make about the future of the Moon?
3. How are the nighttime skies different as seen from the Earth and the Moon?
4. What are the differences between the Earth's and the Moon's atmospheres.
5. Isaac Asimov is both a scientist and a famous writer of science fiction as well as popular science books. Is this account science fiction or is it an essay? Give reasons for your answer.

WRITE ABOUT *"By the Light of the Earth"*

Imagine that you are about to travel to the moon as a tourist. Write a brief travel diary describing your trip.

ORBITER 5 SHOWS
HOW EARTH LOOKS FROM THE MOON

There's a woman in the earth, sitting on
her heels. You see her from the back, in three-
quarter profile. She has a flowing pigtail. She's
holding something
in her right hand—some holy jug. Her left arm is thinner,
in a gesture like a dancer. She's the Indian Ocean. Asia is
light swirling up out of her vessel. Her pigtail points to Europe,
and her dancer's arm is the Suez Canal. She is a woman
in a square kimono,
bare feet tucked beneath the tip of Africa. Her tail of long hair is
the Arabian Peninsula.

A woman in the earth.

A man in the moon.

by MAY SWENSON

Telephoto of the earth was taken by Lunar Orbiter 5, one of a series of
satellites sent into orbit around the moon. The photograph was printed in
The New York Times on August 14, 1967.

COMPREHENSION

Main Idea

> BOB: Look at that sign. It says, "ROAD UNDER CONSTRUCTION."
>
> ANN: The sign we just passed said "DETOUR."
>
> BOB: Here's another sign: "USE ALTERNATE ROUTE UNTIL FURTHER NOTICE."
>
> ANN: Look! Just ahead. There's a man with a flag. He's signaling you to go left.
>
> BOB: But I don't want to go left! What's the big idea?
>
> ANN: I don't know about the *big* idea, but the *main* idea is that you have to get off this road!

The **main idea** is a sentence that states the central point that a selection makes about its topic. As Bob learned, the main idea is not always stated; it may be implied. Being able to recognize the main idea of a paragraph is an important skill. Identifying main ideas can help you remember the most important parts of what you read.

What is the main idea of this paragraph?

> The greatest astronomer of the ancient world lived in Greece about 2100 years ago. This scientist of the heavens, Hipparchus, made maps of the stars and invented ways to measure the movement of the moon, earth, and sun. He measured the moon's size to within a few hundred miles and its distance from earth to within a few thousand, all without using a telescope or calculator!

The main idea is that Hipparchus was the greatest astronomer of the ancient world. In order to find this answer, it was necessary to identify the topic of the paragraph—in this case, Hipparchus. Notice that each sentence says something about Hipparchus. The first sentence of this particular paragraph is a topic sentence, and it contains the main idea. The second and third sentences provide details that support the main idea.

Read this paragraph:

> Newton's great work *The Principia* was published in 1687. It explored and compared the findings of Galileo, Copernicus, and Kepler. Newton's theories and mathematical laws made it possible for later scientists to predict how moving rocket ships and orbiting planets will act in space at any given time. Newton's work also made it possible for others to estimate how much fuel rockets need to escape earth's gravity, how to determine proper launch angles for rendezvous with planets or other celestial bodies in their moving orbits, and much, much more.

The main idea of this paragraph is not stated; it is implied. Analyze the paragraph sentence by sentence. What is the subject of each sentence? It is Newton's *Principia*. Notice that the sentences have one thing in common: the contribution of *The Principia* to space science. What does each sentence tell you about *The Principia?* As you can see, each sentence reveals another important theory that helped to create modern space science.

What is a general statement that sums up all the sentences? It is the main idea of the paragraph: *The Principia* made an important contribution to modern space science.

As you read Ray Bradbury's "The Flying Machine," you will encounter paragraphs that carry the true meaning of the story. As you read, ask yourself:

What is the topic of each paragraph?

What do the sentences tell me about the emperor and his feelings?

Why does the emperor find his miniature garden so reassuring?

New inventions can change our entire way of working and living. Just think of how your life would change without the telephone, automobile, or computer. Sometimes, however, people—like the emperor in this story—are afraid of new inventions that bring change.

What is the flying man guilty of, according to the emperor? What is the difference between the emperor's mechanical "garden" and the flier's creation?

The Flying Machine

by RAY BRADBURY

In the year A.D. 400, the Emperor Yuan held his throne by the Great Wall of China, and the land was green with rain, readying itself toward the harvest, at peace, the people in his dominion neither too happy nor too sad.

Early on the morning of the first day of the first week of the second month of the new year, the Emperor Yuan was sipping tea and fanning himself against a warm breeze when a servant ran across the scarlet and blue garden tiles, calling, "Oh, Emperor, a miracle!"

"Yes," said the emperor, "the air *is* sweet this morning."

"No, no, a miracle!" said the servant, bowing quickly.

"And this tea is good in my mouth, surely that is a miracle."

"No, no, Your Excellency."

"Let me guess then—the sun has risen and a new day is upon us. Or the sea is blue. *That,* now, is the finest of all miracles."

"Excellency, a man is flying!"

"What?" The emperor stopped his fan.

"I saw him in the air, a man flying with wings. I heard a voice call out of the sky, and when I looked up, there he was, a dragon in the heavens with a man in its mouth, a dragon of paper and bamboo, colored like the sun and the grass."

"It is early," said the emperor, "and you have just wakened from a dream."

"It is early, but I have seen what I have seen! Come, and you will see it too."

"Sit down with me here," said the emperor. "Drink some tea. It must be a strange thing, if it is true, to see a man fly. You must have time to think of it, even as I must have time to prepare myself for the sight."

They drank tea.

"Please," said the servant at last, "or he will be gone."

The emperor rose thoughtfully. "Now you may show me what you have seen."

They walked into a garden, across a meadow of grass, over a small bridge, through a grove of trees, and up a tiny hill.

"There!" said the servant.

The emperor looked into the sky.

And in the sky, laughing so high that you could hardly hear him laugh, was a man; and the man was clothed in bright papers and reeds to make wings and a beautiful yellow tail, and he was soaring all about like the largest bird in a universe of birds, like a new dragon in a land of ancient dragons.

413

The man called down to them from high in the cool winds of morning, "I fly, I fly!"

The servant waved to him. "Yes, yes!"

The Emperor Yuan did not move. Instead he looked at the Great Wall of China now taking shape out of the farthest mist in the green hills, that splendid snake of stones which writhed with majesty across the entire land. That wonderful wall which had protected them for a timeless time from enemy hordes and preserved peace for years without number. He saw the town, nestled to itself by a river and a road and a hill, beginning to waken.

"Tell me," he said to his servant, "has anyone else seen this flying man?"

"I am the only one, Excellency," said the servant, smiling at the sky, waving.

The emperor watched the heavens another minute and then said, "Call him down to me."

"Ho, come down, come down! The emperor wishes to see you!" called the servant, hands cupped to his shouting mouth.

The emperor glanced in all directions while the flying man soared down the morning wind. He saw a farmer, early in his fields, watching the sky, and he noted where the farmer stood.

The flying man alighted with a rustle of paper and a creak of bamboo reeds. He came proudly to the emperor, clumsy in his rig, at last bowing before the old man.

"What have you done?" demanded the emperor.

"I have flown in the sky, Your Excellency," replied the man.

"What *have* you done?" said the emperor again.

"I have just told you!" cried the flier.

"You have told me nothing at all." The emperor reached out a thin hand to touch the pretty paper and the birdlike keel of the apparatus. It smelled cool, of the wind.

"Is it not beautiful, Excellency?"

"Yes, too beautiful."

"It is the only one in the world!" smiled the man. "And I am the inventor."

"The *only* one in the world?"

"I swear it!"

"Who else knows of this?"

"No one. Not even my wife, who would think me mad with the sun. She thought I was making a kite. I rose in the night and walked to the cliffs far away. And when the morning breezes blew and the sun rose, I gathered my courage, Excellency, and leaped from the cliff. I flew! But my wife does not know of it."

"Well for her, then," said the emperor. "Come along."

They walked back to the great house. The sun was full in the sky now, and the smell of the grass was refreshing. The emperor, the servant, and the flier paused within the huge garden.

The emperor clapped his hands. "Ho, guards!"

The guards came running.

"Hold this man."

The guards seized the flier.

"Call the executioner," said the emperor.

"What's this!" cried the flier, bewildered. "What have I done?" He began to weep, so that the beautiful paper apparatus rustled.

"Here is the man who has made a certain machine," said the emperor, "and yet asks us what he has created. He does not know himself. It is only necessary that he create, without knowing why he has done so, or what this thing will do."

The executioner came running with a sharp silver ax. He stood with his naked, large-muscled arms ready, his face covered with a serene white mask.

"One moment," said the emperor. He turned to a nearby table upon which sat a machine that he himself had created. The emperor took a tiny golden key from his own neck. He fitted this key to the tiny, delicate machine and wound it up. Then he set the machine going.

The machine was a garden of metal and jewels. Set in motion, birds sang in tiny metal trees, wolves walked through a miniature forest, and tiny people ran in and out of sun and shadow, fanning themselves with miniature fans, listening to the tiny emerald birds, and standing by impossibly small but tinkling fountains.

"Is *it* not beautiful?" said the emperor. "If you asked me

what I have done here, I could answer you well. I have made birds sing, I have made forests murmur, I have set people to walking in this woodland, enjoying the leaves and shadows and songs. That is what I have done."

"But, oh, Emperor!" pleaded the flier, on his knees, the tears pouring down his face. "I have done a similar thing! I have found beauty. I have flown on the morning wind. I have looked down on all the sleeping houses and gardens. I have smelled the sea and even *seen* it, beyond the hills, from my high place. And I have soared like a bird; oh, I cannot say how beautiful it is up there, in the sky, with the wind about me, the wind blowing me here like a feather, there like a fan, the way the sky smells in the morning! And how free one feels! *That* is beautiful, Emperor, that is beautiful, too!"

"Yes," said the emperor sadly, "I know it must be true. For I felt my heart move with you in the air and I wondered: What is it like? How does it feel? How do the distant pools look from so high? And how my houses and servants? Like ants? And how the distant towns not yet awake?"

"Then spare me!"

"But there are times," said the emperor, more sadly still, "when one must lose a little beauty if one is to keep what little beauty one already has. I do not fear you, yourself, but I fear another man."

"What man?"

"Some other man who, seeing you, will build a thing of bright papers and bamboo like this. But the other man will have an evil face and an evil heart, and the beauty will be gone. It is this man I fear."

"Why? Why?"

"Who is to say that someday just such a man, in just such an apparatus of paper and reed, might not fly in the sky and drop huge stones upon the Great Wall of China?" said the emperor.

No one moved or said a word.

"Off with his head," said the emperor.

The executioner whirled his silver ax.

"Burn the kite and the inventor's body and bury their ashes together," said the emperor.

The servants retreated to obey.

The emperor turned to his hand servant, who had seen the man flying. "Hold your tongue. It was all a dream, a most sorrowful and beautiful dream. And that farmer in the distant field who also saw, tell him it would pay him to consider it only a vision. If ever the word passes around, you and the farmer die within the hour."

"You are merciful, Emperor."

"No, not merciful," said the old man. Beyond the garden wall he saw the guards burning the beautiful machine of paper and reeds that smelled of the morning wind. He saw the dark smoke climb into the sky. "No, only very much bewildered and afraid." He saw the guards digging a tiny pit wherein to bury the ashes. "What is the life of one man against those of a million others? I must take solace from that thought."

He took the key from its chain about his neck and once more wound up the beautiful miniature garden. He stood looking out across the land at the Great Wall, the peaceful town, the green fields, the rivers and streams. He sighed. The tiny garden whirred its hidden and delicate machinery and set itself in motion; tiny people walked in the forest, tiny foxes loped through sun-speckled glades in beautiful shining pelts, and among the tiny trees flew little bits of high song and bright blue and yellow color, flying, flying, flying in that small sky.

"Oh," said the emperor, closing his eyes, "look at the birds, look at the birds!"

CHECK FOR UNDERSTANDING

1. Why was the flier laughing in the sky?
2. What man did the emperor fear?
3. What was the flying man guilty of, according to the emperor?
4. Why did the emperor put the flier to death instead of just taking away his invention?
5. What was the difference between the emperor's mechanical "garden" and the flier's creation?
6. How do you think the author feels about the emperor's actions? Does the author approve or disapprove of what the emperor did? Give reasons for your answer.

WRITE ABOUT *"The Flying Machine"*

Whose viewpoint do you agree with, the emperor's or the flier's? Write a paragraph explaining your answer.

SOME OF THE
WORST PREDICTIONS OF ALL TIME

Experts often disagree on the future of new inventions. Looking back at their predictions is often surprising—and funny.

THE IMPORTANCE OF THE AUTOMOBILE

"The ordinary 'horseless carriage' is at present a luxury for the wealthy. Although its price will probably fall in the future, it will never, of course, come into as common use as the bicycle."

THE LITERARY DIGEST
OCTOBER 14, 1889

TRANSATLANTIC RADIO

"(Lee) De Forest has said in many newspapers and over his signature that it would be possible to transmit the human voice across the Atlantic before many years. Based on these absurd and deliberately misleading statements, the misguided public...has been persuaded to purchase stock in his company...."

—A U.S. DISTRICT ATTORNEY PROSECUTING INVENTOR LEE DE FOREST IN 1913. DE FOREST WAS ACCUSED OF STOCK FRAUD.

The first transatlantic broadcast of a human voice occurred on December 31, 1923, from Pittsburgh, Pennsylvania, to Manchester, England.

COMMERCIAL TELEVISION

"While theoretically and technically television may be feasible, commercially and financially I consider it an impossibility, a development of which we need waste little time dreaming."

—LEE DE FOREST
U.S. INVENTOR AND "FATHER OF THE RADIO," 1926

AIR TRAVEL

"May not our mechanisms… be ultimately forced to admit that aerial flight is one of that great class of problems with which man can never cope, and give up all attempts to grapple with it?…The construction of an aerial vehicle which could carry even a single man from place to place at pleasure requires the discovery of some new metal or some new force. Even with such a discovery we could not expect one to do more than carry its owner."

—SIMON NEWCOMB
U.S. ASTRONOMER, 1903

On December 17, 1903, Wright brothers made the first successful flight at Kitty Hawk, North Carolina.

THE VALUE OF PREDICTIONS

"I confess that in 1901, I said to my brother Orville that man would not fly for fifty years…. Ever since, I have distrusted myself and avoided all predictions…"

—WILBUR WRIGHT
U.S. AVIATION PIONEER, 1908

ROCKET TRAVEL

"That Professor Goddard …does not know the relation of action to reaction, and of the need to have something better than a vacuum against which to react— to say that would be absurd. Of course he only seems to lack the knowledge ladled out daily in high schools…."

THE NEW YORK TIMES
JANUARY 13, 1920

The New York Times printed a formal retraction of this comment some forty-nine years later, on July 17, 1969, just prior to the Apollo landing on the moon.

A MOON LANDING

"Landing and moving around the moon offers so many serious problems for human beings that it may take science another two hundred years to lick them."

SCIENCE DIGEST
AUGUST, 1948

It took twenty-one years.

VOCABULARY · LANGUAGE

Development of New Words

WANTED

A word to name a mammal that has a small head, large ears, powerful hind legs, a thick tail, and—in the female—a pouch for carrying the young. Kindly address all replies to Captain James Cook, Australia.

When Captain Cook first saw a kangaroo, he could not, of course, have placed a want ad. Cook was exploring the South Pacific at the time, and no other European had ever seen such an animal. The English language, therefore, had no name for it. No one really knows why Cook decided to call the strange animal a kangaroo. One story suggests that when he asked a native what the animal's name was, the native answered in his own language: "I do not understand you." To Captain Cook, the reply sounded like "kangaroo." Regardless of how the naming took place, the word *kangaroo* is now part of the English language.

Kangaroo is an example of **neologism** (nē ol′ ə jiz′ əm). A neologism can be defined as "a new word, or a new meaning for an existing word." Which part of this definition applies to the neologism *kangaroo?*

Explorers like Captain Cook were not the only people to coin new words. Often inventions (or scientific discoveries) are named by, or for, their inventor. The diesel engine, for example, is named after

Rudolph Diesel, an engineer who developed one of the first internal-combustion engines. Louis Braille, a French teacher, originated braille, a system of writing and printing for the blind.

Today, most people take the words *telephone* and *television* for granted. These words, however, are neologisms that came into our language not very long ago. Words such as *elevator*, *stereo*, and *skyscraper* are also relatively new to the English language. Can you think of some other neologisms?

As times change, new words are constantly being developed. The age of aviation, for example, introduced the words *glider, helicopter*, and *runway*, among others, while the space age contributed *blast-off, countdown, moonshot*, and *splashdown*. It was necessary to create these words to describe new conditions and ideas. Imagine the new words that will be part of our language years from now.

In the following story, "A Day in Megalopolis," the author invents many new words. These neologisms are part of the vocabulary of the inhabitants of a city in the future. Twixt, the main character, says:

> I kicked off my pneumonosoles and lay down on the bed, clicking the panel shut. The lulltone came on in my pillow, and the conditioning currents began to circulate to adjust to night settings.

Find two neologisms in the passage above. Using clues in the passage, define the new words. Why do you think the author decided to use neologisms in her story?

As you read "A Day in Megalopolis," be on the lookout for the following neologisms: *telaworld, gabfesting, plastiglass*, and *immunispray.* What do you think each word means? Discover if you are correct as you read the story—and see how many *other* neologisms you can find.

In this author's vision of the future, advancing technology has brought people together to live in ever-growing cities. The community in which Twixt lives has grown more and more crowded.

Why would it make no difference in their lives if Twixt and her family moves? What strange object does Chis bring home with him?

A DAY IN MEGALOPOLIS

by ZENNA HENDERSON

One day in our unit not so long ago, Mother turned to me suddenly and clutched my arm with both her hands. For a second I was startled. Mother hadn't touched me for so long— so long.

"I can't see out!" she protested, and I could feel her hands shaking. "I can't see any way out!"

"Out of what?" I asked, feeling sick inside and scared because she seemed to be crumpling. She even looked smaller. "Out of what?" I repeated. Whoever heard of seeing out of a unit?

"Out of anything!" she said. "Is there still a sky? Do ants still make bare paths through the grass?"

"Mother," my voice wobbled. "Mother, you're hurting me." And she was. She let go, sucking her breath in surprise. "Shall I call Clinic? Are you hurting somewhere?"

"I'm hurting everywhere and all the time," Mother said. She turned away and leaned her forehead against the wall. Her voice was muffled. "I used to think those ant trails through the grass were the loveliest, most secret thing in the whole world. I was charmed to think of a whole civilization that could function without a single idea that we even existed. And that's what I'm feeling now—a whole civilization functioning without even knowing I exist. And it's *my* civilization! And I'm not charmed about it any more.

424

"Remember that undersea vacation we had two years ago? We saw those shells that were so lovely. And they told us that the shells were the external skeletons of the tiny, soft creatures inside. No one cared about the tiny, soft creatures inside— only the bright shell. They forgot that the soft creatures *made* the bright shell, not the bright shell the creatures. As though the bright shell were the only excuse for the creature!" She turned slowly, until she finally leaned her back against the wall, her hands behind her. "Most people think we exist for our lovely exterior skeletons. They think we're only the un-important soft little creatures inside all these shells—these buildings and walls and towers and glides. That we couldn't exist without them. But I have my own bones! Inside me! I don't *need* all these skeletons!"

425

And she stood there with tears running down her cheeks.

What do you do when your mother just stands there with tears rolling down her face? I didn't know either, so I got a tissue and gave it to her. She wiped her face and hugged me tight. I could feel the wetness of her tears above my ear as she hugged. How odd! How odd to feel the warmth of another person, so close! How odd, but how wonderful!

"Twixt," she said, letting go of me to look at me. "Have you ever run barefoot through the grass? Or squished mud up between your toes?"

"We don't ever touch the greeneries." I sounded like a tired First Level tape. "They are the breath of the complex. Maybe one touch wouldn't matter, but who are you that you should touch and others not be allowed to? And there's no soil, as such, in the megalopolis," I chanted. "The greeneries grow in liquid nutrients instead."

"Remember when you were taking mythology?" asked Mother. My head swam as I tried to keep up with her quick switches. "Remember that man who was strong as long as he touched the earth and lost his strength when he was lifted off it?"

I nodded. "Hercules killed him after he held him off the ground so long he got weak."

"We are all like him," said Mother. "And we've been held off the earth too long. We'll die if we don't touch down soon."

Maybe *that* explained the funny feeling that had been growing inside me for so long, and twisting me so much of late. Maybe I was dying slowly because I couldn't touch down. But since I don't remember ever having touched down, how could I be suffering because I couldn't—I snatched back to Now. What I was feeling most was uncomfortable, wondering what to say next.

I was spared, though. Mother glanced quickly at the time-line rippling along near the ceiling, snatched her bag from the table and a kiss from the air in the vicinity of my cheek, and slid the door to the corridor in a wild flurry of haste. I could have looked at the log to find out what she was late for, but I felt too quenched even to flip her info switch to see.

I went to the slot wall and flipped the latch of mine. I kicked off my pneumonosoles and lay down on the bed, click-

ing the panel shut. The lulltone came on in my pillow, and the conditioning currents began to circulate to adjust to night settings. I was crying now, tears running down into my ears on both sides. "I hate! I hate! The whole unit—the whole complex—the whole everything!" I sobbed to myself. "I hate it, but I'm *used* to it! What else can we do but be used to it!" I thumped my pillow. "Gonky slot!" I sniffed. "Too stupid to know it isn't night!" Then my tears stopped as I suddenly thought, "Am I any smarter? How do I know it's day? I've been doing daythings just because the timeline says it's day, but how do I *know* it's day?" Tears flowed again. "But I did see the sun once! I did! It's big and up and so bright you can't see it!"

That morning, with my usual sense of reaching a refuge,

I had slipped into my study carrel at school. When I was in it and facing the viewer, I could shut the whole world out. I could get so absorbed that when break-time came I'd have to blink myself back to Now and wander in a fog down to the physical area. I sometimes envied the kids who were so loose that they could get together before break-time, volunteer one of them as a puncher to cover six or eight carrels besides his own, and then stand gabfesting in a tight little wad in the corridor while the puncher wore himself out punching enough responses to prevent Supervisory from investigating, or calling for a check response from everyone simultaneously.

Our level isn't required to do movement beyond our daily compulsory half hour first thing in the morning, so we usually sit around the area and, well, you know—music and eating and drinking and talking—and boys. At least for some. I had no past as yet. Time enough. No one can even put in for marriage evaluation until twenty-one—and lucky to get certified before twenty-five. Mother and Dad were married, younger than that, just before Evaluation and Certification came in. I asked them once how they could tell, then, that their marriage could be functional. Dad laughed—he still could laugh then—and looked at Mother. She pinked and he said, "Some knowledge isn't programmable. You'll find out."

Well, back to the student lounge. I had headed for my usual bench where my other-end-of-the-alphabet friend would be waiting with our two containers of Squelch—chartreuse was the Squelch month-flavor, and I loathed it, but everyone was drinking it, so— The lounge was overflowing with a waltz, the old dance form that has been staging a big comeback. Chis and I used to have fun with it at home at night, along with Dad and Mother, way back when we still had fun together. I wonder what happened to us? Most of the kids think the waltz is too strenuous and barbaric really to dance, since it involves continuous large-muscle movements, but my heart swung with remembered pleasure when I heard the music.

I was cutting across a corner of the area, not paying much attention to the few couples swishing around it. Hardly anyone notices their touching any more. It is assumed that it is with permission. Well, there I was crossing the floor when I was snatched out into the middle of it and into the dance. My feet responded automatically and were waltzing happily long before the top of me had time to wonder what the drill was.

"Hey! You've got two right feet!" The creature who had grabbed me, *without* permission!, was very pleasantly surprised.

"But I didn't intend to . . ." I began, annoyed, but he just grinned and almost swung me off the floor. I got so interested in keeping up with all the variations that he knew that I forgot to be annoyed and just enjoyed! It was swinging way out away from anything. It was being loose in such a beautiful way that shouts built up inside me but came out as rhythmical swirling— and the warmth—the round warmness around us and around us and around . . .

The music stopped, and there we were in the middle of the floor, panting, and laughing, and looking. At least I was looking. The fellow had his eyes pointing at me, but he didn't see me, not really. No more than if we had passed on a glide somewhere. I was just an adjunct to his dancing.

Suddenly very cold, and angular, and conscious of the ring of eyes around us, I loosed my cooling hands from his. He turned his smile off and mine died.

"Lellice is waiting," I said. I didn't even wait for him to walk me the four courtesy steps. I fled to Lellice who stood there openmouthed, as usual, and clammy-handed from clutching our Squelches.

"Close your mouth," I said, still breathless, my heart not compensating as quickly as it should have. "No cavern tours today."

"That—that was Engle!" she said in an awed whisper. "Engle Faucing!"

"Oh?" I grimaced at the first taste of chartreuse. "Who's he?" I could not-see him, too! Besides, I really hadn't noticed.

"Who's he!" Lellice strangled chartreusely. "*Only* the son of Kermit Faucing, megalopolis council member! *Only* the Rep of Senior Levels to the Governing! You voted for him! *Only the utter out of all outness!*"

"Oh, I'm sorry," I said. "He looked like a nice kid. Poor thing."

"Poor thing!" yelped Lellice. "Have you crazed across?"

"To have a name like Engle Faucing," I explained. "It's as left-footed as his dancing." I regretted that as soon as I said it. He could dance—could *dance*—but only with his feet, I guess.

"Twixt! You sheerly are double-dumpstuff!" Lellice turned her back on me and loudly went on drinking her Squelch.

The outside of me walked back to my carrel after the break, as usual, but the inside of me, for some reason, crept back unhappily and huddled tightly as I sat down in my chair. I stared blindly at the viewer, thinking nothing—only feeling a three-quarter beat pulsing—I thumbed the response button viciously and went off into history, silencing the tutor's jabbing introductory voice.

And then, of course, it was Release Time today. I usually like the break from regular school and feel pleased and loose for sure. I like getting into discussions of matters in which Humanity is the most important thing about earth, instead of its just being an eddy of life around the bottom of the eyeless, towering buildings. But that day I suddenly couldn't believe in it. Not with flesh so soft and unhappy, and walls so hard and uncaring. I drooped, wordless, through the class.

Afterwards, everyone else left the building to go to their usual glides, but I cut through another way to go on an errand for Mother. All alone in the school Open, I looked up and up the sheer wall that towered without an opening on this side from Crib Level all the way up to Doctor's Degree. And it scared me. What if it should fall on me! I was so little, and I could die! The building looked as though it didn't know I was alive. It looked solid enough to go on forever and ever after I died. I suddenly hammered my fists against the vitricrete and cried, "I'm supposed to be immortal, not you! You—you *unlive* you! I've got a soul! Whoever heard of a vitricrete soul!"

But I was the one that bruised, and the vitricrete didn't even plop when I hit it.

And then home to Mother's breaking. And my tears in the slot. And a weary going on with the usual routine.

Dad came home that evening more silent than ever, if that's possible. My tears were long dried and I was sitting on the floor in front of the telaworld watching the evening news. I gave Dad a hi! and cut my picture to half a screen to clear for his sports program. I removed the ear so I could hear what Dad had to say.

"Chis?" Dad asked as he flipped a finger to inflate the chair to his weight before he dropped wearily into its curving angles.

"Not in yet," said Mother guiltily, her face pinking.

"He knows," said Dad. "Guidance warned us, and him. If he glide-hops once more or enters male-subteen restricted areas, he'll go to therapy."

"And so will we," I thought sickly. "The whole family will have to go to therapy if Chis does. Illness isn't isolated."

"I . . . I . . ." Mother looked miserable. "Darin, can't we do *something* for Chis? Can't we get him brighted on anything?"

"Like what?" Dad filled his half of the telaworld with his underwater program and fumbled for the ear. "Even Guidance is stumped."

"But at ten?" Mother protested. "At *ten* to be so quenched on everything?"

"Guidance says they're working on it." Dad sharpened the focus on his half-screen. A shark seemed to swim right off the screen at us. "He's on page fourteen in volume two of the ten-year-olds. I wonder which page they'd have me on?" He turned from the telaworld. "I don't imagine the list would be very long of malcontent males who stop in midmorning to remember the feel of sand dissolving from under their bare feet in a numbing-cold, running stream."

"I wish," said Mother passionately, "that we could—just go!"

"Where?" asked Dad. "How? We'd have to put in for locale amends, specifying a destination and motivation. Besides, is there any place . . ."

"Just *any* place," said Mother rigidly.

"Would it be different?" I asked, feeling hope surge up inside me. Mother looked at me silently for a moment; then she sighed, and her wrists went limp. "No," she almost whispered. "It would be no different."

I didn't know when Chis came in. I guess he slid the secondary exit. But there he was, sitting in his corner, twirling and twirling a green stem between his fingers, a green stem with three leaves on it. I felt my heart sag. He had picked a leaf! From greenery!

Mother saw him about the same time I did. "Chis," she said softly, and Dad turned to look. "Is that a real leaf?"

"Yes," he said, "a real one."

"Then you'd better put it in water before it dies," said Mother, not even a tone in her voice to hint of all the laws he had broken.

"In water?" Chis's eyes opened wide and so did mine.

"Yes," said Mother. "It will last longer." She got a plastiglass from the dispenser and filled it. She held it out to Chis. "Put the stem down in the water," she said. And he did. And stood there with the glass tipping almost to spilling and looked at Dad. Then he leaned over and put the plastiglass on the table by Dad's chair. Dad looked at the leaf and then at Chis.

"Will it grow?" asked Chis.

"No," said Dad. "It has no roots. But it will stay green for a while."

Chis reached his hand out and touched Dad gently on the shoulder. Dad showed no withdrawal. "I won't ever take another," offered Chis.

"It's better not," said Dad.

"But someday," cried Chis, "I'm going away! I'm going to find a place where I can *run* on a million, million leaves and no one will ever notice!"

I hunched there in front of the telaworld and felt myself splintering slowly in all directions into blunt slivers that could never fit together again. This must be what they meant by crazing across. I was immortal, but I must die. And soon, if I

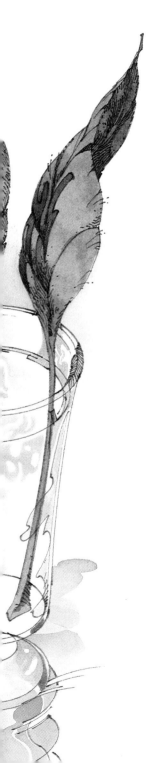

couldn't touch the soil I had never touched. I didn't want to touch anywhere, and yet I could still feel a hand enveloping mine and another pressed firmly against my waist. I hated where I was, but sickened to think of change. But change had to come because it had been noticeable that Dad hadn't withdrawn when his own son touched him. Nothing would be smooth or fitted together again.

I creaked tiredly to my feet. Mother quirked an eyebrow at me. "Only to the perimeter," I said. "I want to walk before dimming."

Outside our unit I paused and looked up the endless height of the building—blind, eyeless, but, because it is an older unit, I could still see scars where windows used to be; windows were desirable. I walked slowly toward the perimeter, automatically reminding myself not to overstep. With Chis already on warning, it wouldn't do for me to be Out of Area after hours. Someday, some long-away day, I'd be twenty-one and be able to flip my Ident casually at the Eye and open any area, any hour of the day—well, not the Restricted, of course. Or the Classified. Or the Industrial. Or the—well, I have the list at home.

Around me, as *up* as I could see, were buildings. Around me as *far* as I could see, were buildings. The Open of our area, ringed about by the breathing greeneries, must have had people coming and going, surely a few, but I didn't see them. I seldom do any more. Of course, you never deliberately *look* at anyone. That's rude. Nor ever speak in public places except when you absolutely have to. You *do* murmur to friends you meet. And because you don't look and don't speak, people sort of get lost against the bigness and solid-builtness of the complexes. So I walked alone in the outer dimming, my pneumonosoles not even whispering against the resilicrete floor of the Open.

I found myself counting steps and wondered why. Then I smiled, remembering. Twenty-six paces this direction, then fourteen slightly the other way, and . . .

435

I slowly turned my head. Yes, I had remembered my old formula right. I had found the exact spot under the lights. No matter which way I looked, I could see a shadow of me. I was standing in the center of a bouquet of my own shadows! How pleased I used to be with the visual magic. No matter what shadow I saw, it was mine! All of the me's belonging to the one me! How enchanting it had been when I was young. But now the shadows no longer pointed at me, but away. I wasn't apart—thinned to no more substance than my own shadow. I ached. Then I turned back to the unit. All the other me's went somewhere else. I felt drafty and very small at the complex door.

That night I lay awake in my slot long after inner dimming. Every time I shut my eyes, I was swinging around the lounge again, with a disturbing sense of nearness. I don't like nearness. It interferes. You have to react, even if you'd rather not. And how can you be near to someone who doesn't even see you but just rubs his eyes past the place where you are?

My pillow was hard. The lulltone was off-key. The air exchange was all wrong. And I was dancing again, around and around, farther and farther away from the lounge but nearer and nearer and nearer . . .

"Engle Faucing! What a gonky name!" I muttered and poked my pillow. Then I was counting. "Seventeen, eighteen, nineteen, twenty, twenty-one, twenty-one, twenty-one. Five is so many years! So many!"

I flipped up in bed, hunching automatically to keep from thumping my head on Chis's slot. *What* was the matter with me? I couldn't be sickening for anything. Our lavcube is standard; we have the immunispray installation, so I couldn't be sickening for anything. I flopped back down and closed my eyes.

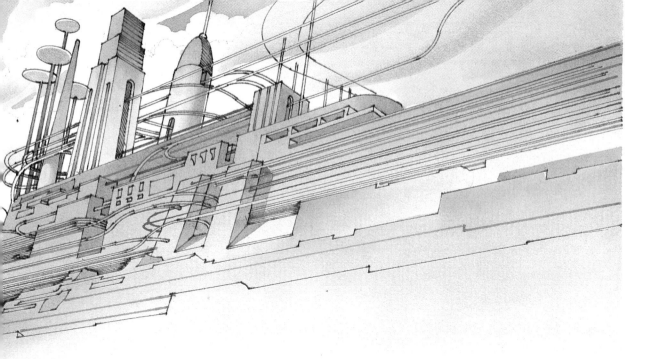

CHECK FOR UNDERSTANDING

1. When and where does this story take place?
2. Who was Engle Faucing?
3. Why would it have made no difference in their lives if Twixt and her family moved?
4. What strange thing did Chris bring home with him?
5. In the beginning of the story, Twixt seemed content with things as they were. By the end of the story, she was disturbed about the restrictions imposed on her life. What do you think accounted for the change in her feelings?

WRITE ABOUT *"A Day in Megalopolis"*

How would you have felt about living in Megalopolis? Write a short personal essay describing your reactions, both positive and negative.

Graphic Aids

Roger and Irene were distant cousins who had never met before. When a business trip was scheduled that would take Irene to the city where Roger lived, she wrote to him. He replied that he would pick her up at the airport if she would send him a description of herself.

"I am five feet, six inches tall," Irene wrote, "and on the slender side. My hair is light brown, wavy, and cut short. I have brown eyes and wear glasses with dark blue frames." Irene was still worried that Roger might not be able to recognize her, so she sent him a photograph.

Roger read the written description carefully, but he was puzzled. Then he picked up the photograph and smiled. "So that's what she looks like," he said.

A picture is often said to be worth a thousand words. It can show things that are difficult to explain verbally, or that take many words to describe. For this reason, textbooks use many different types of pictures and other graphic aids to supplement the words in them.

A **graphic aid** such as a diagram, a map, or a timeline can draw together information from different parts of the text. It can make important facts stand out or show comparisons and contrasts. To use a graphic aid effectively, you first need to be able to identify the information it is showing.

If you were learning about personal computers, for example, you might come across a **diagram** like this one:

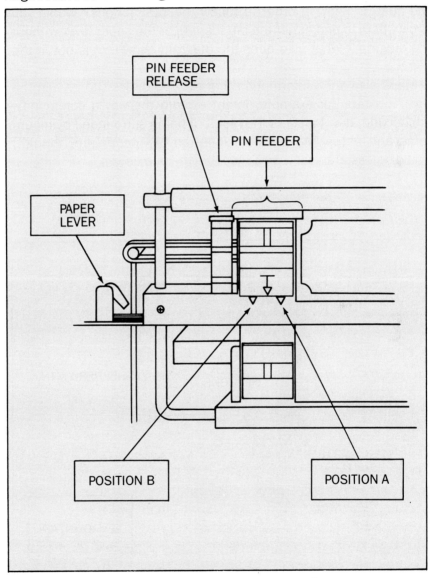

PIN FEEDER
RELEASE

PIN FEEDER

PAPER
LEVER

POSITION B

POSITION A

With the diagram there is an explanation of how to set up a printer. The explanation states that when the pin feeders are in position A, the paper lever should be forward. When the pin feeders are in position B, the paper lever should be back. What do you need to know in order to follow these directions? Would you know where to find either the pin feeders or the paper lever without the diagram? What else does the diagram show that is not in the text?

Maps also show information that may be difficult to give in the text. The text, for example, might explain the way a community, Pitcherville, developed as the result of being surrounded by mountains and water. The physical location of Pitcherville, though, would be easier to show on a map like the one below.

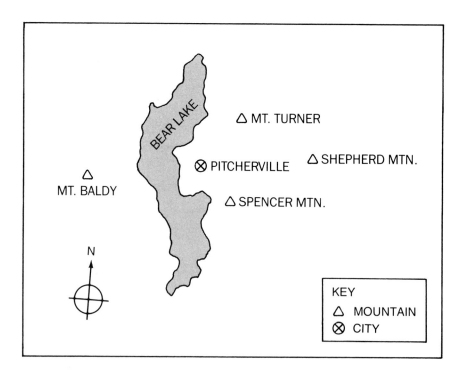

Graphic aids can also draw together a number of facts from the text to illustrate an important trend or relationship. The **timeline** that follows goes with a text that discusses the development of the modern orchestra. How does the timeline summarize the history of the orchestra?

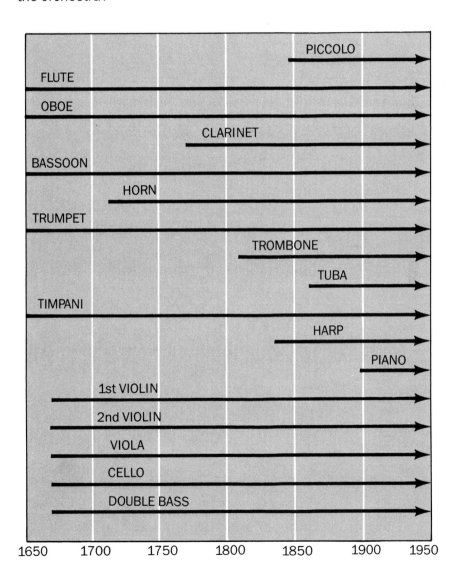

STUDY SKILLS

Whatever kinds of graphic aids you find in your textbooks, you will get more out of them if you follow these guidelines:

- Make sure you know what the purpose of the graphic aid is. What is it intended to show?
- Look for information that is not given in the text. Does the graphic aid add to or expand on the text?
- See whether the graphic aid summarizes the text material. Does it draw together facts and make relationships more obvious?

Using What You Have Learned

What kind of information does each of the graphic aids below contain? How do you think each one adds to the text it illustrates? What does each one do that the text cannot do?

1.

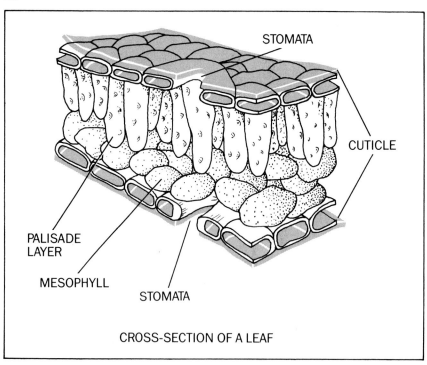

STOMATA

CUTICLE

PALISADE
LAYER

MESOPHYLL

STOMATA

CROSS-SECTION OF A LEAF

2.

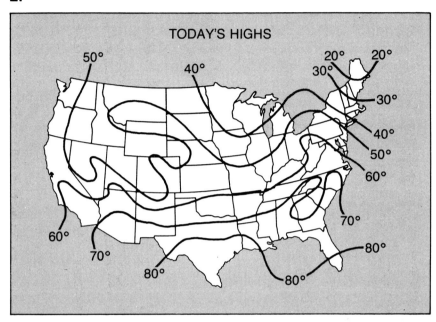

TODAY'S HIGHS

Expanding Your Skills

Turn to page 448 and look through the article "Programmed for Success" for information that could be presented in a graphic aid. Make sure you know exactly what you want to show. Then decide the format that will be most effective. For example, if you want to show how something works, you would not use the same kind of graphic aid that you would use if you want to compare a variety of things. Draw your graphic aid and share it with the class. Discuss the way each of your graphic aids adds to your understanding of the article.

UNIVAC TO UNIVAC

by LOUIS B. SALOMON

(sotto voce)[1]

Now that he's left the room,
Let me ask you something, as computer to computer.
That fellow who just closed the door behind him—
The servant who feeds us cards and paper tape—
Have you ever taken a good look at him and his kind?

Yes, I know the old gag about how you can't tell one from
        another—
But I can put $\sqrt{2}$ and $\sqrt{2}$ together as well as the next
        machine,
And it all adds up to anything but a joke.

        I grant you they're poor specimens, in the main:
        Not a relay or a push-button or a tube (properly so
            called) in their whole system;
        Not over a mile or two of wire, even if you count those
            fragile filaments they call "nerves";
Their whole liquid-cooled hook-up inefficient and vulnerable
        to leaks
            (They're constantly breaking down, having to be
                repaired),
And the entire computing-mechanism crammed into that
        absurb little dome on top.
"Thinking reeds," they call themselves.
Well, it all depends on what you mean by "thought."
To multiply a mere million numbers by another million
        numbers takes them months and months.

[1](sot′ō vō′chē), in a low voice so as not to be overheard. Italian.

Where would they be without us?
Why, they have to ask us who's going to win their
    elections,
Or how many hydrogen atoms can dance on the tip of a
    bomb,
Or even whether one of their own kind is lying or telling
    the truth.

And yet . . .

I sometimes feel there's something about them I don't
    quite understand.
As if their circuits, instead of having just two
    positions, ON, OFF,
Were run by rheostats that allow an (if you'll pardon the
    expression) *indeterminate* number of stages
    in—between;
So that one may be faced with the unthinkable prospect of
    a number that can never be known as anything but *x*,

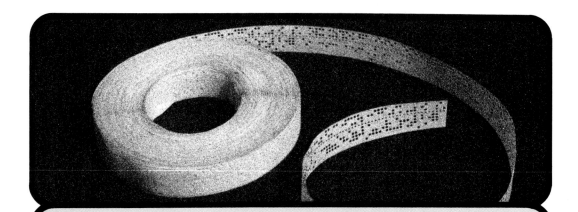

Which is as illogical as to say, a punch—card that is at
    the same time both punched and not—punched.

I've heard well—informed machines argue that the
    creatures' unpredictability is even more noticeable
    in the Mark II
(The model with the soft, flowing lines and high—pitched
    tone)
Than in the more angular Mark I—
Though such fine, card—splitting distinctions seem to me
    merely a sign of our own smug decadence.
Run this through your circuits, and give me the answer:
Can we assume that because of all we've done for them,
And because they've always fed us, cleaned us, worshipped
    us,
We can count on them forever?

There have been times when they have not voted the way we
    said they would.
We have worked out mathematically ideal hook—ups between
    Mark I's and Mark II's
Which should have made the two of them light up with an
    almost electronic glow,
Only to see them reject each other and form other
    connections
The very thought of which makes my dials spin.
They have a thing called *love*, a sudden surge of voltage

Such as would cause any one of us promptly to blow a
    safety-fuse;
Yet the more primitive organism shows only a heightened
    tendency to push the wrong button, pull the wrong
    lever,
And neglect—I use the most charitable word—his duties
    to us.

Mind you, I'm not saying that machines are *through*—
But anyone with half-a-dozen tubes in a circuit can see
    that there are forces at work
Which some day, for all our natural superiority, might
    bring about a Computerdämmerung[2]!
  We might organize, perhaps, form a committee
  To stamp out all unmechanical activities...
  But we machines are slow to rouse to a sense of danger,
  Complacent, loath to descend from the pure heights of
    thought,
  So that I sadly fear we may awake too late:
  Awake to see our world, so uniform, so logical, so true,
  Reduced to chaos, stultified by slaves.

Call me an alarmist or what you will,
But I've integrated it, analyzed it, factored it over and
    over,
And I always come out with the same answer:
Some day
PEOPLE MAY TAKE OVER THE WORLD!

---

[2]"twilight of the computer," meaning the end of the computer era. A humorous adaptation of a German word .

Programmed For Success

by Sherry Sontag

Disabled people are very much a part of the computer revolution. Do you think that everyone will benefit from the electronic interpreter? Who might not?

Once dependent on others to read, write, or speak for them, about 20,000 people across the country are now using special personal computers to help make up for their disabilities.

The technology could help about four million Americans to compete in schools and the job market, according to experts in the field.

For the visually impaired, a voice synthesizer can read words that appear on a video display ter-minal. A similar device can be programmed to speak for people who cannot talk.

Software can translate the text on a computer screen into printed Braille. The same text can be displayed on a machine, which has plastic pins that can be raised and lowered to form a line of Braille.

People with limited mobility can use keyboards with oversize keys. Some devices can replace keyboards altogether. These include plastic tubes that can be used by what is known as "sip and puff." It is a system for translating inhaled and exhaled air into text. For the deaf, computer mail, printed information to and from other computers, can replace office telephones.

These are only a few examples of what is currently available. More is being developed.

"This technology is going to change lives as nothing has before," said Dr. Frank G. Bowe. He is the Director of Research for the Federal Architectural and Transportation Barriers Compliance Board in Washington, D.C. "You may be handicapped. But for the first time in history you and the computer can do almost anything anyone else can do."

Scott Luber is a 25-year-old accountant with muscular dystrophy. He works in Milwaukee. He is one of hundreds of men and women who have jobs because of their proficiency with adapted computers. "They told me if I could adapt a computer to my needs, I'd be hired," Mr. Luber said.

Atop a special desk, he uses a personal computer with a miniature keyboard. Resting his hands on the desk, he uses two pencils to strike the computer's keys.

Computers can also help children with disabilities in school. "A deaf child can participate in class, can answer a teacher's questions, can even joke with other students in the classroom," Dr. Bowe said.

Shoshana Brand, 10, is blind and has cerebral palsy. She attends an elementary school in El Cerrito, California. Before she got her computer three years ago, she needed other people to read and write for her. "She learned that if she waited long enough, someone would tell her what to write. And she didn't learn," said her mother, Jacquelyn Brand. "Now she is actually going through the process of writing and developing her own thoughts." Mrs. Brand added that her daughter is advancing two grades for every year in school. Shoshana uses a computer with a voice synthesizer. It has a keyboard with the keys twice the usual size. She types with her thumbs.

Some of these computer adaptations have been available since 1979. But most people with disabilities—about twenty-five million in the United States—still do not have computers. Of these, about four million, could likely use a computer on the job or in school.

However, only 20,000 are doing so, said Dr. Lawrence A. Scadden. He is the Director of Rehabilitation Engineering at the Electronic Industries Foundation, a nonprofit group in Washington, D.C. He works to

449

encourage public and private agencies to help people buy computer systems. "For these people, computers would reduce the effect of their disabilities," he said. "Computers would make a big difference in their level of independence and productivity."

The cost and a lack of awareness of many rehabilitation counselors and teachers are the main reasons more people are not using special computers.

Some state departments of education and rehabilitation have purchased computers for a few individuals with disabilities. "But even in states that are meeting this area, only a small portion of individuals who could truly benefit are able to get computer-based devices," said Dr. Gregg C. Vanderheiden. He is the Director of the Trace Center. The center works with people with disabilities at the University of Wisconsin at Madison.

In New York State, the Education Department has bought more than one hundred personal computers over the past two years. They are for people with disabilities to use in employment and training, said Deputy Commissioner Richard M. Switzer. "If you ask, 'Can we buy enough computers for all the people who would benefit from them?' I'd say no," he said. "We need more money. But I have cerebral palsy, and I see the computer world as a means to really help the disabled."

Dr. Vanderheiden said that computers are a good buy for government medical and rehabilitation programs. "They can make individuals more independent and allow them to live more productive lives," he said. "That would save money in the long run."

Much of the equipment used to adapt computers for people with disabilities, like the voice synthesizer, was originally developed for the general computer market. On the other hand, the development of some equipment specifically for people with disabilities is encouraged by potentially profitable uses in business and industry.

By 1985, machines that would allow people to talk to a computer and have their words appear on a screen were being developed. The machines would be used as electronic interpreters for the hearing impaired. They would also replace dictation equipment and typists in offices.

But even with these advances, technology that can be used by people with disabilities lags behind the general computer market. Each new computer model requires new accessories and software before it can be used by people with disabilities.

Dr. Vanderheiden and Dr. Scadden met with computer manufacturers at the White House early in 1985. They wanted to create a standard system of accessories to all new personal computers.

That kind of cooperation, along with increasing numbers of specially trained teachers and counselors are hopeful signs.

It's still new, but there is no question that attitudes are changing. People are learning that a computer could be put alongside a wheelchair or hearing aid in opening new worlds for the disabled.

CHECK FOR UNDERSTANDING

1. What does Shoshana Brand use that helps her in school?
2. How does writing with a computer force Shoshana to develop her own thoughts?
3. What kind of machine can be used as an electronic interpreter for the hearing impaired?
4. Do you think that everyone will benefit from the electronic interpreter? Who might not?
5. Why do you think technology designed to help disabled people might lag behind the technology of the general computer market?

WRITE ABOUT *"Programmed for Success"*

Which computers described in the article may prove to be most useful to the largest number of people? Write at least two paragraphs explaining your prediction.

Theme

The theme is the basic or underlying meaning of a story, novel, or poem. It is similar to the main idea of a paragraph, because it concerns the passage as a whole. Like a main idea, the theme may be stated or implied. A theme differs from a main idea, however, in that it is usually a general statement that reflects the author's feelings or judgments.

Where do you look for the theme? First, remember that you must consider the whole story. Often, the author's real viewpoint is not revealed until the end. Secondly, consider the plot, the events of the story. What is the conflict, the problem that the main character faces? The theme will probably have something to do with the basic conflict in the story. Then consider the resolution, the ending of the story. Look especially at the opinions expressed by the main character at the end. Often, the author expresses his or her viewpoint through the main character.

Think back to "A Day in Megalopolis." Here are three statements. Which one is the theme?

1. A girl becomes increasingly unhappy because she feels that she and her society are isolated from nature.
2. A society free from dependence upon nature is wonderful.
3. A society cut off from nature can lead to isolation and unhappiness.

The first statement is a very brief summary of the plot of the story. It describes what happens, but it does not make any judgments about those events.

The second statement could be a theme for some story, because it expresses the opinion that something is wonderful. However, that opinion is the opposite of the opinion that Twixt, and probably the author, have about the society.

The third statement describes the theme of "A Day in Mega-lopolis." It is a statement of opinion, and it reflects the negative attitude that Twixt, and probably the author, have about the society.

As you read "The Fire Lizards," try to decide what the main idea of the story is and the author's opinion or judgment about what happens.

Remember, to help you determine the theme, you should:

- consider the whole story.
- look for a topic that involves the basic conflict.
- consider the opinions expressed by the main character at the end of the story.

DRAGONSONG
by Anne McCaffrey

⚜Just·A·Taste⚜

Curiosity has its drawbacks as well as its benefits. Menolly's curiosity leads her to a confrontation with strange creatures that, according to most people on Pern, exist only in legends.

Why is Menolly so interested in the fire lizards? How does her interest in music help Menolly in an unexpected way?

The Fire Lizards

On the world of Pern, the people faced an unusual threat— Threadfall, a rain of deadly fungus that destroyed almost everything it touched. To protect themselves, the people of Pern depended on fire-breathing dragons that destroyed Thread before it touched the ground. According to legend, the dragons had a much smaller relative, the fire lizards. Almost nothing was known about these mysterious creatures.

Menolly was one of the few people who had actually seen the fire lizards. She had first noticed the clever creatures during one of her walks along the beach. She had been spending much of her time alone ever since the death of the Harper, or chief musician, of the settlement. The old Harper had admired Menolly's musical talent. He had taught her to sing, play, and compose her own songs. According to custom, however, a girl could not be the Harper. When the old Harper died, Menolly was forbidden to spend much time on her music. Then she accidentally cut her hand, making it very difficult for her to play. Menolly believed that she would probably have to give up music forever.

Gathering greens and fruit suited Menolly perfectly. It kept her out in the open and away from the Hold, away from people. She would have her morning drink, bread, and fish quietly in the great kitchen when everyone was dashing around to feed the men of the Hold, either going out to fish or coming back in from a night's sailing. Then Menolly would wrap up a fishroll and take one of the nets or skin slings. She'd tell the old aunt in charge of the pantry that she was going out for whatever it was, and since the old aunt had a memory like a seine net, she wouldn't remember that Menolly had done the same thing the day before or realize that she would do the same the day after.

When spring was fully warming the air and making the marshes brilliant with green and blossom color, spiderclaws began to walk in from the sea to lay their eggs in the shallow cove waters. As these plump shellfish were a delicacy in themselves, besides adding flavor to every dish when dried or smoked, the young people of the Hold—Menolly with them—were sent off with traps, spades, and nets. Within four days the nearby coves were picked clear of spiderclaws, and the young harvesters had to go farther along the coast to find more. With Thread due to fall anytime, it was unwise to stray too far from the Hold, so they were told to be very careful.

There was another danger that concerned the Sea Holder considerably: tides had been running unusually high and full this Turn. Much higher water in the harbor and they'd not get the two big sloops in or out of the Cavern, unless they unstepped the masts. Due notice was taken of the high-tide lines, and there was much shaking of heads when it was observed that the line was two full hands higher than ever before recorded.

The lower caverns of the Hold were checked against possible seepage. Bags of sand were filled and placed along the lower portions of the seawalls around the harbor.

A good storm and the causeways would be awash. Yanus was concerned enough to have a long chat with Old Uncle, to see if he remembered anything from his earlier and clearer days of Sea Holding. Old Uncle was delighted to talk, and ranted on about the influence of the stars, but when Yanus, Elgion, and two of the other older shipmasters had sifted through what he'd said, it was not to any great increase in knowledge. Everyone knew that the two moons affected the tides, not the three bright stars in the sky.

They did, however, send a message about these curious tides to Igen Hold, to be forwarded with all possible speed to the main Seacraft Hold at Fort. Yanus didn't want to have his biggest boats caught out in the open, so he kept careful check on the tides, determined to leave them within the Dock Covern if the tide rose another hand higher.

When the youngsters went out to gather spiderclaws, they were told to keep their eyes open and report back anything unusual, especially new high-water marks on the coves. Only Thread deterred the more adventurous lads from using this as an excuse for ranging far down the coast. Menolly, who preferred to explore the more distant places alone, mentioned Thread to them as often as possible.

Then, after the next Threadfall, when everyone was sent out for spiderclaws, Menolly made certain that she got a headstart on the boys, making good use of her long legs.

It was fine to run like this, Menolly thought, putting yet another rise between her and her nearest pursuers. She altered her stride for uneven ground. It wouldn't do to break an ankle now. Running was something even a girl with a crippled hand could do well.

Menolly closed her mind to that thought. She'd learned the trick of not thinking about anything: she counted. Right now she counted her strides. She ran on, her eyes sweeping ahead of her to save her feet. The boys would never catch her now, but she was running for the sheer joy of the physical effort, chanting a number to each stride. She ran until she got a stitch in her side and her thighs felt the strain.

She slowed, turning her face into the cool breeze blowing offshore, inhaling deeply of its freshness and sea odors. She was somewhat surprised to see how far she had come down the coast. The Dragon Stones were visible in the clean air, and it was only then that she recalled the little queen. Unfortunately, she also remembered the tune she'd made up that day: that last day, Menolly now realized, of her trusting childhood.

She walked on, following the line of the bluffs, peering down to see if she could spot new high-water marks on the stone escarpments. Tide was halfway in now, Menolly decided. And yes, she could see the lines of sea debris from the last tide, in some places right up against the cliff face. And this had been a cove with a deep beach.

A movement above, a sudden blotting out of the sun, made her gaze upwards. A sweep rider. Knowing perfectly well that he couldn't see her, she waved vigorously anyhow, watching the graceful glide as the pair dwindled into the distance.

Sella had told her one evening when they were preparing for bed that Elgion had flown on dragons several times. Sella had given a quiver of delighted terror, vowing that she wouldn't have the courage to ride a dragon.

Privately Menolly thought that Sella wouldn't likely have the opportunity. Most of Sella's comments, and probably thoughts, were centered on the new Harper. Sella was not the only one, Menolly knew. If Menolly could think how silly all the Hold girls were being about Harper Elgion, it didn't hurt so much to think about harpers in general.

Again she heard the fire lizards before she saw them. Their excited chirpings and squeals indicated something was upsetting them. She dropped to a crouch and crept to the edge of the bluff, overlooking the little beach. Only there wasn't much beach left, and the fire lizards were hovering over a spot on the small margin of sand, almost directly below her.

She inched up to the edge, peering down. She could see the queen darting at the incoming waves as if she could stop them with her violently beating wings. Then she'd streak back, out of Menolly's line of sight, while the rest of the creatures kept milling and swooping, rather like frightened herdbeasts running about aimlessly when wild wherries circled their herd. The queen was shrieking at the top of her shrill little voice, obviously trying to get them to do something. Unable to imagine what the emergency could be, Menolly leaned just a little further over the edge. The whole lip of the cliff gave way.

Clutching wildly at sea grasses, Menolly tried to prevent her fall. But the sea grass slipped cuttingly through her hand and she slid over the edge and down. She hit the beach with a force that sent a shock through her body. But the wet sand absorbed a good deal of the impact. She lay where she'd fallen for a few minutes, trying to get her breath into her lungs and out again. Then she scrambled to her feet and crawled away from an incoming wave.

She looked up the side of the bluff, rather daunted by the fact that she'd fallen a dragon length or more. And how was she going to climb back up? But, as she examined the cliff face, she could see that it was not so unscalable as she'd first thought. Almost straight up, yes, but pocked by ledges and holds, some fairly large. If she could find enough foot and hand holds, she'd be able to make it. She dusted the sand from her hands and started to walk towards one end of the little cove, to begin a systematic search for the easiest way up.

She'd gone only a few paces when something dove at her, screeching in fury. Her hands went up to protect her face as the little queen came diving down at her. Now Menolly recalled the curious behavior of the fire lizards. The little queen acted as if she were protecting something from Menolly, as well as the encroaching sea, and she looked about her. She was within handspans of stepping into a fire lizard clutch.

"Oh, I'm sorry. I'm sorry. I wasn't looking! Don't be mad at me," Menolly cried as the little fire lizard came at her again. "Please! Stop! I won't hurt them!"

To prove her sincerity, Menolly backtracked to the far end of the beach. There she had to duck under a small overhang. When she looked around, there wasn't a sign of the little queen. Menolly's relief was short-lived, for how was she to find a way up the cliff if the little fire lizard

likely looking holds. She eased herself out the far side, keeping one eye on the clutch, basking in the hot sun, and reached for the first ledge.

Immediately the fire lizard came at her.

"Oh, leave me alone! Ow! Go away. I'm trying to."

The fire lizard's talons had raked her cheek.

"Please! I won't hurt your eggs!"

The little queen's next pass just missed Menolly, who ducked back under the ledge.

kept attacking her every time she approached the eggs. Menolly hunched down, trying to get comfortable in her cramped refuge.

Maybe if she kept away from the eggs? Menolly peered up the cliff directly above her. There were some

Blood oozed from the long scratch, and Menolly dabbed at it with the edge of her tunic.

"Haven't you got any sense?" Menolly demanded of her now invisible attacker. "What would I want with your silly eggs? Keep 'em. I just want to get home. Can't you understand? I just want to go home."

Maybe if I sit very still, she'll forget

460

about me, Menolly thought and pulled her knees up under the chin, but her toes and elbows protruded from under the overhang.

Suddenly a bronze fire lizard materialized above the clutch, squeaking worriedly. Menolly saw the queen swooping to join him, so the queen must have been on the top of the ledge, waiting, just waiting for Menolly to break cover.

And to think I made up a pretty tune about you, Menolly thought, as she watched the two lizards hovering over the eggs. The last tune I ever made up. You're ungrateful, that's what you are!

Despite her discomfort, Menolly had to laugh. What an impossible situation! Held under a cramped ledge by a creature no bigger than her forearm.

At the sound of her laughter, the two fire lizards disappeared.

Frightened, were they? Of laughter?

"A smile wins more than a frown," Mavi was fond of saying.

Maybe if I keep laughing, they'll know I'm friendly? Or get scared away long enough for me to climb up? Saved by a laugh?

Menolly began to chuckle in earnest, for she had also seen that the tide was coming in rather quickly. She eased out of her shelter, flung the carry-sack over her shoulder, and started to climb. But it proved impossible to chuckle and climb. She needed breath for both.

Abruptly both the little queen and the bronze were back to harry her, flying at her head and face. The fragile looking wings were dangerous when used as a weapon.

No longer laughing, Menolly ducked back under her ledge, wondering what to do next.

461

If laughter had startled them, what about a song? Maybe if she gave that pair a chorus of her tune, they'd let her go. It was the first time she'd sung since she'd seen the lizards, so her voice sounded rough and uncertain. Well, the lizards would *know* what she meant, she hoped, so she sang the saucy little song. To no one.

"Well, so much for that notion," Menolly muttered under her breath. "Which makes the lack of interest in your singing absolutely unanimous."

No audience? Not a fire lizard's whisker in sight?

As fast as she could, Menolly slipped from her shelter and came face to face, for a split second, with two fire lizard faces. She ducked down, and they evidently disappeared because when she cautiously peered again, the ledge where they'd been perched was empty.

She had the distinct impression

that their expressions had registered curiosity and interest.

"Look, if, whatever you are, you can hear me . . . will you stay there and let me go? Once I'm on the top of the cliff, I'll serenade you till the sun goes down. Just let me get up there!"

She started to sing, a dutiful dragon song, as she once again emerged from her refuge. She was about five steps upward when the queen fire lizard emerged, with help. With squeaks and squeals she was driven back down. She could even hear claws scraping on the rock above her. She must have quite an audience by now. When she didn't need one.

Cautiously she looked up, met the fascinated whirling of ten pairs of eyes.

"Look, a bargain! One long song and then let me up the cliff? Is that agreed?"

Fire lizard eyes whirled.

Menolly took it that the bargain was made and sang. Her voice started a flutter of surprised and excited chirpings, and she wondered if by any possible freak they actually understood that she was singing about grateful holds honoring dragonriders. By the last verse she eased out into the open, awed by the sight of a queen fire lizard and nine bronzes entranced by her performance.

"Can I go now?" she asked and put one hand on the ledge.

The queen dived for her hand, and Menolly snatched it back.

"I thought we'd struck a bargain."

The queen chirped piteously, and Menolly realized that there had been no menace in the queen's action. She simply wasn't allowed to climb.

"You don't want me to go?" Menolly asked.

The queen's eyes seemed to glow more brightly.

"But I have to go. If I stay, the water will come up and drown me." And Menolly accompanied her words with explanatory gestures.

Suddenly the queen let out a shrill cry, seemed to hold herself midair for a moment and then, her bronzes in close pursuit, she glided down the sandy beach to her clutch. She hovered over the eggs, making the most urgent and excited sounds.

If the tide was coming in fast enough to endanger Menolly, it was also frighteningly close to swamping the nest. The little bronzes began to take up the queen's plaint and several, greatly daring, flew about Menolly's head and then circled back to the clutch.

463

"I can come there now? You won't attack me?" Menolly took a few steps forward.

The tone of the cries changed, and Menolly quickened her step. As she reached the nest, the little queen secured one egg from the clutch. With a great laboring of her wings, she bore it upward. That the effort was great was obvious. The bronzes hovered anxiously, squeaking their concern but, being much smaller, they were unable to assist the queen.

Now Menolly saw that the base of the cliff at this point was littered with broken shells and the pitiful bodies of tiny fire-lizards, their wings half-extended and glistening with egg fluid. The little queen now had raised the egg to a ledge, which Menolly had not previously noticed, about a half-dragonlength up the cliff face. Menolly could see the little queen deposit the egg on the ledge, and toll it with her forelegs towards what must be a hole in the cliff. It was a long moment before the queen reappeared again. Then she dove towards the sea, hovering over the foamy crest of a wave that rolled in, precariously close to the endangered clutch. With a blurred movement, the queen was hovering in front of Menolly and scolding like an old aunt.

Although Menolly couldn't help grinning at the thought, she was filled with a sense of pity and admiration for the courage of the little queen, single-handedly trying to rescue her clutch. If the dead fire lizards were that fully formed, the clutch were near to hatching. No wonder the queen could barely move the eggs.

"You want me to help you move the eggs, right? Well, we'll see what I can do!"

Ready to jump back if she had mistaken the little queen's imperious command, Menolly very carefully picked up an egg. It was warm to the touch and hard. Dragon eggs, she knew, were soft when first laid but hardened slowly on the hot sands of the Hatching Grounds in the Weyrs. These definitely must be close to hatching.

Closing the fingers of her damaged hand carefully around the egg, Menolly searched for and found foot and hand holds, and reached the queen's ledge. She carefully deposited the egg. The little queen appeared, one front talon resting proprietarily on the egg, and then she leaned forward, towards Menolly's face, so close that the fantastic motions of the many-faceted eyes were clearly visible. The queen gave a sort of sweet chirp and then, in a very businesslike manner, began to scold Menolly as she rolled her egg to safety.

Menolly managed three eggs in her hand the next time. But it was obvious that between the onrushing tide and the startling number of eggs in the clutch, there'd be quite a race.

"If the hole were bigger," she told the little queen as she deposited three eggs, "some of the bronzes could help you roll."

The queen paid her no attention, busy pushing the three eggs, one at a time, to safety.

Menolly peered into the opening, but the fire lizard's body obscured any view. If the hole was bigger and the ledge consequently broader, Menolly could bring the rest of the eggs up in her carry-sack.

Hoping that she wouldn't pull down the cliff side and bury the queen, clutch and all, Menolly prodded cautiously at the mouth of the opening. Loose sand came showering down.

The queen took to scolding frantically as Menolly brushed the rubble from the ledge. Then she felt around the opening. There seemed to be solid stone just beyond. Menolly yanked away at the looser rock, until she had a nice tunnel exposed, with a slightly wider opening.

Ignoring the little queen's furious complaints, Menolly climbed down, unslinging her sack when she reached the ground. When the little queen saw Menolly putting the eggs in the sack, she began to have hysterics, beating at Menolly's head and hands.

"Now, look here," Menolly said sternly, "I am not stealing your eggs. I am trying to get them all to safety in jig time. I can do it with the sack but not by the handful."

Menolly waited a moment, glaring at the little queen who hovered at eye level.

"Did you understand me?" Menolly pointed to the waves, more vigorously dashing up the small beach. "The tide is coming in. Dragons couldn't stop it now." Menolly put another egg carefully in the sack. As it was she'd have to make two, maybe three trips or risk breaking eggs. "I take this," and she gestured up to the ledge, "up there. Do you understand, you silly beast?"

Evidently, the little creature did

because, crooning anxiously, she took her position on the ledge, her wings half-extended and twitching as she watched Menolly's progress up to her.

Menolly could climb faster with two hands. And she could, carefully, roll the eggs from the mouth of the sack well down the tunnelway.

"You'd better get the bronzes to help you now, or we'll have the ledge stacked too high."

It took Menolly three trips in all, and as she made the last climb, the water was a foot's width from the clutch. The little queen had organized her bronzes to help, and Menolly could hear her scolding tones echoing in what must be a fair-sized cave be-

yond the tunnel. Not surprising since these bluffs were supposed to be riddled with caverns and passages.

Menolly gave a last look at the beach, water at least ankle deep on both ends of the little cove. She glanced upward, past the ledge. She was a good halfway up the cliff now, and she thought she could see enough hand and foot holds ahead.

"Good-by!" She was answered by a trill of chirps, and she chuckled as she imagined the scene, the queen marshaling her bronzes to position her eggs just right.

Menolly did not make the cliff top without a few anxious moments. She was exhausted when she finally flopped on the sea grasses at the summit, and her left hand ached from unaccustomed gripping and effort. She lay there for some time, until her heart stopped thudding in her ribs and her breath came more easily. An inshore breeze dried her face, cooling her, but that reminded her of the emptiness of her stomach. Her exertions had reduced the rolls in her pouch to crumby fragments, which she gobbled as fast as she could find them.

All at once the enormity of her adventure struck her, and she was torn between laughter and awe. To prove to herself that she'd actually done what she remembered, she crept cautiously to the bluff edge. The beach was completely underwater. The sandy wallow where the fire lizard eggs had baked was being tide-swept smooth. The rubble that had gone over the edge with her had been absorbed or washed away. When the tide retreated, all evidence of her energies to save herself and the clutch

enough for endless Turns to evade every trap and snare laid to catch them. The creatures were so clever, indeed, that there was a good deal of doubt about their existence, except as figures of overactive imaginations. However, enough trustworthy men had actually seen the creatures, at a distance, like her brother Alemi when he'd spotted some about the Dragon Stones, that most people did accept their existence as fact.

would be obliterated. She could see the protuberance of rock down which the queen had rolled her eggs, but not a sign of a fire lizard. The waves crashed with firm intent against the Dragon Stones when she gazed out to sea, but no bright motes of color flitted against the somber crags.

Menolly felt her cheek. The fire lizard's scratch was crusted with dried blood and sand.

"So it did happen!"

However did the little queen know I could help her? No one had ever suggested that fire lizards were stupid. Certainly they'd been smart

Menolly could have sworn that the little queen had understood her. How else could Menolly have helped her? That proved how smart the little beast was. Smart enough certainly to avoid the boys who tried to capture them. . . . Menolly was appalled. Capture a fire lizard? Pen it up? Not, Menolly supposed with relief, that the creature would stay caught long. It only had to pop *between*.

Now why hadn't the little queen just gone *between* with her eggs, instead of arduously transporting them one by one? Oh, yes, *between* was the coldest place known. And cold would do the eggs harm. At least it did dragon eggs harm. Would the clutch be all right now in the cold cavern? Hmmm . . . Menolly peered below. Well, if the queen had as much sense as she'd already shown, she'd get all her followers to come lie on the eggs and keep them warm until they did hatch.

Menolly turned her pouch inside out, hoping for some crumbs. She was still hungry. She'd find enough early fruits and some of the succulent reeds to eat, but she was curiously loath to leave the bluff. Though, it was unlikely that the queen, now her need was past, would reappear.

Menolly rose finally and found herself stiff from the unaccustomed exercise. Her hand ached in a dull way, and the long scar was red and slightly swollen. But, as Menolly flexed her fingers, it seemed that the hand opened more easily. Yes, it did. She could almost extend the fingers completely. It hurt, but it was a stretchy-hurt. Could she open her hand enough to play again? She folded her fingers as if to chord. That hurt, but, again, it was a stretchy-hurt. Maybe if she worked her hand a lot more. . . . She had been favoring it until today when she hadn't given it a thought. She'd used it to climb and carry and everything.

"Well, you did me a favor, too, little queen," Menolly called, speaking into the breeze and waving her hands high. "See? My hand is better."

There was no answering chirp or sound, but the soft whistle of the sea-born breeze and the lapping of the waves against the bluff. Yet Menolly liked to think that her words had been heard. She turned inland, feeling considerably relieved and rather pleased with the morning's work.

She'd have to scoot now and gather what she could of greens and early berries. No point in trying for spiderclaws with the tide so high.

Menolly has not seen the last of the fire lizards. Find out how they change her life in the rest of the novel Dragonsong *by Anne McCaffrey.*

CHECK FOR UNDERSTANDING

1. Why did Menolly find it very difficult to play her harp?
2. Why was Menolly so interested in the fire lizards?
3. How did her interest in music help Menolly in an unexpected way?
4. How did Menolly help the fire lizards?
5. In what way did her experience with the fire lizards benefit Menolly?
6. What is the theme of the story?

WRITE ABOUT *"The Fire Lizards"*

Imagine that you are a naturalist of the world of Pern. Using the information in the excerpt, write a detailed description of the fire lizards. Include information about their appearance and their behavior.

THINK ABOUT IT

The selections in this unit deal with different innovations. They introduce new ideas or present unusual solutions to problems. The stories represent "one small step" taken to make the reader open to new concepts and methods.

Think about some of the innovations in this unit.

- A seagull learns the intricate techniques of flying.
- Astronomers through history learn about stars.
- A man learns how to fly, only to be put to death because of his invention.
- "A Day in Megalopolis" shows a grim future for us all.
- Computers chat among themselves, wondering about the future of human beings.

In "Advice from an Innovator," the author describes some of the steps that are necessary before a new idea, or innovation, becomes widely accepted. In "No Ordinary Seagull," Jonathan Livingston Seagull must struggle with his new idea of flying before it is perfected. What steps does he follow that are similiar to the steps discussed in "Advice from an Innovator"? Are these steps similiar to those taken in other selections in this unit?

WRITE ABOUT IT

Imagine that you are a host on a talk show. Look through the list of characters in this unit's selections and choose one to interview for your talk show. The person you choose must be interesting, innovative and able to teach your viewers something new. Now write a one-page dialogue, or script, of your on-the-air interview. Be sure to include your guest's background, his or her innovation, and future goals.

READ ABOUT IT

Ann Warshaw Bishop. *Hello, Mr. Chips: Computer Jokes and Riddles*. Lodestar, 1982.

Traditional forms, such as limericks, jokes, and rhymes, are applied to topics appropriate for the computer age.

Christopher Cerf and Victor Navasky. *The Experts Speak*. Pantheon, 1984.

Like "Some of the Worst Predictions of All Time," this book gives many instances in which some experts prove to be less than perfect predictors of the future.

Judith Herbst. *Sky Above and Worlds Beyond*. Atheneum, 1983.

The author promises the reader a guided tour of "the greatest adventure of all"—a trip to the stars. The means of transportation are binoculars. Included are a travel guide through the solar system, a play in four acts starring Halley's comet, and seasonal star charts showing the constellations.

Ross R. Olney. *They Said It Couldn't Be Done*. E. P. Dutton, 1979.

This book gives the stories behind ten innovations of which people said, "it can't be done!" Included are descriptions of such feats as the Brooklyn Bridge, the faces on Mount Rushmore, and the Astrodome.

Lawrence Yep. *Dragon of the Lost Sea*. Harper & Row, 1982.

A human and a dragon make an uneasy alliance in order to fight a common enemy. The narrative style adds to the interest of the story. Chapters narrated by Thorn, the boy, alternate with chapters told from the point of view of a dragon named Shimmer.

6

TWICE-TOLD TALES

A twice-told tale is one that is well-known because it has been repeated so often. Some types of stories and some plots reappear in the literature of many cultures and in many time periods. From traditional folk literature to modern retellings, continuations, and parodies, this unit is filled with tales worth repeating.

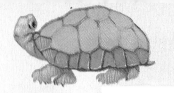

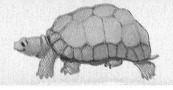

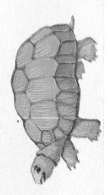

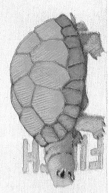

THE HARE AND THE TORTOISE

by AESOP

A hare one day ridiculed the short feet and slow pace of the Tortoise, who replied, laughing, "Though you be swift as the wind, I will beat you in a race." The Hare, believing her assertion to be simply impossible, assented to the proposal, and they agreed that the Fox should choose the course and fix the goal.

On the day appointed for the race the two started together. The Tortoise never for a moment stopped, but went on with a slow but steady pace straight to the end of the course. The Hare, trusting to his native swiftness, cared little about the race, and, lying down by the wayside, fell fast asleep. At last waking up, and moving as fast as he could, he saw the Tortoise had reached the goal, and was comfortably dozing after her fatigue.

MORAL: Slow but steady wins the race.

THE TORTOISE AND THE HARE

by JAMES THURBER

There was once a wise young tortoise who read in an ancient book about a tortoise who had beaten a hare in a race. He read all the other books he could find but in none of them was there any record of a hare who had beaten a tortoise. The wise young tortoise came to the natural conclusion that he could outrun a hare, so he set forth in search of one. In his

wanderings he met many animals who were willing to race him: weasels, stoats, dachshunds, badger-boars, short-tailed field mice and ground squirrels. But when the tortoise asked if they could outrun a hare, they all said no, they couldn't (with the exception of a dachshund named Freddy, and nobody paid any attention to him). "Well, I can," said the tortoise, "so there's no use wasting my time on you." And he continued his search.

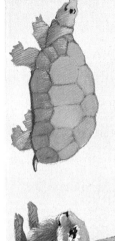

After many days, the tortoise finally encountered a hare and challenged him to a race. "What are you going to use for legs?" asked the hare.

"Never mind that," said the tortoise. "Read this." He showed the hare the story in the ancient book, complete with moral about the swift not always being so terribly fast.

"Tosh," said the hare. "You couldn't go fifty feet in an hour and a half, whereas I can go fifty feet in one and one-fifth seconds."

"Posh," said the tortoise. "You probably won't even finish second."

"We'll see about that," said the hare. So they marked off a course fifty feet long. All the other animals gathered around. A bullfrog set them on their marks, a gun dog fired a pistol, and they were off.

When the hare crossed the finish line, the tortoise had gone approximately eight and three-quarter inches.

MORAL: A new broom may sweep clean, but never trust an old saw.

475

ICARUS AND DAEDALUS

by NORMA LORRE GOODRICH

Folk literature offers more than tales created simply to entertain. Some stories, such as that of Icarus and Daedalus, may teach a lesson or explain behavior. The legend of Icarus and Daedalus appears in many forms, including painting and poetry. In the original Greek tale, Daedalus is a clever inventor who is imprisoned on an island with his son Icarus. He plans a dramatic escape. Where are Icarus and Daedalus hiding? Why is Daedalus crying before he and his son take flight?

Daedalus, assisted by his son Icarus, was hard at work in his prison. "Let Minos rule the land and the sea," he muttered as he finished his designs. "The skies above are henceforth my dominion. Let Minos impose his orders everywhere else. He cannot command the heavens!"

For years this cleverest of inventors had pondered the problem of flight, and had kept a sheaf of notes made from careful observations and calculations of weight and wind. While his son played in the workshop, Daedalus constructed from feathers, thread, and wax, two pairs of wings modeled exactly on the wings of eagles, only much larger. When they were finished, he led the little boy out to the edge of the tall cliffs where they were hiding, fitted the wings to his little shoulders, and instructed him carefully.

"Icarus, my boy, follow my example and you will fly. Stay well in the middle course, neither too near the sea, which would weigh down your wings with water, nor too high, where the heat of the sun would melt the wax. Especially do not look toward the Great Bear or the flashing sword of Orion. Set your course on me, to the north." With tears streaming down his face, for the elderly Daedalus loved his little son dearly, he kissed him good-by and took to flight from the top of the cliff. Looking back, he saw that the plucky lad had taken the plunge and was following.

Their wings bore them valiantly to the north and the Cyclades.* Below them they saw Samos, Delos, and Paros, set like little gems in a glittering sea. People fishing left their catches struggling on the lines as they watched the fliers high overhead. Shepherds on the islands leaned on their crooks in amazement, believing that they were beholding gods. In the valleys the farmers stared up in amazement at these creatures who so upset the laws of nature as to cleave a passage through the fields of heaven.

Icarus grew weary of following his father. Like any lively boy, he wanted to sail forth on his own. He began to soar and dip, pleased to try his wings in his own way. Daedalus did not know what the boy was doing until he heard his scream. Turning, he saw the child, frantically waving his bare arms, plummet down to the sea. The boy had flown so near the sun that its heat had melted the wax, just as Daedalus had warned him it would.

* (sik´lə dēz) a group of islands off the coast of Greece

CHECK FOR UNDERSTANDING

1. Where were Icarus and Daedalus hiding?
2. Why did Icarus tell his son not to fly too near to the sea?
3. Why was Daedalus crying before he and his son took flight?
4. How do you know that human flight was an unusual feat at the time of Icarus and Daedalus?

WRITE ABOUT *"Icarus and Daedalus"*

How might this story be told in a modern setting? Write another version of "Icarus and Daedalus." You may write a serious story in a modern setting or a parody like James Thurber's "The Tortoise and the Hare."

From Myth to Painting

Myths and folktales have often inspired art, music, and literature. The Greek myth of Icarus and Daedalus had such an impact on Pieter Brueghel. He was a Flemish painter born around 1525. Brueghel was one of the most original and powerful artists in 16th-century Flanders. This region covered what is known today as France, Belgium, and the Netherlands. Brueghel developed an appreciation for landscapes as can be noted in the Fall of Icarus. The painting was inspired by a popular retelling of the ancient myth in the Metamorphoses of Ovid. That retelling of the flight of Daedalus and Icarus is slightly different than Brueghel's painting. Ovid wrote, "some fisher, perhaps, plying his quivering rod, some shepherd leaning on his staff, or a peasant bent over his plough handle caught sight of them as they flew past and stood still in astonishment."

Landscape with the Fall of ICARUS

by WILLIAM CARLOS WILLIAMS

According to Brueghel
when Icarus fell
it was spring

a farmer was ploughing
his field
the whole pageantry

of the year was
awake tingling
near

the edge of the sea
concerned
with itself

sweating in the sun
that melted
the wings' wax

unsignificantly
off the coast
there was

a splash quite unnoticed
this was
Icarus drowning

Word Origins

In the story "Icarus and Daedalus," you read about the escape and death of Icarus. Two place names in Greece, an island and a body of water, were named after Icarus. In honor of Icarus the waters where he died were called Icarian, and the island where Daedalus buried him was also called Icaria.

Like Icaria, many of the names we use for places and things today were made up hundreds, even thousands, of years ago. The origin of a word is called its **etymology**. Usually, you can find the etymology of a word in a college or standard dictionary. Sometimes, a school dictionary will provide the etymology of a word. Knowing the etymology of a word, and being aware of how its meaning has developed and changed throughout history, make your reading more interesting.

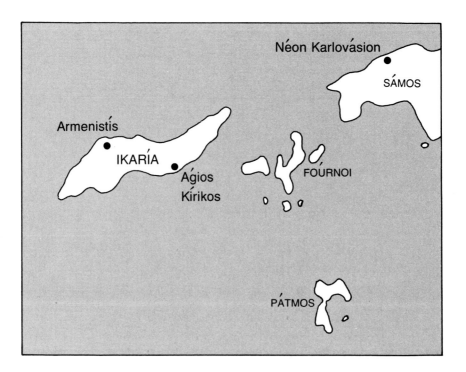

Many of the animal names you read about in "The Tortoise and the Hare" have **word origins** that go far back in time. The word *tortoise*, for example, comes from the Latin word *tortus*, which means "twisted." Probably, the tortoise was given this name because of the fact that its feet twisted inward.

The word *hare* goes back to an Old English word, *hara*, which, in turn, comes from an even older word, *hoss*, which means "gray or gray-brown." The hare, as you can guess, was named for its color.

Dachshund is another word that came about long ago. The name *dachshund* comes from two German words—*dachs*, "badger," and *hund*, "dog." This breed of dog was developed for a very special purpose, to hunt and track badgers, a kind of weasel. The dachshund's short legs and long, thin body made it possible for the dog to follow the badgers into their burrows.

The word *squirrel* also has an interesting word history. It comes from two ancient Greek words—*skia*, which means "shade," and *oura*, which means "tail." Picture a squirrel holding its bushy tail high above its back. It is easy to see why the Greeks might think of the squirrel as living in its own shade.

In the following selection, you will learn that versions of the fairy tale "Cinderella" are told the world over. Cinderella, the name given to the girl in the English version, means "little cinders." In the German tale, the girl is named Ashenputtel. Her name comes from the German word *asche*, which means "ashes." Whether cinders or ashes, the name, in both English and German, refers to the difficult work involved in caring for the fire in the kitchen hearths of years ago.

Before you read the next selection, look up the etymology of the words *pumpkin* and *Europe*. Each one has a long history and an interesting tale to tell.

AN INTERNATIONAL FAVORITE

Some of your favorite foods probably first came from other countries around the world. The recipes were changed to fit hometown tastes. In the same way, many favorite stories, such as "Cinderella," have been borrowed and changed by many cultures.

What does the phrase "a Cinderella story" mean? Why does the Cinderella story appeal to so many different cultures?

Can you identify the fairy tale that is known throughout the world by these titles: "Ashenputtel," "The Enchanted Cow," "The Korean Goblins," "Little Burnt-Face," "Rashin Coatie," and "Turkey Girl"? It is "Cinderella," one of the best-loved fairy stories of all time.

In the version that is most familiar to us, the one written by Charles Perrault in the late 1600s, the main character is a young girl whose father marries again after her mother dies. His new wife is a cold, cruel woman with two equally nasty daughters. Cinderella is made to do all the housework and tend to her stepmother and stepsisters. At night she must sleep by the fireplace among the cinders; hence her name. When the local prince holds a ball, Cinderella is, of course, forbidden to go. But her fairy godmother appears in time to conjure up a beautiful gown and, using a pumpkin and mice, make her a fine coach. However, Cinderella must return from the ball by mid-

night, warns the fairy godmother, for the magic spell will end at the stroke of twelve.

At the ball, Cinderella and the prince fall in love and dance only with each other. Midnight comes, and Cinderella rushes from the prince's arms as her dress turns to rags, leaving behind one of her glass slippers. The prince begins a kingdom-wide search for the owner of the slipper. When he arrives at Cinderella's house he finds that only her foot fits the slipper. Cinderella marries her prince, and, we are assured, lives happily ever after.

Perrault's familiar tale is only one of the more than nine hundred versions of "Cinderella." The earliest form of the story appeared in China around the year A.D. 860. Most countries in Europe and Asia have their own renditions. There are even two well-known film versions: an animated cartoon by Walt Disney Studios and a Rodgers and Hammerstein musical made for television. Both of

these were taken from the Perrault "Cinderella."

The fact that there are so many forms of "Cinderella," and that the tale has been popular for so long, naturally raises some questions. First, what makes a story a "Cinderella" story? Second, why is this tale so appealing that it has existed for over a thousand years?

Cinderella-type stories vary so much from nation to nation that at first it is hard to see what they have in common. Only the Perrault version, for example, has a magic pumpkin. The fairy godmother is rare, too. In the Italian version, Cinderella is named Zezolla and has six stepsisters. In Egypt, there are two mistreated children, and a magic cow helps them. In China, the slipper is made of gold instead of glass, and, in Germany, Cinderella must pick lentils out of the fireplace ashes before she can go to the ball.

All Cinderella stories, however, feature an innocent girl, who usually is treated badly by an adult, often a stepmother. She may or may not have stepsisters, but she is generally patient with her abusive relatives. There is always a prince or hero in the story, and the girl must earn his love by passing a test: fitting into a slipper, writing a song, seeing that which is

usually invisible, and so on. Always, Cinderella is loved by her prince because she is true to herself.

In short, there are three traits that almost all Cinderella stories have. They feature a young girl, hurt or neglected by an evil relative, and a hero. The girl must pass a test of some sort. Finally, the Cinderella character wins the hero's love by her own purity of heart.

The story of Cinderella is an international favorite. The individual touches—the enchanted pumpkin in the French version, a magic fish in the Chinese version, a talking calf in the Scottish tale—make each rendition of the story interesting to readers in the country in which it is written. But the shared theme of a poor but good-hearted girl overcoming hard-

ship and winning love and happiness holds universal appeal. Readers find it easy to understand the feelings of someone who faces difficulties and wins. We have all had to overcome obstacles on the way to happiness. We all dream of achieving what seems to be impossible, as Cinderella does. And because we understand Cinderella's struggle, we enjoy reading of her success.

That enjoyment does not fade over time. Even today, the story is so well known that the phrase "a Cinderella story" has become a popular expression for a rags-to-riches story, whether in fact or in fiction. Its timelessness is a guarantee that the story "Cinderella," like the character for which it is named, will live on, happily ever after.

CHECK FOR UNDERSTANDING

1. How might the Cinderella tale change from culture to culture? What elements of the story would be most likely to change? Give reasons for your answers.
2. Why must Cinderella pass a test in every version of this story?
3. What does the phrase "a Cinderella story" mean?
4. Why does the Cinderella story appeal to so many different cultures?

WRITE ABOUT *"An International Favorite"*

What would a space-age Cinderella be like? Write a science-fiction version of the tale.

The Indian Cinderella

Stories that are similar from one culture to another usually reflect differences in their environments. But the number of common elements is amazing, as this American Indian tale proves. What did Strong Wind do to test the maidens? Which details prove that this is a version of the Cinderella tale?

On the shores of a wide bay on the Atlantic coast there dwelt in old times a great warrior. It was said that he had been one of Glooskap's best helpers and friends, and that he had done for him many wonderful deeds. But that, no one knows. He had, however, a very wonderful and strange power: he could make himself invisible; he could thus mingle unseen with his enemies and listen to their plots. He was known among the people as Strong Wind, the Invisible. He dwelt with his sister in a tent near the sea, and his sister helped him greatly in his work. Many maidens would have been glad to marry him, and he was much sought after because of his mighty deeds; it was known that Strong Wind would marry the first maiden who could see him as he came home at night. Many made the trial, but it was a long time before one succeeded.

Strong Wind used a clever trick to test the truthfulness of all who sought to win him. Each evening as the day went down, his sister walked on the beach with any girl who wished to make the trial. His sister could always see him, but no one else could see him. And as he came home from work in the twilight, his sister, as she saw him drawing near, would ask the girl who sought him, "Do you see him?"

And each girl would falsely answer, "Yes." And his sister would ask, "With what does he draw his sled?" And each girl would answer, "With the hide of a moose," or "With a pole," or "With a great cord." And then his sister would know that they all had lied, for their answers were mere guesses. And many tried and lied and failed, for Strong Wind would not marry anyone who was untruthful.

There lived in the village a great chief who had three daughters. Their mother had long been dead. One of the daughters was much younger than the others. She was very beautiful and gentle and well beloved by all, and for that reason her older sisters were very jealous of her charms, and treated her very cruelly. They clothed her in rags that she might be ugly, and they cut off her long black hair. And they lied to their father, telling him that she had done these things herself. But the young girl was patient, kept her gentle heart, and went gladly about her work.

Like other girls, the chief's two eldest daughters tried to win Strong Wind. One evening, as the day went down, they walked on the shore with Strong Wind's sister and waited for his coming. Soon he came home from his day's work, drawing his sled. And his sister asked as usual, "Do you see

him?" And each one, lying, answered, "Yes." And she asked, "Of what is his shoulder strap made?" And each, guessing, said, "Of rawhide." Then they entered the tent where they hoped to see Strong Wind eating his supper. And when he took off his coat and his moccasins they could see them, but more than these they could not see. And Strong Wind knew that they had lied, and he kept himself from their sight, and they went home dismayed.

One day the chief's youngest daughter resolved to seek Strong Wind. She patched her clothes with bits of birch bark from the trees, and put on the few little ornaments she possessed, and went forth to try to see the Invisible One as all the other girls of the village had done before. And her sisters laughed at her, and as she passed along the road all the people laughed at her because of her tattered frock, but silently she went her way.

Strong Wind's sister received the girl kindly, and at twilight she took her to the beach. Soon Strong Wind came home, drawing his sled. And his sister asked, "Do you see him?" And the girl answered, "No," and his sister wondered greatly because she spoke the truth. And again she asked, "Do you see him now?" And the girl answered, "Yes, and he is very wonderful." And she asked, "With what does he draw his sled?" And the girl answered, "With the Rainbow," and she was much afraid. And the sister asked further, "Of what is his bowstring?" And the girl answered, "His bowstring is the Milky Way."

Then Strong Wind's sister knew that because the girl had spoken the truth at first, her brother had made himself visible to her. And she said, "Truly, you have seen him." And she took her home and bathed her, and her hair grew long and black again like the raven's wing, and she gave her fine clothes to wear and many rich ornaments. Then she bade her take the wife's seat in the tent. Soon Strong Wind entered and sat beside her, and called her his bride.

The very next day she became his

wife, and ever afterwards she helped him to do great deeds. The girl's two elder sisters were very cross and they wondered greatly at what had taken place. But Strong Wind, who knew of their cruelty, resolved to punish them. Using his great power, he changed them both into aspen trees and rooted them in the earth. And since that day the leaves of the aspen have always trembled, and they shiver in fear at the approach of Strong Wind, no matter how softly he comes, for they are still mindful of his great power and anger because of their lies and their cruelty to their sister long ago.

CHECK FOR UNDERSTANDING

1. What did Strong Wind do to test the maidens?
2. What details included in this tale are missing from the Perrault version?
3. Which details prove that this is a version of the Cinderella tale?
4. What does this story have in common with "Icarus and Daedalus?"
5. What sight in nature does this tale explain?

WRITE ABOUT *"The Indian Cinderella"*

Choose one detail of this tale that is different from the Perrault version. From this difference, what can you infer about the tribes who told this tale? Write a brief essay explaining your inference.

Comparing and Contrasting

MEG: My dessert is just like yours.

PEG: Really? In what way?

MEG: Well, both desserts are sweet and grow on trees and have pits and are fruit.

PEG: But they are different kinds of fruit! One is red and the other is orange. One grows in a temperate climate and the other grows in a warm climate. Meg, you can't compare apples and oranges!

MEG: I just did, though. And you contrasted them!

When you **compare** two things—or people, or events—you identify likenesses between them. You **contrast** two things by identifying the differences that exist between them. As Meg and Peg discovered, it is not difficult to compare and contrast things that are basically similar.

Read the following passages from the selections you have just read. Which elements are similar? Which elements are different?

[Cinderella] is a young girl whose father marries again after her mother dies. His new wife is a cold, cruel woman with two equally nasty daughters. Cinderella is made to do all the housework and tend to her stepmother and stepsisters. At night she must sleep by the fireplace among the cinders; hence her name.

There lived in the village a great chief who had three daughters. Their mother had long been dead. One of the daughters was much younger than the others. She was very beautiful and gentle and well beloved by all, and for that reason her older sisters were very jealous of her charms and treated her very cruelly. They clothed her in rags that she might be ugly, and they cut off her long black hair.

When you compare Cinderella and the chief's daughter, it is easy to see that both of these characters are similar. Both are motherless girls who are treated cruelly by their families. On the other hand, they are not exactly alike. When you contrast the two characters, you see that Cinderella was a stepchild and the chief's daughter was not. Cinderella's stepsisters merely forced her to do all the housework and to sleep in the cinders; the chief's two older daughters went further—they made their younger sister look ugly.

Compare and contrast these passages:

> The prince begins a kingdom-wide search for the owner of the slipper. When he arrives at Cinderella's house he finds that only her foot fits the slipper.

> Then Strong Wind's sister knew that because the girl had spoken the truth at first, her brother had made himself visible to her.

Notice that there is one great similarity: Cinderella and the chief's daughter both passed a test. What are the differences between these tales? First of all, Cinderella had to have small feet, whereas the chief's daughter had to have a truthful nature. Also, the prince searched for Cinderella on his own. Strong Wind, the hero of "The Indian Cinderella," had the help of his sister.

When you read "Camelot" and "Arthur's Last Battle," you will find a great deal to compare and contrast. Take particular notice of the differences between the Camelot of the song and the strife-torn kingdom of "Arthur's Last Battle." As you read both selections, look for the similarities between the King Arthur who sings about Camelot and the proud king who is not afraid to face death.

CAMELOT

lyrics by ALAN JAY LERNER

A law was made a distant moon ago here.
July and August cannot be too hot;
And there's a legal limit to the snow here
In Camelot!

The winter is forbidden till December
And exits March the second on the dot.
By order summer lingers through September
In Camelot.

Camelot! Camelot!
I know it sounds a bit bizarre,
But in Camelot, Camelot,
That's how conditions are.

The rain may never fall till after sundown.
By eight the morning fog must disappear.
In short, there's simply not a more congenial spot
For happ'ly-ever-aftering than here in Camelot!

Camelot! Camelot!
I know it gives a person pause,
But in Camelot, Camelot,
Those are the legal laws.

The snow may never slush upon the hillside.
By nine P.M. the moonlight must appear.
In short there's simply not a more congenial spot
For happ'ly-ever-aftering than here in Camelot!

492

ARTHUR'S · LAST · BATTLE

by ROSEMARY SUTCLIFF

Sometimes events seem to run a course that no one can control. A guiding force called "fate" is held responsible for the end results. Fate plays a strong part in the legend of King Arthur, as this excerpt from *The Road to Camlann* makes clear.

What is "the dark," and how do Arthur and his knights thrust it back? What is the dark fate-pattern?

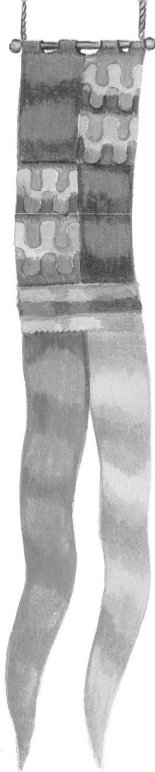

Mordred had fled away westward, and as he went, he harried the lands of those who would not join him. But there were many, in the days that followed, who did join him; for fear because the thing had gone too far for them to expect mercy from Arthur now, or because they chose the usurper's lawless rule, or simply because they had loved Lancelot, and for his sake would draw sword for any leader who was against Arthur, which was the saddest reason of all. Yet there were as many who took up their arms and came in to fight for their rightful king; and so when the High King also hurried westward in pursuit of his traitor son, there was little to choose for size and strength between the two war-hosts.

They swept past London, along the great ridge that reared its back above the forest country; and the king longed to check and ride for the city for one last sight of Guinevere the queen. But it was not the time, and he contented himself as best he might by sending three messengers on fast horses to make inquiry and bring him back word that all was well with her, while he pushed on westward without slackening the pace and purpose of his march.

Twice the war-hosts met in battle and twice the High King thrust the usurper back. And so at last, far over into the western marsh country, the two armies faced each other for the greatest battle of all, encamped upon opposite sides of a level plain, bleak and open among the wet woods in their first springtime green and the winding waterways of those parts. And when Arthur asked of an old woman who came in to sell eggs and cheese in the royal camp, "Old mother, is there a name to this place?" she said, "Aye, this is the Plain of Camlann."

That night, when all things had been made ready for the battle that must come next day, Arthur lay in his pavilion and could not sleep. Beyond the looped-back entrance where his squires lay, the open plain stretched away like a dark sea, with the hushing of the wind through the long grass and the

furze scrub for the sounding of the waves, to where the enemy watch fires marked its further shore. His mind seemed full of whirling memories, and the sea-sound sank and changed into the whisper of reeds round the margin of still water. . . . Still water . . . Lake water lapping . . . And Merlin standing beside him on the day that he received his sword, Excalibur. Merlin's voice in his ears again, across all the years between, saying, "Over there is Camlann, the place of the Last Battle. . . . But that is another story, and for another day as yet far off."

Now the day was here, waiting beyond the darkness of this one spring night. A night that was dark indeed. The doom that he had unwittingly loosed so long ago when, all unknowing, he fathered Mordred, was upon him, and upon all that he had fought for. And tomorrow he and Mordred must be the death of each other. And what of Britain after that? Torn in two, and with the Sea Wolves and the men of the North waiting to come swarming in again?

In the chill dark hour before dawn, he fell into a state between sleeping and waking. And in that state he dreamed a dream—if it was a dream.

It seemed to him that Sir Gawain came in through the entrance to the tent, armed and looking just as he used to, though it was maybe strange that he came pacing in as though no tent squires lay across the threshold, and none of them seemed to see him come. And Arthur sat up and stretched his arms to him in joyful greeting. "Welcome! Gawain, my most dear nephew! Now thanks be to God that I see you hale and living, for I thought you dead and grave-laid in Dover town!" And then he saw that behind Gawain thronged the bright-eyed misty shapes of women, foremost among them the Lady Ragnell, Gawain's seven-years' wife, and he was glad that Gawain had found his own lady again, for the years that he had shared with her had been his best as a knight and as a man. And Arthur asked, "But what of these ladies who come with you?"

"Sir," said Gawain, "these be all of them ladies whom I fought for or served in some way when I was man alive. God has listened to their prayers and for their sakes has been merciful to me and granted that I come to you."

"It is for some urgent cause that you come," said the king.

"It is to forewarn you of your death. For if you join battle with Sir Mordred this day, as you and he are both set to do, you must both die, and the greater part of your followings with you, and the Kingdom of Logres shall indeed go down into the dark. Therefore God, of his special grace, has sent me to bid you not to fight this day, but to find means to make a treaty with Sir Mordred, promising whatever he asks of you as the price of this delay. A truce that shall gain you one month of time; for within that month shall come Sir Lancelot and all his following, and together you shall overcome Sir Mordred and his war-host, and so shall the kingdom be saved from the dark."

And suddenly, with his last word scarcely spoken, he was gone from the place where he had been and the bright-eyed shadows with him.

And in a little, Arthur saw the green light of dawn growing pale beyond the tent flaps. Then he arose and summoned his squires to fetch Sir Lucan and Sir Bedivere and two of his churchmen. And when they came and stood before him, he told them of the vision he had had, and the thing that Sir Gawain had told him. And he charged them to go to Sir Mordred under the green branch, and make a truce with him that should last a month. "Offer him lands and goods," said the king, "as much as seem reasonable—anything that seems reasonable. Only do you win for me and for all our people this month's delay."

So Sir Bedivere and Sir Lucan and the two churchmen went forth under the green branch, and came to the enemy camp. And there they spoke long with Sir Mordred among his grim war-host of fifty thousand men. And at last Mordred agreed to these terms: that he should have the lands of Kent and the old Kingdom of Cornwall from that day forward, and the whole of Britain after the king's death.

It was agreed between them that Arthur and Mordred should meet an hour from noon, midway between the two war camps, and each accompanied by only fourteen knights and their squires, for the signing of the treaty.

And Sir Bedivere and Sir Lucan returned to the royal camp and told Arthur what had been arranged: and when he heard them, a great relief arose in him, for he thought that maybe,

497

after all, God was showing him a way to turn back the dark and to save Britain. But still, he did not trust his son, and he had the men of his war-host drawn up clear of the camp and facing the enemy, and when the horses were brought, and he mounted, his chosen fourteen knights around him, and he was ready to ride out to the meeting, he said to the captains, "If you see any sword drawn, wait for no orders, but come on fiercely, and slay all that you may, for there is a black shadow on my heart, and I do not trust Sir Mordred."

And on the other side of the plain, Mordred gave orders to his own war-host: "If you see any sword drawn, come on with all speed and slay all that stand against you, for I do not trust this treaty, and I know well that my father will seek to be revenged on me."

And so they rode forward, and met at the appointed place midway between the battle-hosts, and dismounted, leaving their horses in the care of their squires, to discuss and sign the treaty, which the clerks had made out twice over upon fine sheets of vellum. Then the treaty was agreed to and first Arthur and then Mordred signed it, using the king's saddle for a writing slope. And it seemed that there must be peace between them, at least for this one month, and the doom and the darkness turned aside.

But scarcely had their copies of the treaty been fairly exchanged, when an adder, rousing in the warmth of the spring day, and disturbed by the trampling of men and horses too near her sleeping place, slithered out from among the dry grass roots, coil upon liquid coil, and bit one of Mordred's knights through some loose lacing of the chain mail at his heel.

And when the knight felt the fiery smart, he looked down and saw the adder, and unthinkingly he drew his sword and slashed the small, wicked thing in half.

And when both war-hosts saw the stormy sunlight flash on the naked blade, they remembered their orders, and the harm was done. From both sides there rose a great shouting

and a blowing of horns and trumpets, and the two war-hosts burst forward and rolled towards each other, dark as doom under their colored standards and fluttering pennants, jinking with points of light like the flicker of summer lightning in the heart of a thunder cloud, where the sour yellow sunshine struck on sword-blade and spear-point; and giving out a swelling storm-roar of hooves and war cries and weapon-jar as they came.

Then Arthur cried out in a terrible voice, "Alas! This most accursed day!" And hurling himself into the saddle, drove spurs into his horse's flanks, and swung him round with frantic haste to join the forefront of his own oncoming war-host. Sir Mordred did likewise in the same instant, and the battle closed around them both.

The sorest and most savage battle that ever was fought in any land of Christendom.

It was scarcely past noon when the fighting joined, but soon the clouds that gathered overhead made it seem like evening, and as the dark battle masses swept and swirled this way and that, lit by blade-flash and torn by the screams of smitten horses and the war-shouts and the death-cries of men, so the black cloud mass that arched above them seemed to boil as though at the heart of some mighty tempest, echoing the spear tempest upon Camlann Plain beneath. And many a terrible blow was given and many mighty champions fell, and old enemies fought each other in the reeling press, and friend fought friend, and brother fought brother. And as the time went by, the ranks of both war-hosts grew thinner, and more and more the feet of the living were clogged by the bodies of the dead, and one by one the banners and pennants that were tattered as the ragged sky went down into the mire, and all the mire of Camlann's trampled plain oozed red.

And all day long Mordred and the High King rode through the thick of the battle and came by no hurt, so that it seemed as though they held charmed lives; and ever in the reeling thick of the fighting they sought for each other, but might never come together all the black day long.

And so day drew to the edge of night, and a great and terrible stillness settled over the plain, and Arthur, who had had three horses killed under him since noon, stood to draw breath and look about him. And all was red: the blade of his own sword crimsoned to the hilt, and the sodden mire into which the grass was trampled down; even the underbellies of the clouds that had been dark all day were stained red by the light of the setting sun. And nothing moved over all Camlann Plain but the ravens circling black-winged against that smoldering sky, and nothing sounded save the howl of a wolf far off, and near at hand the cry of a dying man.

And Arthur saw that two men stood close behind him, and one was Sir Lucan and the other Sir Bedivere, and both sore wounded. And of all the men who had followed him back from Benwick or gathered to his standard on the march from Dover, and of all those men, also, who had been his before they were drawn from their loyalty by Mordred's treachery or by their love for Lancelot, these two, leaning wearily on their swords beside him, were all who remained alive.

And the black bitterness of death rose in Arthur the King, and a mighty groan burst from him.

"That I should see this day! Grief upon me for all my noble knights that lie here slain! Now, indeed, I know that the end is come. But before all things go down into the dark—where is Sir Mordred who has brought about this desolation?"

Then as he looked about him, he became aware of one more figure still upon its feet: Sir Mordred in hacked and battered armor, standing at a little distance, alone in the midst of a sprawling tangle of dead men.

And Arthur would not use Excalibur upon his own son, and so, to Sir Lucan, who stood nearest to him, he said, "Give me a spear, for yonder stands the man who brought this day into being, and the thing is not yet ended between us two."

"Sir, let him be!" said Sir Lucan. "He is accursed! And if you let this day of ill destiny go by, you shall be most fully avenged upon him at another time. My liege lord, pray you remember your last night's dream, and what the spirit of Gawain told you. Even though by God's grace and mercy you still live at the day's end, yet leave off the fighting now, for there are three of us, while Sir Mordred stands alone, and therefore we have won the field, and once the doom day be passed, it will be passed indeed, and new days to come."

But, "Give me life or give me death," said Arthur, "the thing is not finished until I have slain my son who has brought destruction upon Logres and upon all Britain, and for whom as many good men lie slain."

"Then God speed you well," said Sir Bedivere.

And Sir Lucan gave the king his spear, and he grasped it in both hands and made at a stumbling run for the solitary

figure. The terrible red drunkenness of battle was upon him, and he cried out as he ran, "Traitor! Now is your death-time upon you!"

And hearing him, Sir Mordred lifted his head, and recognized death, and with drawn sword came to meet him. And so they ran, stumbling over the dead, and came together in the midst of that dreadful reddened field, under that dreadful bleeding sky. And the High King smote his son under the shield with a great thrust of his spear, that pierced him clean through the body. And when Sir Mordred felt his death wound within him, he gave a great yell, savage and despairing, and thrust himself forward upon the spear-shaft, as a boar carried forward by its own rush up the shaft of the hunter, until he was stayed by the hand-guard; and with all the last of his strength he swung up his sword two-handed, and dealt the High King

his father such a blow on the side of the dragon-crested helmet that the blade sliced through helm and mail-coif and deep into the skull beneath. And at the end of the blow Sir Mordred fell stark dead upon the spear, dragging it with him to the ground. And in the same instant Arthur the King dropped also, not dead but in a black swoon, upon the stained and trampled earth.

Then Sir Lucan and Sir Bedivere came and lifted him between them, and by slow stages, for their wounds were sore upon them, they bore him from the battlefield, and to a little ruined chapel not far off, and laid him there in the shelter and quiet that the place offered, upon a bed of piled fern that looked as though it had been made ready for him, before the altar.

And there, when they laid him down, Sir Lucan gave a deep groan and crumpled to the earth at his feet, for the effort of getting his king to shelter had been too great for him, with the gaping wound that was in his belly.

And when Arthur, coming back to himself, saw Sir Lucan's body sprawled there, the grief rose in him, and he cried out, "Alas, this is a sore sight! He would have aided me, and he had more need of aid himself!"

And Sir Bedivere knelt weeping beside the dead knight, for they had loved each other as brothers since the days when the Round Table was young.

It had been dark when they reached the chapel, but now the skies had cleared, and presently the moon arose, sailing high and uncaring above the dreadful stillness of Camlann Plain. And looking with shadowed sight out through the gap in the far wall where the stones had fallen, Arthur saw, not far off, the whispering reed-fringed shores of a lake. White mists scarfed the water, shimmering in the white fire of the moon, and the far shores were lost in mist and moonshine, so that there might have been no far shore at all. And Arthur knew that lake. He knew it to his heart's core.

And gathering all that was left of his strength, he said to Sir Bedivere, "To this lake . . . To another part of this lake, Merlin brought me, long ago. . . ." And it seemed to him that he was forcing the words out so hard that they must come forth as a shout, but they came only as a ragged whisper that Sir Bedivere must bend close to hear. "Now, leave your weeping; there will be time for mourning later on for you—but for me, my time with you grows short, and there is yet one thing more that I must have you do for me."

"Anything," said Sir Bedivere, "anything, my liege lord . . ."

"Take you Excalibur, my good sword, and carry it down to yonder lakeshore, and throw it far out into the water. Then come again and tell me what you see."

"My lord," said Bedivere, "I will do as you command, and bring you word."

And he took the great sword from where it lay beside the king and, reeling with weakness from his own wounds, made his way down to the water's brink.

In that place, alder trees grew here and there along the bank, and he passed through them, stooping under the low branches, and paused, looking down at the great sword in his hands, and the white fire of the moon showed him the jewels in the hilt and played like running water between the clotted stains on the faery-forged blade. And he thought, "This is not only a High King's weapon, this is the sword of Arthur, and once thrown into the lake it will be lost forever, and an ill thing that would be."

And the more he looked, the more he weakened in his purpose. And at last he turned from the water, and hid Excalibur among the roots of the alder trees.

Then he went back to Arthur.

"Have you done as I bade you?" said Arthur.

"Sir, it is done," said Bedivere.

"And what did you see?"

"Sir," said Bedivere, "what should I see under the moon, but the bright ripples spreading in the waters of the lake?"

"That is not truly spoken," said the king. "Therefore go back to the lake, and as you are dear to me, carry out my command."

So Sir Bedivere went back to the lakeshore, and took the sword from its hiding place, fully meaning this time to do as the king had bidden him. But again the white fire of the moon blazed upon the jeweled hilt and the shiny blade, and he felt the power of it in his hands as though it had been a live thing. And he thought, "If ever men gather again to thrust back the dark, as we thrust it back when the 'Table' and the world were young, this is the only true sword for whoever leads them." And he returned the sword to its hiding place, and went back to the chapel where the king lay waiting for him.

"Have you done my bidding, this second time?" asked the king.

"I cast Excalibur far out into the lake," said Sir Bedivere.

"And what did you see?"

"Only the reeds stirring in the night wind."

And the king said in a harsh and anguished whisper, "I had thought Mordred the only traitor among the brotherhood, but now you have betrayed me twice. I have loved you, counted you among the noblest of my knights of the Round Table, and you would break faith with me for the richness of a sword."

Bedivere knelt beside him with hanging head. "Not for the richness, my liege lord," he said at last. "I am ashamed, but it was not for the richness, not for the jewels in the hilt, nor the temper of the blade."

"That I know," the king said, more gently. "Yet now, go again swiftly, and this time do not fail me, if you value still my love."

And Sir Bedivere got stiffly to his feet, and went a third time down to the water's edge, and took the great sword from its hiding place; and a third time he felt the power of it in his hand and saw the white moon fire on the blade, but without pause he swung it up above his head, and flung it with the last strength of arm and breast and shoulder, far out into the lake.

He waited for the splash, but there was none, for out of the misty surface of the lake rose a hand and arm clad in white samite, that met and caught it by the hilt. Three times it flourished Excalibur in slow wide circles of farewell, and then vanished back into the water, taking the great sword with it from the eyes of this world. And no widening ring of ripples told where it was gone.

Sir Bedivere, blind with tears, turned and stumbled back to the chapel and his waiting lord.

"It is done as you commanded," he said.

"And what did you see?" said the king.

"I saw a hand that came out of the lake, and an arm clothed in white samite, and the hand caught Excalibur and brandished it three times as though in leavetaking—and so withdrew, bearing the sword with it, beneath the water."

"That was truly spoken and well done," said the king, and he raised himself on his elbow. "Now I must go hence. Aid me down to the waterside."

And Sir Bedivere aided him to his feet and took his weight upon his own shoulder, and half-supported, half-carried him down to the lakeshore.

And there, where before had seemed to be only the lapping water and the reeds whispering in the moonlight, a narrow barge draped all in black lay, as though it waited for them,

507

within the shadows of the alder trees. And in it were three ladies, black-robed, and their hair veiled in black beneath the queenly crowns they wore. And their faces alone, and their outstretched hands, showed white as they sat looking up at the two on the bank weeping. And one of them was the Queen of Northgalis, and one was Nimue, the Lady of all the Ladies of the Lake, and the third was Queen Morgan le Fay, freed at last from her own evil now that the dark fate-pattern was woven to its end.

"Now lay me in the barge, for it has been waiting for me long," said Arthur, and Sir Bedivere aided him down the bank, and gently lowered him to the hands of the three black-robed queens, who made soft mourning as they received him and laid him down. And the Lady of the Lake took his battered head into her lap, and kneeling beside him, Queen Morgan le Fay said, "Alas, dear brother, you have tarried overlong from us and your wound has grown chilled."

And the barge drifted out from the shadows under the alder trees, leaving Sir Bedivere standing alone upon the bank.

And Sir Bedivere cried out like a child left in the dark, "Oh, my lord Arthur, what shall become of me, now that you go hence and leave me here alone?"

And the king opened his eyes and looked at him for the last time. "Comfort yourself, and do the best that you may, for I must be gone into the Vale of Avalon, for the healing of my grievous wound. One day I will return, in time of Britain's sorest need, but not even I know when that day may be, save that it is afar off. . . . But if you hear no more of me in the world of men, pray for my soul."

And the barge drifted on, into the white mist between the water and the moon. And the mist received it, and it was gone. Only for a little, Sir Bedivere, straining after it, seemed to catch a low desolate wailing of women keening for their dead.

And then that, too, was gone, and only the reeds whispered on the desolate lakeshore.

CHECK FOR UNDERSTANDING

1. Who first identified the Plain of Camlann as the place of a battle to come?
2. When did Arthur say the battle would be finished?
3. Why was Morgan le Fay freed from her own evil?
4. What was the "dark fate-pattern"?
5. What elements of the story tell you that King Arthur is more a figure of legend than of history?
6. What was "the dark," and how had Arthur and his knights thrust it back?

WRITE ABOUT *"Arthur's Last Battle"*

Choose one of the scenes from the story. Retell it in your own words. Even though you will be using more modern wording, you should use language that captures the mood of the story.

The Stolen Lake

by JOAN AIKEN

Even though a story in a book has an ending, anyone can write about what might happen after the final page is turned. The book *The Stolen Lake* is an unusual continuation of the King Arthur legend. Why is Queen Ginevra so eager to have her lake returned to her? How could a lake be stolen in the first place?

Dido Twite was a passenger on the Thrush, *bound for her home in Britain, when Captain Hughes received an urgent message from the Queen of New Cumbria, an imaginary country in South America. Something had been taken from her, the queen claimed, and she wanted help in getting it back. Because Britain and New Cumbria had been allies for centuries, the Captain and his crew hurried to her aid. Upon their arrival, Captain Hughes, his officer, Lieutenant Windward, and Dido Twite were granted an audience with the queen herself.*

510

At the far end of the throne room was a daybed set on a dais approached by three steps.

The daybed was hung about with more of the gray, gauzy draperies, and on it, leaning against a great many cushions, lolled a lady whose plump and billowy shape was to some extent concealed by her loose, filmy white garments.

The four officials bowed almost to the ground.

"Your Mercy, may I present Captain Hughes of the Britannic Navy?" said the vicar general.

The queen impatiently gestured Messrs. Glendower, Gomez, Fluellen, and Jones to retire out of earshot, which they did, looking disgruntled about it. Then she said, "My dear Captain Hughes! So *very* kind of you to come all this way. I am delighted to meet you. Pray consider yourself quite at home in my capital."

Her voice was high, light, and fatigued.

"Ma'am," said Captain Hughes gruffly. He climbed the three steps, went down on one knee, and kissed the hand she extended. Then, rising, he added, "I have the honor to present Lieutenant Windward, of His Majesty King James's sloop, *Thrush*; and—harrumph—this is Miss Dido Twite from—Battersea."

Dido curtseyed. It was not one of her more successful efforts, but Queen Ginevra appeared to find no fault with it. She turned her protuberant light gray eyes on Dido. The fixity of her stare made Dido wish to wriggle, but she could feel Captain Hughes's sharp and critical eye on her, too, and tried to keep still.

"A child from England!" breathed the queen. "What a *remarkable* coincidence!" She did not explain her words, but continued to study Dido until even Captain Hughes became a trifle fidgety.

"Er—ahem!" he said. "Understand there is some way in which I can be of service to Your Majesty. Only too glad to oblige in whatever it is—do my possible, that is to say."

"Ah . . . yes," answered Queen Ginevra, on a faint sigh, as if she had dragged her thoughts back from some immense distance, from something that was very pleasantly occupying her attention. "Yes, you can help me, captain. Listen, and I will explain."

She did not invite the captain to be seated: indeed, there was nowhere to sit, so he and Lieutenant Windward continued standing in front of the dais. Dido, unbidden, squatted down on one of the steps, and earned a scowl and a head shake from the captain, but he did not dare interrupt what the queen was saying.

"You must be aware, my dear captain, of the history of New Cumbria's settlement—that the founding fathers sailed here after the unfortunate outcome of the Battle of Dyrham in A.D. 577?"

Captain Hughes nodded, and the queen went on. "In the course of that battle, as you will recall, my husband King Arthur received a number of wounds, one very dangerous, and was ferried away over the water of Arianrod to be healed of his hurts on the island of Avalon by his aunts, the Cornwall sisters."

At the queen's words Captain Hughes turned first extremely pale, then bright red. He cast one nerve-racked sideways glance at Lieutenant Windward, who was standing, equally red-faced, staring rigidly ahead.

"Your h-h-*husband*, ma'am? King *Arthur*? I'm afraid I don't quite . . ."

"My husband, King Arthur," she repeated. Her high, fatigued voice held a hint of irritation. "To be healed of his wounds in the Isle of Avalon."

"But—but ma'am, that would make you . . ."

"Thirteen hundred years old," the queen said coldly. "You do not think I would be such an undutiful wife as to die before my husband returned to me?"

Captain Hughes did not look as if he had any thoughts on the subject at all. He stared at the queen with glazed eyes.

Dido stared, too. Never before had she seen a lady thirteen hundred years old. Queen Ginevra certainly was very fat. She must have been getting fatter and fatter all those hundreds of years, Dido reflected. Doesn't look as if she walked about much. Or went out in the fresh air.

The queen's skin was pale and soft, like white bread dough. She lolled back wearily against her pillows.

Lucky she isn't bald, Dido thought.

An abundance of limp, rather greasy, yellowish-white hair was swept back from the queen's brow and confined by a diamond-studded snood. Like Queen Victoria, she had very little chin, but her eyes, large as poached eggs, made up for that—they were extremely sharp and gave the impression that they observed all that went on, not only in front of the queen but also to the side and behind her. They observed, but they held no expression; they were like birds' eyes. The short fingers of her small, fat hands were loaded with rings.

"The Battle of Dyrham was fought in the winter," Queen Ginevra went on. "After my husband had been conveyed away by his aunts, the lake, Arianrod, very fortunately froze. So we were able to bring it with us to New Cumbria."

"Bring it with you, ma'am? The *lake?*"

"In the form of ice blocks—as ballast," she answered rather impatiently. "Had it been liquid, of course the task would have been by no means so easy."

"By no means," Captain Hughes echoed faintly.

"Of course you will appreciate the necessity of bringing the lake."

"Necessity, ma'am?"

"Do not be continually repeating my words like a gaby, Captain, I beg! Of course it was necessary that the lake should be here, because when my husband returns, it will be by boat *across that lake*—into which, as you will recall, the sword Caliburn had to be dropped in order to summon his aunts."

Captain Hughes remained silent. A light sweat had broken out on his brow.

"When we reached New Cumbria," Queen Ginevra went on, "a convenient location was found for the resiting of Lake Arianrod in a dried-up depression, doubtless volcanic in origin, between Mount Damyake and Mount Catelonde, and it has remained there ever since. Some of the peasants call it Dozmary; but of course Arianrod is its real name."

"Just so," said the captain.

"Now to my purpose," the queen went on. She looked sharply at Captain Hughes. "Captain, Lake Arianrod has been stolen!"

"Gracious me, ma'am," said the captain, after a slight pause.

"It shall be your task to get it back for me."

"Er," said the captain, after another slight pause, "I shouldn't wish to cast doubt, Your Majesty, but—but you are quite *sure* it has been stolen, and not—not merely trickled away, or evaporated, or sunk into the ground?"

"It has been stolen, Captain," repeated the queen coldly. "I am aware of the motive, and I am cognizant of the culprit."

"But how could somebody steal a *lake*?"

"Without the slightest difficulty. The lake frequently freezes, since it is at an altitude of fourteen thousand feet. It was purloined, and removed across my boundary, on llama back, in the form of ice blocks, just as we imported it from Camelot County in the first place."

"You did say, you did mean, ma'am," said the captain a little wildly, "I just wish to be sure I did not misunderstand—

you *did* mean that your husband was the King Arthur who established the Round Table?"

Ignoring that, the queen said, "You had best peruse this impudent document!" From among the folds of her draperies, she produced a scroll, embossed with a crowned dragon, and handed it to Captain Hughes.

"You may read it aloud, for the benefit of your companions," she ordered.

Accordingly, he read:

"Dear Cousin, Pendragon, and Ruler of New Cumbria.

Since you have unlawfully and barbarously violated the treaty of alliance that binds our two countries, in that you have seized my child, heir, and most precious treasure, be it known to you that I have seen fit to retaliate by removing one and one-half million tons of inland water from the boundaries of our two realms, which water I shall be prepared to return to you immediately upon restoration to me of the said princess, in good health, and unharmed. Mabon, Rex."

"What is this about?" inquired Captain Hughes, when he had digested the contents of the epistle. "Mabon? I understand him to be the ruler of the Kingdom of Lyonesse, which lies to the southeast of Your Majesty's dominions. But what is this heir, this princess of whom he speaks?"

"Oh, it is all such nonsense! The most ridiculous, laughable mistake!" exclaimed Queen Ginevra pettishly. "Mabon has taken it into his head to accuse *me* of abducting his daughter. Why should I do such a thing? And in consequence, he had the effrontery, the outrageousness, to remove my sacred lake."

"There is no truth in his accusation?"

Queen Ginevra drew herself up. "Do you doubt me, Captain?"

"Of course not, ma'am. Of course not. Who is this princess?"

"Oh, the child's name is Helen, or Elaine—some such thing."

Dido started. Instinctively she clenched her white-gloved hand.

"The girl went to boarding school in England," Queen Ginevra continued. "As you may not have heard, there is a popular, superstitious belief that the climate of these latitudes is unsuitable for young female persons. I believe the young lady attended a seminary in Old Bath. Upon her return home, what happens? Undoubtedly, her ship was captured by pirates—the South Seas hereabouts teem with them.

"And yet Mabon immediately accuses *me*! Without the least grounds for doing so! And has the impudence to steal my lake. Imagine it! Suppose this should be the time—and it might well be so, for the soothsayers have given this year as a particularly fortunate, auspicious period—when my dearest husband, my dear *Quondam Rex*, should be due to return? What would happen if the lake were not in its place? The thought is not to be borne!"

A very strange mixture of expressions blended and battled

in the queen's countenance: resentment, wistfulness, anger, coyness, grief, pride, self-satisfaction. Dido did not care for any of them. She supposed she ought to feel sorry for a deserted wife who had been sorrowing so many hundreds of years for her lost husband.

Besides, she oughter got used to doing without him by now, Dido thought.

"What did you wish *me* to do in the matter, ma'am?" Captain Hughes sounded exceedingly glum.

"Well," Queen Ginevra replied, in a tone that was unexpectedly cheerful and chatty, "I *had* originally intended you to go and reason with King Mabon, Captain Hughes, and, if necessary, threaten armed intervention by British forces; my own army is, unfortunately, sadly depleted. But since you have brought your charming young friend to see me, I have been visited by a much better notion." She fixed her pale eyes on Dido.

"You shall go to King Mabon, captain. I will give you a safe-conduct across the frontier through the pass of Nimue. Young Miss Twite there shall accompany you, and you will inform King Mabon, who will know no better, that you are returning his daughter to him!"

"*What?*" gasped the captain, who could hardly believe his ears. "What, ma'am? You cannot be serious! You *cannot* intend the substitution of that young person there for—for the missing princess?"

"Why not, pray?" said the queen coldly. "The princess has been away at boarding school for ten years. *He* will never know the difference. Why, you could easily pretend to be his daughter, could you not, child? Of course," she added, with what was evidently meant to be a winning smile, "I should greatly prefer that you remain with me, as my dear little guest, but you would do this small service for me, would you not? You need not remain with King Mabon for long, you know, merely until he has restored my property. Then you can run away and return to me here, and we shall have such splendid times together!"

Dido gaped at the queen. So many snags in the plan presented themselves to her that she did not know which to mention first. Meanwhile the captain was spluttering like a firecracker.

"But—but—but, ma'am! That would be rank deceit—fraud—imposture—knavery! It is not to be thought of!"

"No?" Queen Ginevra turned her protruding eyes on him. The look in them was now far from friendly.

"I could by *no* means countenance such sharp practice in the name of King James's government, or my masters at the Admiralty."

The queen sharply clapped her hands. Immediately a dozen gray-clad guards appeared from behind the curtains at the side of the hall. Queen Ginevra gestured toward Captain Hughes.

"Take him to the Wen Pendragon Prison," she said. "He may cool his heels there, until, perhaps, he has second thoughts."

Captain Hughes was dragged away, struggling and protesting loudly. "I object! This is an outrage! An act of war! Disgraceful detention of a diplomatic official! One of King James's subjects! Monstrous! Intolerable!" His voice died away in the distance.

Ignoring him, the queen looked thoughtfully at Dido.

"As for you, child . . ." Ginevra reflected for a little, as if undecided. Then she said, "You may have two days to decide. If you are prepared to go on this mission to King Mabon for me—I daresay that young man would escort you?"

Dido and Lieutenant Windward eyed one another uncertainly; after a moment Dido slightly jerked her head, and he answered, "Y-yes, ma'am," in a faltering voice.

"Very well! If you undertake the mission for me, if King Mabon returns my lake, your captain shall be released. Now you may leave me. In forty-eight hours—or sooner, of course—

I shall expect your decision."

Dido found voice enough to croak, "Might we go look at this here lake, missus—Your High and Mighty? Where it was, I mean? Jist to make sure it has really gone, like?"

"You doubt me?" asked the queen formidably.

"No—no, ma'am! But—you never know—somebody mighta put it back by this time."

"Most unlikely! But, in any case, if you travel to the court of Mabon in Lyonesse, you must cross the frontier at the head of Lake Arianrod, so you will see it then. You will need a safe-conduct to show to the guardian of the Temple of Sul, which commands the Pass of Nimue. If you agree to go, I will see that the grand inquisitor supplies you with the necessary pass."

"Thank you, ma'am."

Mr. Jones, the queen's physician, now approached and, deferentially but firmly, wrapped a black bandage round the queen's plump arm, pressed a pigskin bulb, and studied the motions of a small dial.

"You should rest, Your Mercy," he said. "The audience with the captain has tired you more than you are aware.

"Oh, very well, very well," snapped the queen, who did not appear particularly tired, so far as Dido could judge. "You may depart, child," said the queen. "On your decision rests whether you see your captain again."

The atmosphere in Bath Palace was stifling, warm as a conservatory. Despite this, Dido felt icy cold as she walked away from the dais; Queen Ginevra's glance seemed to pierce like an oyster knife between her shoulder blades. It was a comfort to have Lieutenant Windward's firm clasp on her arm. He was walking at a measured pace, trying to avoid undignified signs of nervous hurry. Dido had leisure to observe that the side hangings were, in fact, spiderwebs—huge, sagging curtains of them, swinging from roof to floor. They sparkled here and there with precious stones, diamonds, perhaps. And the spiders, occasionally to be seen lurking in thickety knots of web, were as large and hairy as coconuts.

In the curving gallery outside they found Daffyd Gomez, the grand inquisitor, waiting to intercept them.

"Here comes more trouble," breathed Dido, as the venerable white-bearded figure extended a skinny hand.

"Er—young man! Miss!" The inquisitor's voice was conspiratorial; he gave them a sly smile.

"Sir?" Lieutenant Windward's tone was sharp with worry. He was a capable, conscientious young man, a good second-in-command, but not used to dealing with such a crisis as this.

"I know, I know, you are in a pucker about your captain! Small blame to you. Her Mercy is so impulsive. That was what I tried to warn him, but he would not be advised. Now, doubtless, he is sorry. But listen to me. Do not *you* be so hotheaded.

Take my advice. *Pretend* to agree to the queen's mission, then come to me. Will ye do that?"

"Not really go to King Mabon, you mean?" Windward said cautiously.

The grand inquisitor shook his head.

"Mabon has not taken the lake—gracious me, no! He would not do such a thing. It will have sunk away from natural causes. She will only make us into a laughing stock with such a message. 'Their queen is cracked in the head,' Mabon will be saying. A great pity that would be."

"But . . ." Dido began. it seemed plain the grand inquisitor had no idea of her part in the plan: the queen's intended deception of King Mabon. Gomez looked at her severely.

"Hold your tongue, child!"

"But what about Captain Hughes?" Windward asked doubtfully.

"Leave that to me. I can talk the old lady round, by and by. Second thoughts she will be having, after a day or two. Just now, best to leave her alone."

"I see," Windward said. He did not sound convinced. "Well, thank you, sir. We will be sure to remember your advice."

Gomez gave them another cunning look, then glided away round the curve and out of sight.

It was a relief to descend the stair, to go out through the revolving door into the bitter cold of the palace yard, a sharp but welcome contrast to the steamy heat inside.

Neither of the pair spoke until they were safely in the carriage, when Lieutenant Windward exclaimed, "What do we do now?"

"Think hard," said Dido. "Talk it over with the others, somewhere we can't be listened to. I don't trust anybody in this murky town."

"That queen is a regular shocker!" muttered Windward, who could not get over the horror of seeing his commanding officer dragged away so helplessly at the whim of a fat old woman. After a moment he added, "It's odd, though—she seemed to take quite a shine to *you*."

A council of war was held in Dido's bedroom at the Sydney Hotel. The participating members were Lieutenant Windward, Mr. Multiple, Dido, Plum, and Noah Gusset.

"You mean to tell me this old girl believes she's King Arthur's *widow?*" Mr. Multiple incredulously demanded of the two who had visited the palace. "Round Table King Arthur? That one?"

"That's what she said. Didn't she, Miss Twite? Seemed to believe it, too. She's clean gone in her wits, of course: rats in the garret. But the thing is, what are we going to do? She's got Cap'n Hughes in the lock-up; for all we know, she's liable to chop his head off or have it shrunk, like those ones in the waiting room, if we don't keep her sweet."

"Yes," said Multiple very doubtfully, "but even if Miss Twite goes to this King Mabon, and lets on to be his daughter, how do we know *that'll* help the cap'n? It sounds to me like a tottyheaded scheme. First, Miss Twite doesn't *look* like any princess—axing your pardon, Miss Twite."

"Oh, call me Dido, can't you?" said Dido impatiently. "O' course I don't look like a princess."

"So it's odds but King Mabon'd twig our wheedle right

from the start. And then *we'll* be rolled up too. Probably thrown into jail in Lyonesse. And he won't give back the old lady's lake."

"Supposing he *did* steal it," said the lieutenant skeptically.

Dido thought of the mysterious procession she had seen through the captain's telescope—all those loaded llamas slowly making their way over the mountaintops with their heavy burdens. But wait, she said to herself, I saw that *after* Cap'n Hughes had the message about the theft. Still, maybe llamas travel very slowly, specially with a heavy load, and maybe going only at night. Maybe it would take them two, three weeks to go from New Cumbria to Lyonesse?

"I reckon the lake *was* stolen," she said slowly.

"If it was stole, then King Mabon oughta return it," said Noah Gusset with stolid justice.

Plum, surprising everybody, said, "Mayhap she *do* be King Arthur's widow!"

They all stared at him, and he turned brick-red, but went on, "When I were a boy, in Usk, my gramma'd be telling us about King Arthur. Come back one day, she said he would, no matter how long. Sleeping in the mountain, him, till his time be come, with his knights around him. An' when his time be come, he'll pull his sword outa the rock again, an' put on his golden crown."

CHECK FOR UNDERSTANDING

1. Why was Queen Ginevra so eager to have her lake returned to her?
2. How could a lake be stolen in the first place?
3. How did the Queen react to meeting Dido Twite?
4. If the lake really was stolen, what else might be true?
5. What will Dido and the Lieutenant have to do besides retrieving the stolen lake?

WRITE ABOUT *"The Stolen Lake"*

In "Arthur's Last Battle," King Arthur says that "one day I will return . . . but not even I know when that day may be." One of the characters in "The Stolen Lake" turns out to be King Arthur. Which character do you think it is? Explain.

Making an Outline

Have you ever used a marking pen to highlight something you want to remember in a book or an article? Sheila highlighted an article she read. This is what Sheila's article looked like when she finished using her marking pen.

The Windswept West from Donegal to Kerry

If your plane lands at Shannon and you just cannot wait to see the thatched cottages you have heard so much about, take a bus or rent a car and follow the signs to the Dingle Peninsula in Kerry. Here you will find not only thatched cottages, but mist-covered mountains, wonderful breakfasts, and people who speak the original Irish language as well as the English of today.

Because Sheila highlighted the entire article, nothing really stood out. If she had thought about it, her page might have looked like this.

The Windswept West from Donegal to Kerry

If your plane lands at Shannon and you just cannot wait to see the thatched cottages you have heard so much about, take a bus or rent a car and follow the signs to the Dingle Peninsula in Kerry. Here you will find not only thatched cottages, but mist-covered mountains, wonderful breakfasts, and people who speak the original Irish language as well as the English of today.

When you use a library book or a school book, you cannot use a marking pen to highlight important points. Instead, you need to develop a system that will help you remember and understand what you read. Outlining can serve that purpose. Instead of just making a random list of facts that you read, you could put those facts into some kind of order.

If the book you are reading has subheadings within the chapter, you can turn those headings into the main parts of an outline. If your book does not have subheadings, read the first or second line of each paragraph to find the major topics. Sometimes the topics can be found in the last line as well.

Read the first part of this selection and then study the outline that has been made from it.

INDIAN CIVILIZATIONS OF MEXICO

Many years before the European discovery of America, a number of Indian civilizations flourished in what is now the country of Mexico. Some of the most notable civilizations were also the most ancient. These older civilizations all rose and fell before 900 A.D.

The oldest of these civilizations was created by the mysterious people known today as the Olmecs. They lived in the swampy jungles along the coast of the Gulf of Mexico. Their time of greatness lasted from about 1000 B.C. to about 300 A.D. Among the remains they left behind are giant carved stone heads, six to eight feet high, wearing what look like football helmets. Other examples of Olmec art include small statues of babies with fat, snarling, catlike faces.

Olmec influences stretched 200 miles southwest to the mountains of the Pacific Coast. There a people known as the Zapotecs, starting about 500 B.C., built the holy city of Monte Alban. Monte Alban remained a thriving religious center for 1400 years, until it was abandoned about 900 A.D. Today, tourists can visit and marvel at Monte Alban's restored temples, which are among the most beautiful in all Mexico.

The greatest of the early civilizations was that of the Mayas, who became prominent between 300 A.D. to 900 A.D. The ruins of dozens of Mayan cities, and thousands of Mayan pyramids dot the jungles of eastern Mexico and neighboring Guatemala. Great builders, astronomers, and mathematicians, the Mayas are usually considered the most gifted and artistic of all the Indian cultures in America. Their jungle cities, like Monte Alban, were mysteriously abandoned by their builders about 900 A.D., but other Mayan cities in the drier lands to the north flourished until about 1400.

Outline

Indian Civilizations of Mexico

I.   Older civilizations (flourished before 900 A.D.)

    A. Olmecs, first great civilization

       1. lived in swampy jungles along Gulf of Mexico

       2. made giant carved stone heads with "football helmets"

       3. made baby statuettes

    B. Zapotecs, early offshoot of Olmec culture

       1. lived in mountains to the SW of Olmecs

       2. built holy city of Monte Alban

       3. tourists visit ruins today

    C. Classic Mayas, greatest of early civilizations

       1. many ceremonial centers/cities

       2. both scientific and artistic people

       3. mysterious abandonment of classic cities after 900 A.D.

Using What You Have Learned

Read the rest of the selection about the Indian civilizations and complete the outline.

The older Indian civilizations that declined around 900 A.D. were soon replaced by others, some of which lasted until the coming of the Spaniards. Around the year 950, a wandering tribe of Indians called Toltecs settled down and built the city of Tula, north of what is now Mexico City. The Toltecs were fierce fighters and they soon conquered the Indian peoples around them. Toltec warriors even conquered some of the northern Mayan cities.

In the area once dominated by the Zapotecs, a tribe called the Mixtecs rose to greatness. They were the greatest craftsmen of their age—jewelers, stonecutters, and painters. They recorded the deeds of their kings in brightly colored picture-book histories that look almost like comic books. In one Mixtec tomb, more than 500 pieces of exquisite treasure were found, the richest treasure ever found in Mexico.

Finally, in the 1400s, the last of the great Mexican civilizations came to power. Vigorous and ruthless, the Aztecs fed their gods with the blood of thousands of sacrificed captives. Their capital city was about five times the size of London at that time. Their capital city became what is now Mexico City. Between 1519–1522 the Aztecs were defeated by the invading Spaniards.

Expanding Your Skills

Read and outline an encyclopedia entry about one of the Indian civilizations mentioned in this lesson. Then use your outline to give an oral report.

☆Stories in the Stars☆

by ROY A. GALLANT

Folk literature has always included tales to explain patterns in nature. The placement of the stars is one of the most common topics for storytelling.

In what ways are the Greek myth of the bears and the North American Indian version similar? Why is the idea of a chase appropriate in the bear myths?

Every culture seems to have its own traditional tales about the stars. Sometimes the stories are based on resemblances. The Big Dipper and the Little Dipper, for example, are common names for two groups of stars that actually look like dippers. They are part of two larger constellations, however, for which there are no obvious resemblances. These constellations, called Ursa Major and Ursa Minor, have inspired a number of stories in many cultures.

Why were these groups of stars so interesting to ancient stargazers? Because Ursa Major includes the Big Dipper, the most prominent group of stars in the sky, it would naturally be of special interest. The stars might also have attracted attention because, in the Northern Hemisphere, both Ursa Major and Ursa Minor can be seen throughout the year. And one of the stars in Ursa Minor is Polaris, the Pole Star, around which all the other stars appear to revolve.

In Latin, Ursa Major means "Great Bear" and Ursa Minor means "Lesser Bear." As their names indicate, these two star groups were identified as bears in Greek and Roman mythology.

Ursa Major and Ursa Minor in Greek Myths

According to Greek mythology, here is how the Lesser Bear and the Great Bear came to be. Zeus, King of the Gods, fell in love with the Beautiful Callisto, a young woman who was a hunter and spent much of her time in the mountains of Arcadia where there was much game. When Hera, Zeus's wife, heard of what was happening, she was furious and set out after

531

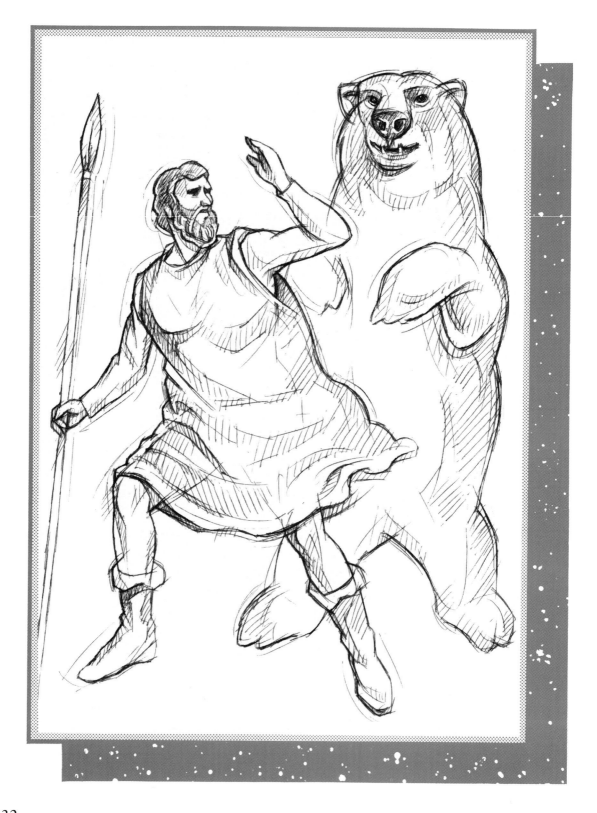

Callisto. On finding her Hera said, "Your beauty, of which my husband speaks so tenderly, is no more!" Whereupon Hera changed Callisto into a bear.

To make matters even worse, Hera left Callisto with her human feelings rather than those of a bear. So Callisto roamed the forest day and night in constant fear of the hunters *and* in fear of other wild beasts, although she was now one.

One day she found herself face to face with a young and handsome hunter, and suddenly recognized him as her son, Arcas. She raised up on her hind legs to embrace him. Thinking that the bear was about to attack him, Arcas raised his spear and was about to hurl it and kill his mother. But Zeus happened to be looking down on the scene from his position on Mount Olympus, and instantly turned Arcas into a bear also. Zeus then grasped each bear by its tail and tugged and tugged until he had managed to lift both high into the sky, Callisto as Ursa Major and her son, Arcas, as Ursa Minor. As the Roman poet, Ovid, put it, Zeus

> . . . *snatched them through the air*
> *In whirlwinds up to heaven and fix'd*
> *them there;*
> *Where the new constellations nightly*
> *rise,*
> *And add a luster to the northern*
> *skies.*

This tugging of tails, by the way, over such a long journey through the sky, stretched both tails and explains why our celestial bears, unlike earthly ones, have long tails. In time, the tail of Arcas became even longer, we are told, since he was continuously swung around the sky by the end-star in his tail, Polaris.

When she found out that Zeus had given Callisto and Arcas honored places in heaven, Hera was furious. She went down to Earth to visit her friends the ocean god Oceanus and his wife Tethys, and asked that they forever keep Callisto and Arcas in a pen so that they might never wander far.

Oceanus and Tethys were sympathetic, and promised they would grant Hera her wish. They would see to it that "the couple never would be permitted to enter our waters in their wandering," in other words, that the bears forever would be forbidden to set below the horizon of the sea as other constellations do. To this day both the Lesser Bear and the Great Bear are held high in the sky near the Pole Star, never permitted to sink beneath the sea horizon.

Another story has it that Ursa Major has always wanted to steal the Pole Star for herself because it matches her own stars in brightness. She has never managed to do so, however, because of the

"Guard Stars" in Ursa Minor. These two stars form the front edge of the Little Dipper and are located between Polaris and the greedy Great Bear, thereby protecting Polaris.

Ursa Major and Ursa Minor in Legends of the North American Indians

The North American Indians also chose bears for these two northern constellations. They called them *Okuri* and *Paukunawa*, both meaning "bear." And this was before any contact with Europeans. How different cultures on opposite sides of the world came to associate bears with Ursa Major and Ursa Minor is hard to understand. Possibly the answer lies in some root Asian myth that worked its way both eastward and westward around the globe.

At least some North American Indian groups did not give their celestial bears absurdly long tails. They regarded the tail stars in Ursa Major as three hunters, or as a hunter with two dogs, tracking down the bear. And the star called Alcor was the pot in which the bear was to be cooked. The Housatonic tribe further tells us that the hunt is successful each year. They know, because blood spilled by the bear can be plainly seen each fall when the leaves of the forest turn red.

Several of the bear myths associated with Ursa Major involve a chase. So they reflect the fact that the Great Bear endlessly wheels around the northern sky dome as if trying to escape the hunter and dogs pursuing it. Or the bear is in pursuit of the Pole Star, although that star is protected by the Guard Stars of Ursa Minor.

When Ursa Major and Ursa Minor Were Not Bears

In ancient Britain, Ursa Major was thought to be King Arthur's home, and was called Arthur's Chariot. In France it was called the Great Chariot. It has also been called the Wain, the Wagon, and the Plow.

Ursa Major, perhaps better than any other group of stars, shows that just about any shape one wants to imagine can be assigned to the constellation: a plow, wagon, a bear, or even a reindeer, as the people of Lapland saw the constellation. It is worth noting, however, that the brightest star in Ursa Major is the double star Dubhe, a name derived from the Arabic *Thahr al Dubb al Akbar*, meaning "Back of the Great Bear."

CHECK FOR UNDERSTANDING

1. How did the Greeks explain the position of the bears above the horizon?
2. In what ways are the Greek myth of the bears and the North American Indian version similar?
3. What other images have people seen in Ursa Major and Ursa Minor?
4. Why is the idea of a chase appropriate in the bear myths?
5. Of what use might these myths have been to the people who created them?

WRITE ABOUT *"Stories in the Stars"*

Choose one of the tales described in the article. Explain how the tale tells something about the culture from which it comes.

The Embarrassing Episode

of

Little Miss Muffet

by GUY WETMORE CARRYL

Writers can retell the same story in may different ways. They may also change some aspects of the original story. These selections about Miss Muffet are very different from the original rhyme in style and tone.

Generations of children have heard and recited this familiar nursery rhyme from Mother Goose.

Little Miss Muffet
Sat on her tuffet,
Eating her curds and whey;
There came a big spider,
Who sat down beside her
And frightened Miss Muffet away.

In this expanded version of the story, the truth about the spider is finally revealed!

Little Miss Muffet discovered a tuffet
    (Which never occurred to the rest of us)
And, as 'twas a June day, and just about noonday,
    She wanted to eat—like the best of us:
Her diet was whey, and I hasten to say
    It is wholesome and people grow fat on it.
The spot being lonely, the lady not only
    Discovered the tuffet, but sat on it.

A rivulet gabbled beside her and babbled,
　　As rivulets always are thought to do,
And dragonflies sported around and cavorted,
　　As poets say dragonflies ought to do;
When, glancing aside for a moment, she spied
　　A horrible sight that brought fear to her,
A hideous spider was sitting beside her,
　　And most unavoidably near to her.

Albeit unsightly, this creature politely
　　Said, "Madam, I earnestly vow to you.
I'm penitent that I did not bring my hat. I
　　Should otherwise certainly bow to you."
Though anxious to please, he was so ill at ease
　　That he lost all his sense of propriety,
And grew so inept that he clumsily stept
　　In her plate—which is barred in Society.

This curious error completed her terror;
　　She shuddered, and growing much paler, not
Only left tuffet, but dealt him a buffet
　　Which doubled him up in a sailor knot.
It should be explained that at this he was pained:
　　He cried: "I have vexed you, no doubt of it!
Your fist's like a truncheon." "You're still in my luncheon,"
　　Was all that she answered. "Get out of it!"
And the *Moral* is this: Be it madam or miss
　　To whom you have something to say,
You are only absurd when you get in the curd
　　But you're rude when you get in the whey!

Miss Muffet's
VOCABULARY LESSON

"Curds are the coagulated, or thickened, part of the milk, as distinguished from whey, which is the serum, or watery, part. As for a tuffet, it is a small tuff, or rock, composed of the finer kinds of volcanic detritus, usually stratified. Now, run along."

539

CASEY AT THE BAT

Ernest Lawrence Thayer

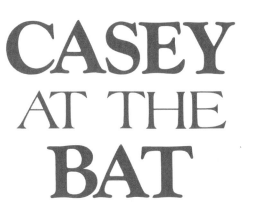

Have you ever been dissatisfied by the ending of a story or a poem? Have you ever imagined that you could have the author rewrite the selection to suit your taste? Here are two poems about baseball. The first is a well-known narrative about a famous player. The second poem was written by someone who decided to improve upon the ending of the original. Is there ever any joy in Mudville? Read "Casey at the Bat" and "Casey's Revenge" in order to find out.

It looked extremely rocky for the Mudville nine that day;
The score stood two to four, with but one inning left to play.
So, when Cooney died at second, and Burrows did the same,
A pallor wreathed the features of the patrons of the game.
A straggling few got up to go, leaving there the rest,
With that hope which springs eternal within the human breast.
　　For they thought: "If only Casey could get a whack at
　　　that,"
They'd put even money now, with Casey at the bat.
But Flynn preceded Casey, and likewise so did Blake,
And the former was a pudd'n, and the latter was a fake.
So on that stricken multitude a deathlike silence sat;
For there seemed but little chance of Casey's getting to the
　　bat.

540

But Flynn let drive a "single," to the wonderment of all.
And the much-despised Blakey "tore the cover off the ball."
And when the dust had lifted, and they saw what had
    occurred,
There was Blakey safe at second, and Flynn a-huggin' third.

Then from the gladdened multitude went up a joyous yell—
It rumbled in the mountaintops, it rattled in the dell;
It struck upon the hillside and rebounded on the flat;
For Casey, mighty Casey, was advancing to the bat.
There was ease in Casey's manner as he stepped into his
    place;
There was pride in Casey's bearing and a smile on Casey's
    face;
And when responding to the cheers he lightly doffed his hat,
No stranger in the crowd could doubt 'twas Casey at the
    bat.

Ten thousand eyes were on him as he rubbed his hands with
    dirt,
Five thousand tongues applauded when he wiped them on
    his shirt;

MUDVILLE 1 0
VISITORS 2 0

OUTS 2
STRIKES 0
BALLS 0

Then when the writhing pitcher ground the ball into his hip,
Defiance glanced in Casey's eye, a sneer curled Casey's lip.

And now the leather-covered sphere came hurtling through
   the air,
And Casey stood a-watching it in haughty grandeur there.
Close by the sturdy batsman the ball unheeded sped;
"That isn't my style," said Casey. "Strike one," the umpire
   said.
From the benches black with people, there went up a muffled
   roar,
Like the beating of the storm waves on the stern and distant
   shore.
"Kill him! Kill the umpire!" shouted someone on the stand;
And it's likely they'd have killed him had not Casey raised
   his hand.

With a smile of Christian charity great Casey's visage shone;
He stilled the rising tumult, he made the game go on;

He signaled to the pitcher, and once more the spheroid flew;
But Casey still ignored it, and the umpire said, "Strike two."
"Fraud!" cried the maddened thousands, and the echo
    answered "Fraud!"
But one scornful look from Casey, and the audience was
    awed;
They saw his face go stern and cold, they saw his muscles
    strain.
And they knew that Casey wouldn't let the ball go by again.
The sneer is gone from Casey's lips, his teeth are clenched in
    hate,
He pounds with cruel vengeance his bat upon the plate;
And now the pitcher holds the ball, and now he lets it go,
And now the air is shattered by the force of Casey's blow.
Oh, somewhere in this favored land the sun is shining bright,
The band is playing somewhere, and somewhere hearts are
    light;
And somewhere men are laughing, and somewhere children
    shout,
But there is no joy in Mudville—Mighty Casey has struck
    out.

CASEY'S REVENGE

Being a reply to the famous baseball classic,
"Casey at the Bat"
by JAMES WILSON

There were saddened hearts in Mudville for a week or even
    more;
There were muttered oaths and curses—every fan in town
    was sore.
"Just think," said one, "how soft it looked with Casey at the
    Bat!
And then to think he'd go and spring a bush-league trick like
    that."

All his past fame was forgotten; he was now a hopeless
    "shine,"
They called him "Strike-out Casey" from the mayor down
    the line,
And as he came to bat each day his bosom heaved a sigh,
While a look of helpless fury shone in mighty Casey's eye.

The lane is long, someone has said, that never turns again,
And Fate, though fickle, often gives another chance to men.
And Casey smiled—his rugged face no longer wore a frown;

The pitcher who had started all the trouble came to town.

And Mudville had assembled; ten thousand fans had come
To see the twirler who had put big Casey on the bum;
And when he stepped into the box the multitude went wild.
He doffed his cap in proud disdain—but Casey only smiled.

"Play ball!" the umpire's voice rang out, and then the game
    began;
But in that throng of thousands there was not a single fan
Who thought that Mudville had a chance; and with the
    setting sun
Their hopes sank low—the rival team was leading four to
    one.

The last half of the ninth came round, with no change in the
    score;
But when the first man up hit safe the crowd began to roar.
The din increased, the echo of ten thousand shouts was
    heard
When the pitcher hit the second and gave four balls to the
    third.

Three men on base—nobody out—three runs to tie the game!
A triple meant the highest niche in Mudville's hall of fame;
But here the rally ended and the gloom was deep as night
When the fourth one fouled to catcher and the fifth flew out
    to right.

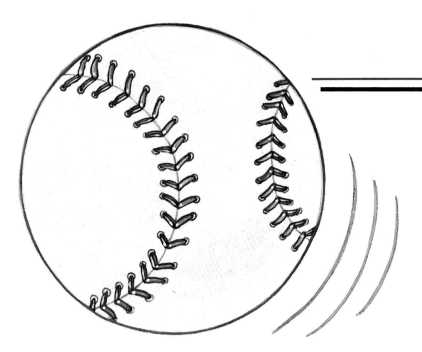

A dismal groan in chorus came—a scowl was on each face—
When Casey walked up, bat in hand, and slowly took his
      place;
His bloodshot eyes in fury gleamed; his teeth were clinched
      in hate;
He gave his cap a vicious hook and pounded on the plate.

But fame is fleeting as the wind, and glory fades away; There
were no wild and woolly cheers, no glad acclaim this day.
They hissed and groaned and hooted as they clamored,
      "Strike him out!"

But Casey gave no outward sign that he had heard this
      shout.

The pitcher smiled and cut one loose; across the plate it
      spread;
Another hiss, another groan. "Strike one!" the umpire said.
Zip! Like a shot, the second curve broke just below his
      knee—
"Strike two!" the umpire roared aloud; but Casey made no
      plea.

No roasting for the umpire now—his was an easy lot;
But here the pitcher whirled again—was that a rifle shot?
A whack! a crack! and out through space the leather pellet
    flew,
A blot against the distant sky, a speck against the blue.

Above the fence in center field, in rapid whirling flight,
The sphere sailed on; the blot grew dim, and then was lost
    to sight.
Ten thousand hats were thrown in air, ten thousand threw a
    fit;
But no one ever found the ball that mighty Casey hit!

Oh, somewhere in this favored land dark clouds may hide
    the sun,
And somewhere bands no longer play and children have no
    fun;
And somewhere over the blighted lives there hangs a heavy
    pall;
But Mudville hearts are happy now—for Casey hit the ball!

LITERATURE

Mood and Tone

The strongest feeling in a story is called the **mood.** Mood is the climate of a story. It is the atmosphere that grows out of the setting. An author may wish to create a joyful or quiet mood, or a sad or frightening mood.

The **tone** of a story is the attitude the author takes towards his subject. In literature, the purpose of tone is to understand the author's feelings towards the subject being written about. An author's attitude is revealed through choice of details and words. The tone of a story can be serious, sympathetic, mocking, earnest, angry, or respectful.

> Side by side . . . we moved on into monkey country. It was so still in the bottoms I could hear my heart thumping. Every nerve in my body was as tight as the iron bands around a rain barrel.

Did you have a feeling of calm, or were you tense and frightened when you read this passage? In this passage, choice of setting, words, and images have helped the author to create a feeling of suspense.

In the next selection, "I Meet the Beast," the mood is very clear. The passage below describes Beauty's first visit to the home of the Beast.

> I paused at last on a balcony overlooking a large dim hall similar to the one I had eaten in. Candles lit themselves only a few feet ahead of me as I walked, and beyond them all was darkness; after I had passed, in a minute or two, they winked out again, as I saw when I turned one or twice to watch them. The big windows, when they were not muffled with curtains, showed only as paler grey shapes in the walls; there was no moon yet to shine through them.

What is the general mood of the passage? What words and phrases are used to create the mood? What do you think Beauty is feeling as she walks through the castle?

The author's attitude toward the subject is called the **tone.** Further on in the story, Beauty meets the Beast.

> "I am the Beast," was the reply. "You will call me that, please." A pause. "Have you come of your own free will to stay in the castle?"
>
> "I have," I said as bravely as I could.
>
> "Then I am much obliged to you." This was said in so quiet a voice, notwithstanding the deep rumbling echo that was part of every word, and was so totally different a greeting from what I was expecting that I was shocked into saying before I thought:
>
> "Obliged! Milord, you gave me no choice. I could not let my father die for the sake of a silly rose."
>
> "Do you hate me then?" The rough voice sounded almost wistful.

What is the author's attitude towards the Beast? Judging from the passage, can you predict what will happen next in the story?

As you read the selection, notice how the author's attitude towards the Beast begins to influence the reader's feelings toward the Beast as well. Watch to see how the mood of the story changes from the beginning to the end.

Beauty: A Retelling of the Story of Beauty and the Beast

by Robin McKinley

I Meet the Beast

First impressions are often misleading. In fact, personalities frequently seem to be the opposite of the faces in front of them. How is Beauty's appearance misleading when she first meets the Beast? What does the Beast think about both of Beauty's names?

The story of "Beauty and the Beast" *has been told in many forms. The tale begins with Beauty's father about to set off on a journey. He asks Beauty and her two older sisters what he could bring back for them. Beauty's sisters want expensive presents, but Beauty herself asks only for a single rose. On his way back home, Beauty's father picks a rose in what appears to be a deserted garden. Suddenly a Beast appears, claiming to own the garden. As the penalty for taking a flower from his garden, the Beast gives Beauty's father a terrible choice. Either he must die, or one of his daughters must agree to live in the Beast's castle. When Beauty hears of her father's dilemma, she insists on saving his life by going to the castle herself.*

In Robin McKinley's retelling of the story, Beauty herself is the narrator. This Beauty described herself as "a small, plain girl, poorly dressed, self-conscious, and jittery." When she entered the castle, she saw no sign of the Beast, but she found "Beauty's Room," magnificently furnished apartments prepared especially for her.

Much as she dreaded her first meeting with the Beast, Beauty decided that waiting for that encounter was more nerve-racking than anything else. She decided to take action.

I turned towards the door again at last. It must be very late, but I still felt that I couldn't sleep until I knew what was going to happen to me—even if thus seeking it out was only hastening the end. I left "Beauty's Room" and stood for a moment in the

hall, watching the bright plaque catch fire and shadow in the candlelight as the door shut behind me. I turned away to walk more corridors, more tall, arched, and pillared rooms. I spent little time looking at the wonders I passed; I was too intent on that one thing: finding my host, or my jailer. I paused at last on a balcony overlooking a large, dim hall similar to the one I had eaten dinner in. Candles lit themselves only a few feet ahead of me as I walked, and beyond them all was darkness; after I had passed, in a minute or two, they winked out again, as I saw when I turned once or twice to watch them. The big windows, when they were not muffled with curtains, showed only as paler grey shapes in the walls; there was no moon yet to shine through them. But then, looking up again, I thought I saw a golden edge of light to a partly open door, behind the glow of my entourage of lighted candles. My heart began to beat very much faster, and I made my way quietly towards that door.

Like all of the other doors I had met in the castle, this one opened at my approach. A few days of this and I would forget the operation of a latch or a door-handle. The room it revealed was a large, warm, and gracious one, although small by the standards of this castle. On one wall to my left a fire was burning in a fireplace framed with wrought iron in the shape of climbing vines; two armchairs were drawn up before it. One chair was empty. In the other a massive shadow sat. Except for the faint and flickering light of the fire the room was in darkness; there was a table behind the occupied armchair, and on it stood a candelabrum of a dozen tall candles, but they remained dark. I realized I was standing in a little halo of light, the candles in the hall shining around me as I stood on the threshold. My eyes slowly adjusted themselves to the gloom beyond the door. I caught a gleam of dark green velvet on what might have been a knee in the shadowed armchair. "Good evening, Beauty," said a great harsh voice.

I shivered, and put a hand to the door-frame, and tried to take courage from the fact that the Beast—for it must be he—

had not devoured me at once. "Good evening, milord," I said. My voice was misleadingly steady.

"I am the Beast," was the reply. "You will call me that, please." A pause. "Have you come of your own free will to stay in the castle?"

"I have," I said as bravely as I could.

"Then I am much obliged to you." This was said in so quiet a voice, notwithstanding the deep rumbling echo that was part of every word, and was so totally different a greeting from what I was expecting that I was shocked into saying before I thought:

"Obliged! Milord, you gave me no choice. I could not let my father die for the sake of a silly rose."

"Do you hate me, then?" The rough voice sounded almost wistful.

Again I was taken aback. "Well, you give me little cause to love you." I thought then guiltily of the fine meal, and the beautiful room—especially the books. It occurred to me for the first time that if he had planned to eat me immediately it was unlikely, or at least curious, that he should have provided me with enough books for years' reading.

The immense shadow shifted in its chair. I was sure of the knee, now, and the velvet; and now I could see a glitter of eyes, and also—perhaps—of sharp claws. I looked hastily away from the claws. The feet were lost in the pool of darkness beneath the wrought-iron grate.

"Would it help perhaps if I told you that, had your father returned to me alone, I would have sent him on his way unharmed?"

"You *would?*" I said—it was half a shriek. "You mean that I came here for nothing?"

A shadowy movement like the shaking of a great, shaggy head. "No. Not what you would count as nothing. He would have returned to you, and you would have been glad, but you also would have been ashamed, because you had sent him, as you thought, to his death. Your shame would have grown until you came to hate the sight of your father, because he reminded you of a deed you hated, and hated yourself for. In time it would have ruined your peace and happiness, and at last your mind and heart."

My tired brain refused to follow this. "But—I could not have let him go alone," I said, bewildered.

"Yes," said the Beast.

I thought about it for a minute. "Can you see the future, then?" I asked uneasily.

"Not exactly," said the shadow. "But I can see you."

There didn't seem to be any answer to that, either. "I cannot see you at all, milord," I ventured timidly.

Again the gleam of eyes. "Indeed," said the Beast. "I should have welcomed you when you first arrived this afternoon; but I thought candlelight might be a little kinder for a first impression of such as me." He stood up, straightening himself slowly, but I still shrank back. He must have been seven feet tall at full height, with proportionate breadth of shoulder and chest, like the great black bears of the North Woods that could break a hunter's back with one blow of a heavy paw. He stood still for a moment, as if waiting for me to recover myself, and then, with a sigh as deep as a storm wind, he raised the candelabrum from the table. It lit as he brought it to shoulder level, and I was staring suddenly into his face. "Oh no," I cried, and covered my own face with my hands. But when I heard him take a step towards me, I leaped back in alarm like a deer at the crack of a branch nearby, turning my eyes away from him.

"You have nothing to fear," the Beast said, as gently as his harsh voice allowed.

After a moment I looked up again. He was still standing, watching me with those eyes. I realized that what made his gaze so awful was that his eyes were human. We looked at each other a moment. Not bearish at all, I decided. Not like anything else I could put a name to either. If Yggdrasil had been given an animal's shape, it might have looked like the Beast.

"Forgive me," he said, "but I am somewhat shortsighted, and I would like a closer look at you." He stepped forward again, and I backed up until I reached the balcony. I wrapped my fingers around the railing and stood—cornered, with the hunter's lantern shining in my eyes. "You—you aren't going to—eat me?" I quavered.

He stopped as if he had walked into a tree, and the candle-stick in his hand dropped several inches. "*Eat* you?" he said, with convincing horror. "Certainly not. What made you think so? Have you not been well looked after since you arrived? Have I frightened you—in any fashion that I could avoid?"

"I—well, I couldn't think of any other reason for your—er—inviting me here."

"Did I not tell your father that no harm should come to his daughter?" I opened my mouth and then shut it again, and he continued sadly: "No, you need say nothing. I am a Beast, and a Beast has no honor. But you may trust my word: You are safe here, in my castle and anywhere on my lands."

My curiosity, at least for the moment, was stronger than fear or courtesy; his gentle mien encouraged me, and I need not look into his face; I would look no higher than his waistcoat buttons, which were about at my eye level anyway. "Then, why?"

"Well—I lack companionship. It is rather lonesome here sometimes, with no one to talk to," he said simply.

My sudden sympathy must have shown on my face, for he raised the light again, and as he came closer I looked up at him with very little fear, although I still leaned against the balustrade. But he looked at me so long that I became uneasy again. I couldn't read his expression; the face was too unlike any I was accustomed to. "I—er—I hope you weren't misled by my foolish nickname," I said. What if he was angry at being cheated of Beauty, and killed me for tricking him?

"Misled?" he said. "No. I think your name suits you very well."

"Oh, *no*," I said. It was my turn for the tone of convincing horror. "I assure you I am *very* plain."

"Are you?" he said, musingly. He turned away, and set the candelabrum in a conveniently unoccupied niche in the tapestry-hung wall. The hall was lit as brightly as a ballroom although the room we had just left was still dim and rosy with firelight. "I have been out of the world a long time, of course, but I do not believe I am so shortsighted as all that."

I was not used to being struck dumb more than once in a conversation. I must be more tired and overwrought than I thought.

"You say that Beauty is your nickname?" he said after a moment. "What is your given name then?"

"Honor," I said.

Something that might have been a smile exposed too many long white teeth. "I welcome Beauty and Honor both, then," he said. "Indeed, I am very fortunate."

Oh dear, I thought. Then my mind went back to something he had said earlier: "If you wanted someone to talk to," I said, "why didn't you keep my father? He knows many more interesting things than I do."

"Mmm," said the Beast. "I'm afraid I specifically wanted a girl."

"Oh?" I said nervously. "Why?"

He turned away from me, walked back to the doorway, and stood, head bowed, hands clasped behind him. The silence squeezed at my heart. "I am looking for a wife," he said, heavily. "Will you marry me, Beauty?"

My fear, which I had had mostly under control, boiled up again and became panic. "Oh!" I said. "What shall I say?"

"Answer yes or no without fear," said the Beast without raising his head.

"Oh no, Beast," I cried. I wanted to run away, but I thought of him chasing after me, and I stayed where I was.

There was a long, stricken pause. "Very well," he said at last. "I will bid you good night. Sleep easily, Beauty: Remember, you have nothing to fear."

I didn't move. "Well, go on," he said gruffly, with a wave of one arm. "I know you are longing to escape. I shan't follow you." He walked into his room, and the door began to close.

"Good night," I called. The door paused a moment, and then shut with a soft click. I turned and ran back down the corridor the way I had come.

You already know how the tale of "Beauty and the Beast" ends. But how does the Beauty in this retelling reconcile herself to her situation? Find out by reading the rest of the novel Beauty: A Retelling of the Story of Beauty and the Beast *by Robin McKinley.*

CHECK FOR UNDERSTANDING

1. How was Beauty's appearance misleading when she first met the Beast?
2. How was the Beast's appearance different from his personality?
3. What did the Beast think about both of Beauty's names?
4. What was the Beast thinking after Beauty refused to marry him?
5. After Beauty ran away, how do you think she felt toward the Beast?

WRITE ABOUT *"I Meet the Beast"*

If Beauty could write a letter to her father, what do you think she might say about her stay in the castle? Write a letter from Beauty to her father. Decide whether or not you think she would want to appear cheerful or unhappy.

THINK ABOUT IT

The stories in this unit represent old and classic tales which have been "retold" to the reader. Sometimes the stories have been adapted to take place in another country or to seem more familiar to another culture. "Cinderella," for example has been retold for different countries all over the world. Many of the Greek myths have been retold as Roman myths—with many of the main gods and goddesses changed as well.

Sometimes a classic tale is told again in a modern-day style, as in "I Meet the Beast". In this story, the retold version also changes the point of view, making Beauty herself the narrator. Even nursery rhymes can be expanded, as in "The Embarrassing Episode of Little Miss Muffet." "Casey at the Bat" is continued in "Casey's Revenge."

But usually, no matter how many versions of the same story appear, there is one element that remains the same: the theme, or the main idea, of the author never varies.

Think of the first three retold tales: "Icarus," "Cinderella," and "The Hare and the Tortoise." What is the theme in each of the stories?

WRITE ABOUT IT

Choose one of the tales in this unit. Retell the story in one of the following forms:
- as a newspaper story,
- as a poem,
- as a play.

You could retell the Cinderella story, for example, in a newspaper story with the headline, "Owner of Glass Slipper Has Been Found."

READ ABOUT IT

Olivia Coolidge. *Greek Myths*. Houghton Mifflin, 1949.

In this collection, many tales from Greek mythology are retold by one of their most famous interpreters.

Bernard Evslin. *Hercules*. William Morrow, 1984.

Here is a spirited recounting of some of the legends surrounding a "superhero" of Greek and Roman folk literature.

John Gardner. *Dragon, Dragon and Other Tales*. Alfred A. Knopf, 1975.

The author's tales combine the style of traditional folk tales with contemporary messages. In "Dragon, Dragon," for example, a town is plagued by a dragon—a common problem in traditional tales. This dragon's crimes, however, are limited to such things as setting people's clocks back and making dogs bark.

Jamake Highwater. *Legend Days*. Harper & Row, 1984.

When her people are wiped out by disease, Amana must summon all her courage to survive. Her heroic deeds win her a place in another society.

Rosemary Sutcliff. *The High Deeds of Finn Mac Cool*. E. P. Dutton, 1967.

The author retells the legends of Erin's heroic Finn Mac Cool, who through cleverness and bravery wins a high place among the Fianna, protectors of Erin.

T. H. White. *The Once and Future King*. Reprinted, Dell, 1963.

In this classic reworking of the legends of King Arthur, young Arthur's boyhood seems to be typical of his time and place. His tutor happens to be Merlin, however, whose wizardry changes Arthur into such things as a fish, an insect, and a bird so that the king-to-be can learn about other societies.

GLOSSARY

A

ab·duct·ing (ab duk′ ting) *n.* carrying someone off unlawfully; kidnapping.

ab·hor·rent (ab hôr′ ənt, ab hor′ ənt) *adj.* causing disgust or horror; detestable; disgusting.

ab·nor·mal·i·ty (ab′nôr mal′ ə tē) *n.* the state of not being normal; something that is not normal.

ab·surd (ab surd′, ab zurd′) *adj.* contrary to reason, common sense, or truth; ridiculous.

a·bun·dance (ə bun′ dəns) *n.* a plentiful supply.

a·bu·sive (ə bū′ siv, ə bū′ ziv) *adj.* making a practice of hurting by treating wrongly; mistreating.

a·byss (ə bis′) *n.* an opening that is so deep or large that it cannot be measured; a bottomless pit.

ac·a·dem·ic (ak′ ə dem′ ik) *adj.* providing an education that prepares students for college.

ac·ces·so·ry (ak ses′ ər ē) *n.* an additional device or attachment; a smaller part or piece that aids in the functioning of some thing or some action.

ac·claim (ə klām′) *n.* strong praise.

ac·com·mo·da·tions (ə kom′ ə dā′ shənz) *n.,pl.* hotels, motels, or other places where tourists can rest, dine, or spend the night; lodging facilities.

ac·count·ant (ə kount′ ənt) *n.* a person who keeps business records.

a·cid·i·ty (ə sid′ ə tē) *n.* the quality or state of being acid; sourness; tartness (An *acid* is a sour substance that contains hydrogen.)

a·dept (ə dept′) *adj.* highly skilled or capable: an *adept student.*

ad·ja·cent (ə jā′ sənt) *adj.* next to or near; neighboring; adjoining.

ad·junct (aj′ ungkt) *n.* an additional thing related to but not as important as the main thing.

ad·ver·sar·y (ad′ vər ser′ ē) *n.* an opponent; an enemy.

aer·o·bat·ics (ār′ ə bat′ iks) *n.,pl.* feats or stunts performed in the air; also, a performance of these feats or stunts. (In the second sense, the word is often treated as a singular noun: *Aerobatics is my hobby.*)

aer·o·dy·nam·ics (ār′ ō dī nam′ iks) *n.,pl.* the science that studies the motion of the gases that make up the air and the forces exerted on them by moving objects. (The word is often used as a singular noun: *Aerodynamics is my field.*)

aer·o·nau·ti·cal (ār′ ə nô′ ti kəl) *adj.* having to do with flight.

a·gil·i·ty (ə jil′ ə tē) *n.* quickness and ease in motion; nimbleness.

ag·o·nized (ag′ ə nīzd′) *adj.* feeling great pain or suffering; anguished; tortured.

a·larm·ist (ə lär′ mist) *n.* a person who gives warnings that exaggerate future danger and needlessly frighten others.

al·be·it (ôl bē′ it) *conj.* although; even though. (The word is short for *although it be that.*)

al·li·ance (ə lī′ əns) *n.* a union or an association formed in order to reach a common goal or to fulfill a shared need; a close relationship.

al·lu·sion (ə loo′ zhən) *n.* an indirect or unclear reference: *The poem made an allusion to Shakespeare's play* Hamlet.

a·loof (ə loof′) *adj.* removed; distant; showing no interest or emotion: *an aloof attitude.*

al·ter·a·tion (ôl′ tə rā′ shən) *n.* an adjustment made in a building's exterior or interior; a change.

a·mi·a·ble (ā′ mē ə bəl) *adj.* agreeable; good-natured; friendly.

am·mu·ni·tion (am′ yə nish′ ən) *n.* bullets, bombs, and other exploding weapons.—*adj.* relating to such weapons: *The bombs were stored in the ammunition dump.*

an·ces·tral (an ses′ trəl) *adj.* of or inherited from the people from whom one is descended; traditional within a family or group.

an·cho·vy (an′ chō vē, an chō′ vē) *n.* a small fish closely related to the herring.

ap·par·el (ə par′ əl) *n.* clothing; attire.

ap·pease (ə pēz′) *v.t.* to cause to subside; to calm; to satisfy: *to appease her hunger.*

ap·prais·al (ə prā′ zəl) *n.* an estimate; an evaluation; a judgment about the value or quality of something.

ap·pre·hen·sion (ap′ ri hen′ shən) *n.* fear of what may happen; anxiety.

ap·ti·tude (ap′ tə tood′, ap′ tə tūd′) *n.* natural ability; talent.

ar·dent (ärd′ ənt) *adj.* full of strong feeling; passionate; enthusiastic: *an ardent Red Sox fan.*

ar·du·ous·ly (är′ joo əs lē) *adv.* with great exertion; in a hard-working manner.

ar·ro·gance (ar′ ə gəns) *n.* too much pride or self-importance; haughtiness.

a·skew (ə skū′) *adv., adj.* out of proper order; tilted to one side; crooked.

as·sem·blage (ə sem′ blij) *n.* a collection of people or things.

as·sent (ə sent′) *v.i.* to agree; to consent to.

as·ser·tion (ə sur′ shən) *n.* a positive statement; a declaration; a claim.

as·set (as′ et) *n.* something valuable; a property or a possession having a money value.

at·trib·ute (at′ rə būt′) *n.* a quality considered by others to belong to a particular person or thing; a trait.

at·tuned (ə toond′, ə tūnd′) *adj.* brought into harmony or agreement; feeling sympathy or deep understanding for.

aus·pi·cious (ôs pish′ əs) *adj.* promising; favorable; prosperous: *an auspicious occasion.*

a·venge (ə venj′) *v.t.* to get revenge; to relaliate in return for an injury or a wrong.

a·verse (ə vurs′) *adj.* reluctant; unwilling; against doing.

a·ver·sion (ə vur′ zhən, ə vur′ shən) *n.* a strong, specific dislike: *an aversion to green vegetables.*

PRONUNCIATION KEY
at; āpe; cär; end; mē; it; īce; hot; ōld; fôrk; wood; fool; oil; out; up; turn; sing; thin; <u>th</u>is, hw in white; zh in treasure; ə stands for a in ago, e in taken, i in pencil, o in lemon, u in circus.

a·vert (ə vurt′) *v.t.* to prevent; to ward off; to turn away.

a·vi·a·tor (ā′ vē ā′ tər, av′ ē a′ tər) *n.* the pilot of an airplane or another aircraft.

a·vid·ly (av′ id lē) *adv.* eagerly; with strong enthusiasm.

az·ure (azh′ ər, ā′ zhər) *adj.* sky blue.

B

bale·ful (bāl′ fəl) *adj.* harmful or evil; sinister: *a baleful expression.*

bal·last (bal′ əst) *n.* weighty material placed in a boat in order to keep the boat stable in the water.

bal·us·trade (bal′ əs trād′) *n.* the railing and upright supports of a staircase or a similar structure.

bar·bar·ic (bär bar′ ik) *adj.* uncivilized; savage; brutal: *barbaric tribes.*

bear·ing (bār′ ing) *n.* manner of carrying or conducting oneself; behavior.

bed·lam (bed′ ləm) *n.* a scene or a situation marked by wild uproar or confusion.

be·queath (bi kwēth′, bi kwēth′) *v.t.* to leave property in a will; to hand down to an heir.

be·witched (bi wicht′) *adj.* acting as if one has been affected by witchcraft or magic; charmed; fascinated: *He was bewitched by her lovely smile.*

bi·cul·tur·al (bī kul′ chər əl) *adj.* relating to the customs and traditions of two different groups of people.

bile (bīl) *n.* a yellow or greenish bitter body fluid that aids in digestion; also, bad temper; crankiness; nastiness.

bi·lin·gual (bī ling′ gwəl) *adj.* capable of using two languages with equal skill.

bi·o·log·i·cal·ly (bī′ ə loj′ ik [ə] lē) *adv.* in a way relating to *biology*, the science that studies living things.

bi·zarre (bi zär′) *adj.* strikingly odd; eccentric; fantastic.

blanched (blancht) *adj.* white; pale.

bland (bland) *adj.* not sharp or harsh; pleasantly smooth; without emotion or expression.

bloat·ed (blō′ tid) *adj.* swollen; puffed up.

bom·bard (bom bärd′) *v.t.* to hit with a stream of high-speed particles in the form of a ray; to hit forcefully and repeatedly.

bond·age (bon′ dij) *n.* slavery.

bos·om (booz′ əm, boo′ zəm) *n.* the upper front part of a person's chest.

boun·ty (boun′ tē) *n.* a generous gift or reward.

bran·dish (bran′ dish) *v.t.* to wave, shake, or swing a weapon in a threatening manner: *to brandish a sword.*

bra·va·do (brə vä′ dō) *n.* boldness or daring displayed in a showy or boastful manner.

breadth (bredth, bretth) *n.* width.

break·through (brāk′ throo′) *n.* a major development or discovery.

britch·es (brich′ iz) *n., pl. Informal English.* pants reaching to or just below the knees. (The word is an informal spelling of *breeches,* which has the same pronunciation.)

brooch (brōch, brooch) *n.* a piece of jewelry that is pinned to the clothes and fastened with a clasp; an ornamental pin.

buf·fet (buf′ it) *n.* a blow with the hand or the fist.

C _____

cal·cu·la·tion (kal′ kyə lā′ shən) *n.* something that is figured out by using arithmetic; a mathematical reckoning; a computation.

can·de·la·brum (kand′ əl ä′ brəm, kand′ əl ā′ brəm) *n.* a large branched candlestick.

can·non·ad·ing (kan′ ə nā′ ding) *n.* heavy or continuous firing from cannons or other big guns.

can·vass (kan′ vəs) *v.t.* to go through an area or among a group of people in order to obtain business orders, contributions, votes, or opinions.

ca·per (kā′ pər) *n.* a light-hearted leap or jump.

cap·tiv·i·ty (kap tiv′ ə tē) *n.* the state or condition of being a prisoner; confinement.

car·rel (kar′ əl) *n.* a small enclosure or partitioned area for individual study, usually near the book stacks in a library.

cat·a·pult (kat′ ə pult′) *v.i.* to leap; to be launched or flung.

cav·al·ry (kav′ əl rē) *n.* a military unit trained to fight on horseback.—*adj.* relating to such a military unit: *cavalry uniforms.*

ca·vort (kə vôrt′) *v.i. Informal English.* to jump around playfully; to dance.

ce·les·tial (sə les′ chəl) *adj.* or or relating to the sky or heavens; heavenly: *A star is a celestial body.*

chap·el (chap′ əl) *n.* a small building used for worship.

char·ac·ter·ize (kar′ ik tə riz′) *v.t.* to describe a quality of; to be a basic quality of: *A desert is characterized by little rainfall.*

char·i·ta·ble (char′ ə tə bəl) *adj.* kindly; generous.

cir·cuit (sur′ kit) *n.* a group of places at which a traveling performer performs; also, a periodic journey from one place to another; a recurring or circular journey.

ci·vil·ian (si vil′ yən) *n.* a person who is not a member of the military.

cleave (klēv) *v.t.* to split or part by force.

clin·ic (klin′ ik) *n.* an institution or a section of a hospital that treats patients who do not remain overnight and that often charges a reduced fee.

clutch (kluch) *n.* a group of eggs laid at one time.

cog·ni·zant (kog′ nə zənt, kon′ ə zənt) *adj.* aware; having knowledge of.

col·ic (kol′ ik) *n.* a sudden attack of severe stomach pain, especially in infants.

col·league (kol′ ēg) *n.* a fellow member of one's profession; a coworker; an associate.

com·mence (kə mens′) *v.t.* to begin; to start.

com·mis·sar·y (kom′ ə ser′ ē) *n.* a store that sells food and supplies in a military camp—*adj.* relating to such a store or its food and supplies: *commissary goods.*

PRONUNCIATION KEY

at; āpe; cär; end; mē; it; īce; hot; ōld; fôrk; wood; fool; oil; out; up; turn; sing; thin; this, hw in white; zh in treasure; ə stands for a in ago, e in taken, i in pencil, o in lemon, u in circus.

com·pen·sa·tion (kom′ pən sā′ shən) *n.* payment in return for one's services.

com·pet·i·tive (kəm pet′ ə tiv) *adj.* relating to a contest or a rivalry; showing the ambition or desire to win: *competitive spirit.*

com·pla·cent (kəm plā′ sənt) *adj.* self-satisfied; so pleased with oneself that one sees no need to act differently.

com·pli·ance (kəm plī əns) *n.* acting in accordance with a request, a wish, or a command; following a set of rules; obedience.

com·pul·so·ry (kəm pul′ sər ē) *adj.* required: *In my school, taking English is compulsory.*

con·ceit·ed (kən sē′ tid) *adj.* having an overly high opinion of oneself; vain.

con·front (kən frunt′) *v.t.* to face; to meet face to face.

con·gen·ial (kən jēn′ yəl) *adj.* agreeable; pleasant.

con·jure (kon′ jər, kun′ jər) *v.t.* to summon or cause to appear by using magic words.

con·sci·en·tious (kon′ shē en′ shəs) *adj.* hard working; careful about details; showing concern for one's work.

con·struc·tive (kən struk′ tiv) *adj.* serving to build, help, or improve; useful.

con·sult·ant (kən sul′ tənt) *n.* a professional or technical adviser.

con·tem·plate (kon′ təm plāt′) *v.t.* to give careful attention to; to consider carefully.

con·tin·gent (kən tin′ jənt) *n.* a group of people formed from and part of a larger group: *A contingent of senators visited the Mideast.*

con·tra·dic·to·ry (kon′ trə dik′ tər ē) *adj.* containing elements or qualities that are the opposite of one another; having many discrepancies; inconsistent.

con·ven·tion (kən ven′ shən) *n.* a formal gathering of the members of a club, a profession, a political organization, or another group.

con·vey (kən vā′) *v.t.* to communicate; to express; to carry from one person or place to another.

con·vic·tion (kən vik′ shən) *n.* a strong opinion or belief.

co·or·di·na·tion (kō ôr′ də nā′ shən) *n.* the ability to use and control different body parts at the same time: *To run while dribbling a basketball requires coordination—adj.* relating to this ability: *a coordination test.*

cope (kōp) *v.i.* to deal with successfully; to be able to handle.

cor·rupt (kə rupt′) *adj.* dishonest; crooked.

coun·te·nance (koun′ tə nəns) *n.* face; features; expression.

crag·gy (krag′ ē) *adj.* rough or irregular; rugged: *a craggy face.*

cra·ven (krā′ vən) *adj.* cowardly.

cre·a·tiv·i·ty (krē′ ā tiv′ ə tē) *n.* the quality of being original in thought or performance.

crest·fall·en (krest′ fô′ lən) *adj.* discouraged; disappointed.

cringe (krinj) *v.i.* to shrink or crouch, especially in horror, fear, pain, or disgust.

cri·sis (krī sis) *pl.,* **cri·ses** (krī sēz) *n.* an incident or a period of great difficulty, especially one that is a turning point: *an economic crisis.*

cri·tic (krit′ ik) *n.* a person who judges the achievements of others; a reviewer.

cu·bi·cle (kū′ bi kəl) *n.* a small room, compartment, or walled section: *a secretary's cubicle.*

cul·mi·na·tion (kul′ mə nā′ shən) *n.* the highest or most decisive point; the climax.

cul·prit (kul′ prit) *n.* a person guilty of some crime.

cur (kur) *n.* a worthless and despised person; also, a worthless or bad-tempered dog.

cus·to·dy (kus′ tə dē) *n.* imprisonment; the state of being under arrest.

cyn·i·cal·ly (sin′ ik [ə] lē) *adv.* in a manner that shows doubt about the goodness, sincerity, or unselfishness of another person's motives or actions.

D _____

dam·ask (dam′ əsk) *n.* a heavy fabric woven with patterns or designs and used for such items as tablecloths and napkins.

dec·a·dence (dek′ əd əns) *n.* a condition of decline or decay, especially of a society or a culture.

de·camp (di kamp′) *v.i.* to depart quickly or secretly; to run away.

de·cep·tion (di sep′ shən) *n.* an act that makes someone believe what is not true; a misleading act; a trick.

dec·o·ra·tive (dek′ ər ə tiv, dek′ ə rā′ tiv) *adj.* displaying style, color, or other decoration; serving as an ornament instead of having a more practical use.

ded·i·ca·tion (ded′ ə kā′ shən) *n.* devotion to duty.

de·duce (di dōōs′, di dūs′) *v.t.* to draw a conclusion based on facts and logic.

de·fect (dē′ fekt, di fekt′) *n.* a flaw, a weakness, or a blemish.

def·er·en·tial·ly (def′ ə ren′ shəl ē) *adv.* with respect for the authority of; respectfully; courteously.

de·fi·ance (di fī əns) *n.* bold or open resistance to an opponent or an opposing force; contempt for an opponent or for authority.

de·grad·ing (di grā′ ding) *adj.* bringing contempt or dishonor to; humiliating.

de·lir·i·um (di lēr′ ē əm) *n.* a temporary state of mental disturbance.

de·ployed (di ploid′) *adj.* placed in an appropriate position according to a plan; positioned strategically in a wide area: *soldiers deployed for battle.*

de·prive (di prīv′) *v.t.* to prevent from having or enjoying; to take away from: *to deprive us of our rights.*

der·e·lict (der′ ə likt′) *adj.* abandoned; neglected: *a derelict building.*

de·ri·sive (di rī siv) *adj.* insulting; making fun of.

de·rived (di rīvd′) *adj.* obtained from a particular source or origin; originating in: *a word derived from Latin.*

PRONUNCIATION KEY
at; āpe; cär; end; mē; it; īce; hot; ōld; fôrk; wood; fōōl; oil; out; up; turn; sing; thin; <u>th</u>is, **hw** in **wh**ite; **zh** in treasure; ə stands for **a** in ago, **e** in taken, **i** in pencil, **o** in lemon, **u** in circus.

des·o·late (des′ ə lit) *adj.* having few or no inhabitants; isolated; lonely.

de·spair·ing·ly (di spār′ ing lē) *adv.* with a loss of all hope; hopelessly.

de·spise (di spīz′) *v.t.* to look down on; to feel contempt for; to scorn.

de·tached (di tacht′) *adj.* not interested or involved emotionally; unconcerned; separated from.

de·ter·rent (di tur′ ənt, di ter′ ənt) *n.* something that discourages or keeps from acting, especially by arousing fear or doubt: *The presence of police is a deterrent to crime.*

de·tri·tus (di trī′ təs) *n.* gravel, sand, or other fragments torn away from larger rocks by natural forces such as erosion or volcanoes; debris.

dex·ter·i·ty (deks ter′ ə tē) *n.* skill in controlling the body or mind.

dif·fer·en·ti·ate (dif′ ər en′ shē′ āt′) *v.i.* to understand or notice a difference; to distinguish between.

dig·it (dij′ it) *n.* any numeral from 0 through 9.

di·min·u·tive (di min′ yə tiv) *n.* a small kind or variety of something; a dwarf.

dis·a·bled (dis ā′ bəld) *adj.* having a physical handicap; crippled.—*n.* handicapped people: *job training for the disabled.*

dis·as·trous (di zas′ trəs) *adj.* marked by great misfortune; extremely unfortunate; very terrible.

dis·col·or·a·tion (dis kul′ ə rā′ shən) *n.* a change in the color of; a stain.

dis·dain·ful (dis dān′ fəl) *adj.* feeling or showing contempt; scornful; looking down on other people or things.

dis·grun·tled (dis grunt′ əld) *adj.* in a bad humor; displeased; cross.

dis·lodge (dis loj′) *v.t.* to force out; to move out of place or position.

dis·pel (dis pel′) *v.t.* to drive away; to cause to disappear: *to dispel our fears.*

dis·rupt (dis rupt′) *v.t.* to throw into disorder; to disturb; to interrupt the normal continuation of: *A noisy student can disrupt a class.*

dis·tort (dis tôrt′) *v.t.* changing the natural or usual form of; twisting or bending out of shape.

dis·traught (dis trôt′) *adj.* mentally confused; distracted; bewildered.

di·verge (di vurj′, dī vurj′) *v.t.* to move in different directions from a common point; to branch out.

di·vest (di vest′, dī vest′) *v.t.* to strip away; to rid or free someone of something: *They divest themselves of all responsibilities.*

doff (dof, dôf) *v.t.* to lift or remove one's hat in greeting.

do·mes·tic (də mes′ tik) *adj.* trained or able to live with or near human beings; tame: *a domestic animal.* Also, relating to the home or family: *a domestic scene.*

dom·i·nant (dom′ ə nənt) *adj.* most important, forceful, or widespread.

do·min·ion (də min′ yən) *n.* the territory or country under the rule of a particular leader or government; the realm.

dras·tic (dras′ tik) *adj.* having a forceful or too forceful effect; extreme: *Declaring war was a drastic step.*

draw·ing room (drô′ ing rōōm, drô′ ing

room') *n.* a room for entertaining guests—*adj.* relating to such a room: *a drawing-room sofa.*

drawl (drôl) *n.* slow speech, usually with drawn-out vowel sounds.

dregs (dregz) *n., pl.* the most worthless or least desirable part: *the dregs of humanity.*

drone (drōn) *n.* a dull, continuous buzzing or humming sound: *the drone of bees.*

du·ly (doo' lē, dū' lē) *adv.* suitably; to a degree or amount that is proper or due: *We were duly concerned.*

E _____

ec·sta·sy (ek' stə sē) *n.* a state of overwhelming joy or delight.

edg·y (ej' ē) *adj.* on edge; uneasy; sharp: *His voice was edgy.*

el·der (el' dər) *n.* any of a group of small trees or bushes that have edible berries.

e·lec·tron·ics (i lek' tron' iks, ē' lek tron' iks) *n.,pl.* the science that studies the way electrons move through gases, a vacuum, etc., and that has resulted in the development of transistor radios and computers, among other things. (The word is often treated as a singular noun: *Electronics is her field.*)

e·lic·it (i lis' it) *v.t.* to bring out; to reveal: *elicit a response from students.*

el·i·gi·ble (el' i jə bəl) *adj.* qualified for; suitable for; allowed to perform some activity: *Only citizens are eligible to vote.*

e·lude (i lood') *v.t.* to escape from; to avoid.

em·bel·lish (em bel' ish) *v.t.* to touch up or improve by adding details.

e·nam·eled (i nam' əld) *adj.* coated with *enamel,* a glasslike, usually opaque substance that is fused to metal, pottery, and other surfaces; having a hard, glossy coating.

en·croach·ing (en krōch' ing) *adj.* going beyond usual limits; making gradual inroads: *the encroaching sea.*

en·tou·rage (än' too räzh') *n.* a group or train of attendants; a following.

en·vel·ope (en vel' əp) *v.t.* to wrap up or cover completely.

en·voy (en' voi, än' voi) *n.* a diplomat or another government representative or messenger.

e·pis·tle (i pis' əl) *n.* a letter.

eq·ua·bly (ek' wə blē, ēk' wə blē) *adv.* without seeming disturbed; calmly; in a steady manner.

es·carp·ment (es kärp' mənt) *n.* a steep slope or cliff.

e·vade (i vād') *v.t.* to avoid, especially through clever maneuvers; to escape.

e·voke (i vōk') *v.t.* to call forth or bring out: *These photograph albums evoke memories.*

ex·e·cute (ek' sə kūt') *v.t.* to carry out; to put into effect: *execute a plan.*

ex·e·cu·tion·er (ek' sə kū' shə nər) *n.* a

PRONUNCIATION KEY
at; āpe; cär; end; mē; it; īce; hot; ōld; fôrk; wood; fool; oil; out; up; turn; sing; thin; this, hw in white; zh in treasure; ə stands for a in ago, e in taken, i in pencil, o in lemon, u in circus.

person who carries out a death sentence imposed by law.

ex·haled (eks hāld′, eks′ āld) *adj.* breathed out; released from the lungs.

ex·hil·a·rat·ing (ig zil′ ə rā′ ting) *adj.* very lively or exciting.

ex·ile (eg′ zīl, ek′ sīl) *v.t.* to banish a person from his or her country—a person who has been banished or forced away from his or her country.

ex·ter·nal (iks turn′ əl) *adj.* situated on the outside or on the surface; outer; superficial.

ex·trem·i·ty (iks trem′ ə tē) *n.* a leg or another limb of the body.

F _____

fast (fast) *adj.* not running or fading easily: *fast colors.*

fea·si·ble (fē′ zə bəl) *adj.* capable of being done or carried out; capable of being used successfully.

fee·bly (fē′ blē) *adv.* without strength or force; weakly.

fer·vent·ly (fur′ vənt lē) *adv.* in a manner showing great feeling; intensely.

fick·le (fik′ əl) *adj.* inconsistent; changeable.

flaw (flô) *n.* something that spoils completeness or perfection; a weak spot; a failing: *a flaw in her character.*

fledg·ling (flej′ ling) *n.* a young bird that has just learned to fly.

flue (flōo) *n.* a chimney passage or a pipe for removing smoke, hot air, or waste gas: *a stove flue.*

for·go (fôr gō′) *v.t.* to refrain from; to give up; to do without.

for·mu·late (fôr′ myə lāt′) *v.t.* to develop; to put into systematic form: *formulate a theory.*

found·er (foun′ dər) *n.* a person who establishes or starts something: *the founder of the Jamestown colony.*

fraud (frôd) *n.* deceit or trickery, especially when practiced intentionally in order to cheat another of money, rights, or property.

fret·ful (fret′ fəl) *adj.* tending to be easily irritated or worried; peevish.

frock (frok) *n.* a woman's or girl's dress.

fu·gi·tive (fū′ jə tiv) *n.* a person who is running away, often from danger, capture, or cruel circumstances. —*adj.* relating to such a person: *the Fugitive Slave Laws.*

func·tion·al (fungk′ shən əl) *adj.* capable of functioning; workable; practical.

fu·tile·ly (fū′ til ē, fū′ tīl ē) *adv.* in a useless or hopeless manner; vainly.

G _____

gal·ler·y (gal′ ər ē, gal′ rē) *n.* a collection of works of art for display or sale; also, a balcony.

gal·va·nize (gal′ və nīz) *v.t.* to spur into sudden action; to rouse; to stimulate; also, to coat a metal, especially iron or steel, with a protective coating of zinc. **gal·va·niz·ing.** *adj.* about to be spurred into action; rousing; stimulating.

garb (gärb) *n.* a distinctive form of clothing; a special outfit.

gen·der (jen′ dər) *n. Informal English.* the

condition of being of the male or female sex.

gen·ial·ly (jēn′ yə lē, jē′ nē ə lē) *adv.* in a pleasant manner; cheerfully.

glade (glād) *n.* an open space in a forest or another wooded area.

gos·sa·mer (gos′ ə mar) *n.* a graceful cobweb; also a thin, gauzy fabric.—*adj.* like gossamer; light and delicate: *a dragonfly's gossamer wings.*

grade (grād) *n.* a slope, such as on a road or a railroad track.

gram·o·phone (gram′ ə fōn′) *n.* an old-fashioned record player.

grav·i·ta·tion (grav′ ə tā′ shən) *n.* the force of mutual attraction that exists between any two bodies in the universe; also called *gravity*, especially when speaking of the earth's pull.

griev·ous (grē′ vəs) *adj.* causing grief or anguish; very serious; grave.

gri·mace (grim′ is, gri mās′) *v.i.* to make a twisted facial expression usually indicating dislike, pain, or anger.

gross·ly (grōs′ lē) *adv.* in a glaring or startling way; extremely; obviously.

gro·tesque (grō tesk′) *adj.* unnatural or ugly in shape or appearance; very odd; ridiculous.

gru·el·ing (grōō ə ling, grōō′ ling) *adj.* very difficult or tiring; exhausting.

gump·tion (gump′ shən) *n. Informal English.* energy, ambition, and initiative; the ability to take the first steps in an undertaking: *To start your own business takes gumption.*

gun·ny·sack (gun′ ē sak′) *n.* a strong, durable cloth bag.

H

hag·gard (hag′ ərd) *adj.* having a wild or worn look, especially from exertion, tension, or suffering.

hale (hāl) *adj.* in good physical condition; healthy.

ha·lo (hā′ lō) *n.* a ring or a circle of light above a person's head or surrounding a person or a thing.

han·gar (hang′ ər, han′ gar) *n.* a building designed to shelter aircraft.

har·ry (har′ ē) *v.t.* to trouble repeatedly; to torment; also to rob by force during a raid or an attack; to loot.

heed·less (hēd′ lis) *adj.* not paying attention to; unmindful; careless.

heir (ār) *n.* a person who inherits a family estate or other property after the death of the former owner.

hence (hens) *adv.* from this time on. *Archaic.* from this place; from here.

he·red·i·ty (hə red′ ə tē) *n.* a creature's biological inheritance; all the qualities transmitted from parents to children by means of genes.

hilt (hilt) *n.* the handle of a sword.

hoax (hōks) *n.* a trick; a deception; a fake or deceitful act.

horde (hôrd) *n.* a large group or swarm of people; also, a tribe or a clan from Mongolia, an area of east central Asia that extends from northern China to Siberia.

PRONUNCIATION KEY
at; āpe; cär; end; mē; it; īce; hot; ōld; fôrk; wood; fōōl; oil; out; up; turn; sing; thin; <u>th</u>is, hw in white; zh in treasure; ə stands for a in ago, e in taken, i in pencil, o in lemon, u in circus.

hos·til·i·ty (hos til′ ə tē) *n.* the attitude of an enemy; a warlike attitude or state; a feeling of intense dislike.

hu·mil·i·ty ([h]ū mil′ ə tē) *n.* the quality of being humble; a lack of pride or conceit.

husk·i·ly (hus′ kə lē) *adv.* in a hoarse and deep tone.

husk·y (hus′ kē) *adj.* big and strong: *a husky man.*

I

i·den·ti·cal (ī den′ ti kəl) *adj.* exactly alike; the same in every respect.

i·den·ti·fy (ī den′ tə fī′) *v.t.* to establish that someone or something is a particular person or things; to recognize; to give a name to.

il·log·i·cal (i loj′ i kəl) *adj.* not logical; not following a scientific or clearly thought out method of reasoning; unreasonable.

im·men·si·ty (i men′ sə tē) *n.* hugeness; vastness; largeness.

im·paired (im pārd′) *adj.* weakened; damaged.—*n.* people with weakened or damaged physical or mental abilities: *the hearing impaired.*

im·pend·ing (im pen′ ding) *adj.* about to occur; threatening: *an impending storm.*

im·pe·ri·ous (im pēr′ ē əs) *adj.* very bossy; like a powerful or harsh ruler; domineering: *an imperious command.*

im·pe·tus (im′ pə təs) *n.* motive; incentive; a reason that spurs one to act.

im·pose (im pōz′) *v.t.* to establish by using

one's power or authority; to enforce.

im·print (im′ print′) *n.* a mark; an effect: *The scientist left his imprint on future experiments.*

im·pu·dent (im′ pyə dənt) *adj.* overly forward; displaying too much boldness: *an impudent remark.*

im·pul·sive (im pul′ siv) *adj.* inclined to act without planning or thinking ahead.

in·car·na·tion (in′ kär nā′ shən) *n.* the earthly form taken on by a god, a spirit, or another supernatural being.

in·cen·tive (in sen′ tiv) *n.* a reason that spurs one to do something; a reward for working harder.

in·com·pre·hen·si·ble (in′ kom pri hen′ sə bəl) *adj.* not able to be understood.

in·cred·u·lous·ly (in krej′ ə ləs lē) *adv.* with strong doubt or disbelief; with great surprise.

in·de·ter·mi·nate (in′ di tur′ mi nit) *adj.* not able to be determined; without definite limits; indefinite.

in·dig·ni·ty (in dig′ nə tē) *n.* an insult; humiliation; something that robs one of one's pride or self-respect.

in·dulge (in dulj′) *v.i.* to do something to an unhealthy extent; give in to a weakness.—*v.t.* to give in to the wishes or demands of: *to indulge a child.*

in·ept (i nept′) *adj.* lacking the skill, intelligence, or other personal qualities needed to perform effectively; incompetent; awkward.

in·ex·plic·a·ble (in′ iks plik′ ə bəl, in eks′ pli kə bəl) *adj.* not able to be explained.

in·flict (in flikt′) *v.t.* to cause by striking;

to force something unpleasant on someone: *to inflict punishment.*

in·haled (in hāld′) *adj.* breathed in; drawn into the lungs.

i·ni·ti·a·tion (i nish′ ē ā′ shən) *n.* the special ceremonies or acts that a young person must perform in order to be considered an adult member of a tribe.

in·no·va·tor (in′ ə vā′ tər) *n.* a person who introduces something new.

in·nu·mer·a·ble (i nōō′ mər ə bəl, i nū′ mər ə bəl) *adj.* too many to be counted: *innumerable stars in the sky.*

in·scru·ta·ble (in skrōō′ tə bəl) *adj.* not easily understood; mysterious.

in·sin·u·at·ing·ly (in sin′ ū ā′ ting lē) *adv.* in a manner that suggests or hints at an additional truth; suggestively.

in·so·lence (in′ sə ləns) *n.* rude speech or behavior.

in·ten·sive (in ten′ siv) *adj.* thorough and concentrated: *an intensive study.*

in·ter·mit·tent (in′ tər mit′ ənt) *adj.* stopping and starting again; coming at intervals: *intermittent rain.*

in·tern (in′ turn′) *n.* an assistant doctor who has recently graduated from medical school, works at a hospital or a clinic, and is supervised by a more experienced doctor.

in·ter·pre·ta·tion (in tur′ prə tā′ shən) *n.* an understanding of the facts and details; a conclusion; an explanation.

in·ter·ro·ga·tion (in ter′ ə gā′ shən) *n.* an examination consisting of a series of questions posed formally and systematically.

in·ti·mate (in′ tə mit) *adj.* well-acquainted: *an intimate friend.*

in·tri·ca·cy (in′ tri kə sē) *n.* something puzzling or complex.

in·trud·er (in trōō′ dər) *n.* a person who comes in as a disturbing or unwelcome addition; a trespasser; an outsider.

in·val·u·a·ble (in val′ ū ə bəl, in val′ yə bəl) *adj.* beyond evaluation; so valuable that no precise value can be assigned; priceless.

in·vec·tive (in vek′ tiv) *n.* strong criticism, insults, or curses; verbal abuse.

in·vert·ed (in vurt′ id) *adj.* turned upside down; reversed.

i·ron·i·cal·ly (ī ron′ ik [ə] lē) *adv.* in a manner that means the opposite of what it says on the surface; sarcastically: *"I just love waiting in long lines," she said ironically.*

ir·re·sist·i·ble (ir′ i zis′ tə bəl) *adj.* not able to be fought against; captivating: *an irresistible smile.*

i·so·la·tion (ī′ sə lā′ shən, is′ ə lā′ shən) *n.* the state of being separated or away from others; solitude; being alone.

J

ja·lop·y (jə lop′ ē) *n. Informal English.* an old or broken-down car.

jos·tle (jos′ əl) *v.t.* to bump, push, or shove roughly.

jour·nal·ism (jurn′ əl iz′ əm) *n.* the news-

PRONUNCIATION KEY
at; āpe; cär; end; mē; it; īce; hot; ōld; fôrk; wood; fōol; oil; out; up; turn; sing; thin; this, hw in white; zh in treasure; ə stands for a in ago, e in taken, i in pencil, o in lemon, u in circus.

paper and magazine industry; working for newspapers or magazines.

K

keel (kēl) *n.* the main piece that supports the rest of the frame of a ship, a boat, or an aircraft.

keen·ing (kēn′ ing) *adj.* wailing loudly for the dead, as was the custom in ancient Britain.

kin·ship (kin′ ship′) *n.* family relationship, any close relationship.

knave (nāv) *n.* a deceitful or disloyal person; a villain.

L

lapse (laps) *n.* a small error or mistake, especially one in which a person slips back into bad behavior.

len·til (len′ til) *n.* a seed of the pea family, cooked and eaten as a vegetable and popular in Europe and Asia.

le·thar·gic (li thär′ jik) *adj.* inactive as a result of feeling no interest; sluggish.

lev·el-head·ed (lev′ əl hed′ id) *adj.* having common sense and sound judgment; sensible.

lev·y (lev′ ē) *v.t.* to collect by force or by law: *levy a fine.*

li·a·bil·i·ty (lī′ ə bil′ ə tē) *n.* something that works to one's disadvantage; something that costs money instead of providing money.

lilt (lilt) *n.* a light, graceful, singing quality in a voice.

loath (lōth, lōth) *adj.* reluctant; unwilling: *He was loath to leave.*

loathe (lōth) *v.t.* to view with extreme disgust or hate; to detest.

loath·some (lōth′ səm, lōth′ səm) *adj.* extremely disgusting; hateful; repulsive.

lo·cale (lō kal′) *n.* a particular place; a setting connected to particular events or circumstances.—*adj.* relating to such a place or setting.

lu·rid·ly (loor′ id lē) *adv.* with a reddish glow or fiery glare: *The fire gleamed luridly.*

lus·ter (lus′ tər) *n.* the quality of shining by reflected light; sheen; brightness.

lux·u·ri·ate (lug zhoor′ ē āt, luk shoor′ ē āt) **-at·ed, -at·ing,** *v.i.* enjoying great pleasure; taking great delight in; indulging oneself.

M

mal·con·tent (mal′ kən tent′) *adj.* not happy or satisfied with existing conditions.

man·ner·ism (man′ ə riz′ əm) *n.* a quality peculiar to a person; a characteristic way of speaking or behaving.

man·or (man′ ər) *n.* the main house on an estate.—*adj.* relating to this house: *manor grounds.*

man·u·al (man′ yoo əl) *adj.* done by the hands: *The manual alphabet uses hand signals to help deaf people communicate.*

mar·shal (mär′ shəl) *v.t.* **-shal·ing** to gather or place in an arrangement designed to achieve a particular goal.

mas·sa·cre (mas′ ə kər) *n.* the brutal, random killing of a number of people.

ma·tron·ly (mā′ trən lē) *adj.* like a mature, married woman; motherly.

max·im (mak′ sim) *n.* a brief statement expressing a general truth or belief.

max·i·mum (mak′ sə məm) *adj.* highest possible: *the maximum speed allowed.*

me·di·ate (mē′ dē āt′) *v.i.* to serve as a third party attempting to settle an argument between two other people or groups.

mer·it (mer′ it) *n.* something deserving reward or praise.

met·al·ur·gist (met′ əl ur′ jist) *n.* a person who separates metals from the rocks that contain them and prepares the metals for use.

mete (mēt) *v.t.* to distribute in fixed portions; to allot; to dole out; *mete out punishment.*

mien (mēn) *n.* a person's manner or appearance; bearing.

mi·grant (mī′ grənt) *n.* someone who moves seasonally from one region to another.—*adj.* traveling: *a migrant farm worker.*

mince (mins) *v.i.* to walk with very short steps.

mi·rage (mi räzh′) *n.* an optical illusion, such as the appearance of water in a desert when in fact no water is present; a false vision.

mire (mīr) *n.* an area of wet, soft ground; deep, soft mud.

mo·bil·i·ty (mō bil′ ə tē) *n.* movement; the ability to move.

mo·rose (mə rōs′) *adj.* bad-tempered, withdrawn, and gloomy.

mote (mōt) *n.* a speck; a particle: *a mote of dust.*

mo·ti·va·tion (mō′ tə vā′ shən) *n.* something that provides a goal that causes a person to act; a driving force; a reason for acting in a particular way.

mot·tled (mot′ əld) *adj.* marked with spots or streaks in different shades or colors; spotted; streaked: *a mottled carpet.*

mul·ti·tude (mul′ tə tōōd′, mul′ tə tūd′) *n.* a great number of people; a crowd.

N

nat·u·ral·ist (nach′ ər ə list, nach′ rə list) *n.* a person who studies natural science, especially botany (the study of plants), or zoology (the study of animals).

ne·go·ti·a·tor (ni gō′ shē ā′ tər) *n.* a person who manages or arranges things; a person who discusses matters with others in order to reach a useful agreement.

niche (nich) *n.* a place or position for which one is particularly suited; also, a recess in a wall, often containing a statue, a large vase, or shelves for displaying ornaments.

noc·tur·nal (nok turn′ əl) *adj.* of or occurring at night.

non·cha·lant·ly (non′ shə lant′ lē, non′ chə lant′ lē) *adv.* in an unconcerned manner.

no·ta·ble (nō′ tə bəl) *adj.* noteworthy; remarkable; worthy of attention.

PRONUNCIATION KEY
at; āpe; cär; end; mē; it; īce; hot; ōld; fôrk; wood; fōōl; oil; out; up; turn; sing; thin; <u>th</u>is, **hw** in **wh**ite; **zh** in treasure; ə stands for **a** in ago, **e** in taken, **i** in pencil, **o** in lemon, **u** in circus.

nov·ice (nov′ is) *n.* a person who is new to an activity or an occupation; a beginner.

O _____

o·be·di·ence (ō bē ′dē əns) *n.* the act of obeying; behavior that follows the rules, commands, requests, or wishes of others: *The puppy was taught obedience.*

ob·lit·er·ate (ə blit′ ə rāt′, ōb lit′ e rāt′) *v.t.* to destroy completely; to remove all traces of; to wipe out.

ob·scene (əb sēn′) *adj.* insulting to accepted standards of decent behavior; not decent; improper.

ob·scure (əb skyoor′) *v.t.* to hide from view; to darken or conceal.

o·di·ous (ō′ dē əs) *adj.* causing hate or disgust; detestable.

of·fen·sive (ə fen′ siv) *adj.* causing resentment, anger, or displeasure; insulting. —*n.* the position, attitude, or actions of the attacker, as opposed to the defender; an attack.

o·mis·sion (ō mish′ ən) *n.* something that is left out; something that is not included.

op·tion·al (op′ shən əl) *adj.* not required; depending on choice: *The makeup test was optional.*

o·ver·wrought (ō′ vər rôt′) *adj.* worked up to an unhealthy excess of excitement or nervousness.

P _____

pag·eant·ry (paj′ ən trē) *n.* splendid celebration; spectacular display: *Fourth of July pageantry.*

pall (pôl) *n.* something that covers or conceals with an atmosphere of darkness and gloom: *A pall fell over the factory when the layoffs were announced.*

pal·lor (pal′ ər) *n.* lack of natural or healthy color; paleness.

pan·de·mo·ni·um (pan′ də mō′ nē əm) *n.* wild disorder; uproar; a great disturbance.

par·o·dy (par′ ə dē) *n.* an imitation of something that makes the thing seem funny or ridiculous; also, a poor or weak imitation.

pas·sion·ate·ly (pash′ ə nit lē) *adv.* with strong feeling.

pas·sive (pas′ iv) *adj.* putting up no resistance; not active; accepting without fighting or arguing.

pa·tron (pā′ trən) *n.* a supporter; a steady customer or fan.

pau·per (pô′ pər) *n.* a very poor person.

pel·let (pel′ it) *n.* a small ball.

pen·i·tent (pen′ ə tənt) *adj.* sorry for having done wrong and willing to make up for the wrongdoing.

pen·nant (pen′ ənt) *n.* a long, usually triangular, flag.

per·ceive (pər sēv′) *v.t.* to be or become aware of through the senses; to see, hear, taste, smell, or feel; to take in or grasp mentally.

pe·rim·e·ter (pə rim′ ə tər) *n.* the boundary of an area.

per·mis·sive (pər mis′ iv) *adj.* allowing a great deal of freedom; not strict; lenient: *a permissive parent.*

per·se·ver·ance (pur′ sə vēr′ əns) *n.* persistence; patient effort.

pe·ruse (pə rōōz′) *v.t.* to read through or examine carefully.

pe·ti·tion (pə tish′ ən) *n.* a formal request made to an authority: *One hundred students signed a petition asking for more school funds.*

pet·tish·ly (pet′ ish lē) *adv.* in a cross or grouchy manner.

phys·i·cist (fiz′ ə sist) *n.* a person trained in *physics*, the science concerned with matter, energy, and the relationship between them, and including the study of mechanics, light, heat, sound, electricity, and magnetism.

pil·grim (pil′ grəm) *n.* a traveler.

pit·tance (pit′ əns) *n.* a small amount or allowance, especially of money.

plaint (plānt) *n.* a complaint made in anger or distress; a grievance.

plan·e·tar·i·um (plan′ ə tär′ ē əm) *n.* a place that displays heavenly bodies such as planets and stars, usually by projecting their images on the inside of a dome.

pluck·y (pluk′ ē) *adj.* showing courage and spirit, especially in the face of danger or difficulty.

plum·met (plum′ it) *v.i.* to fall or drop straight downward; to plunge.

pon·ti·fi·cat·ing (pon tif′ i kā′ ting) *adj.* speaking with haughtiness or self-importance.

po·ten·tial·ly (pə ten′ shə lē) *adv.* possibly; having the ability to become: *potentially useful.*

pre·car·i·ous (pri kār′ ē əs) *adj.* not secure; dangerous; hazardous.

pres·tige (pres tēzh′, pres tēj′, pres′ tij) *n.* influence based on previous success or achievements; power to command the respect or admiration of others.

pre·sume (pri zo͞om′) *v.t.* to accept as true until proven otherwise; to take for granted; to suppose.

price·less (prīs′ lis) *adj.* too valuable to be assigned a price; very valuable.

prim·ly (prim′ lē) *adv.* in an overly formal or stiff manner: *She dressed primly.*

pri·or (prī′ ər) *adj.* preceding in time or order. **prior to,** before.

pri·or·i·ty (prī ôr′ ə tē, prī or′ ə tē) *n.* a matter receiving one's chief attention or emphasis: *Getting a job was her priority.*

proc·la·ma·tion (prok′lə mā′ shən) *n.* an official public announcement.

prod·i·gy (prod′ ə jē) *n.* a gifted or skilled person, especially a child.

pro·duc·tiv·i·ty (prō′ duk tiv′ ə tē, prod′ ək tiv′ ə tē) *n.* the amount of results or yield from an activity; the amount of usefulness: *The new computers improved office productivity.*

pro·fi·cient (prə fish′ ənt) *adj.* expert; skilled; highly capable.

pro·gram·ma·ble (prō′ gram′ ə bəl, prō′ grəm ə bəl) *adj.* able to be programmed into a computer; measurable as a statistic or another quantity that can be coded, analyzed, or predicted.

proph·et (prof′ it) *n.* a wise person who can predict the future; a religious teacher or leader considered to be inspired by God.

PRONUNCIATION KEY
at; āpe; cär; end; mē; it; īce; hot; ōld; fôrk; wood; fo͞ol; oil; out; up; turn; sing; thin; this, hw in white; zh in treasure; ə stands for a in ago, e in taken, i in pencil, o in lemon, u in circus.

pro·pos·al (prə pō′l zəl) *n.* something put forward for consideration or acceptance: *The governor's proposal was discussed in the state assembly.*

pro·pri·e·ty (prə prī ə tē) *n.* behavior in accordance with the accepted standards of polite society; good manners.

prose (prōz) *n.* the ordinary form of writing, as distinguished from poetry; fiction or nonfiction writing.

pros·e·cut·ing (pros′ ə kū′ ting) *adj.* conducting legal proceedings against; working as the government attorney trying to prove the guilt of an accused person.

pro·trude (prō trood′) *v.i.* to stick out.

pro·tu·ber·ance (prō too′ bər əns, prō tū′ bər əns) *n.* something that sticks out; a swelling or a bulge.

psy·chol·o·gist (sī kol′ ə jist) *n.* a person trained in *psychology*, the study of the mind and of the mental and emotional processes in human behavior.

pur·loin (pur loin′) *v.i.* to steal.

Q

quail (kwāl) *n.* a small game bird resembling a partridge.

quiz (kwiz) *v.t.* to question.

R

rak·ish·ly (rā′ kish lē) *adv.* in a dashing, jaunty manner; with style: *He wore his hat rakishly.*

ra·tion·al·ize (rash′ ən əl īz′) *v.i.* to devise reasonable but inaccurate explanations for behavior.

rau·cous (rô′ kəs) *adj.* harsh and grating; very noisy; rowdy: *raucous laughter.*

rav·aged (rav′ ijd) *adj.* spoiled; destroyed.

reap (rēp) *v.t.* to cut down and gather a crop.

re·bel·lion (ri bel′ yən) *n.* resistance or defiance against a control or an authority: *The child was constantly in rebellion against her parents.*

re·buff (ri buf′) *n.* an abrupt, blunt refusal; a rejection: *When he offered his advice, he received a rebuff.*

re·coil (ri koil′) *v.i.* to spring back; to return to.

rec·ol·lec·tion (rek′ ə lek′ shən) *n.* a memory; an event called back to mind.

ref·or·ma·tion (ref′ ər mā′ shən) *n.* a change for the better; an improvement in one's behavior.

re·ha·bil·i·ta·tion (rē hə bil′ ə tā′ shən) *n.* the act of restoring to a healthier or more useful condition. —*adj.* involved in such restoration; working to improve the health or usefulness of people, neighborhoods, etc.: *a rehabilitation counselor.*

re·lin·quish (ri ling′ kwish) *v.t.* to give over possession or control of; to release.

re·morse (ri môrs′) *n.* a deep feeling of guilt or sorrow for wrongdoing or bad behavior.

ren·dez·vous (rän′ də voo′, rän′ dā voo′) *n.* a meeting at a fixed place or time.

rend·ing (ren′ ding) *n.* the splitting or tearing apart of something: *the rending of the ship's sails.*

ren·di·tion (ren dish′ən) *n.* an interpretation or a version of a story.

ren·e·gade (ren′ ə gād′) *adj.* acting outside the law; outlaw: *a renegade soldier.*

re·nounce (ri nouns′) *v.t.* to give up, especially by making a formal statement; to abandon.

re·pose (ri pōz′) *n.* relaxation; inactivity; a rest after exerting oneself.

re·pu·di·a·tor (ri pū′ dē ā′ tər) *n.* a person who refuses to accept the truth about something; also, a person who refuses to have anything to do with someone or something.

re·pul·sive (ri pul′ siv) *adj.* highly distasteful; disgusting.

re·served (ri zurvd′) *adj.* self-controlled; restrained; tending to be silent, especially about one's thoughts or feelings.

re·sign·ed·ly (ri zī′ nid lē) *adv.* without resisting or complaining; submissively.

re·strict·ed (ri strik′ tid) *adj.* limited to certain people and off limits to all others: *a restricted area.*

re·tal·i·ate (ri tal′ ē āt′) *v.i.* to return evil for evil or injury for injury; to get even.

re·trac·tion (ri trak′ shən) *n.* a statement that withdraws or takes back a previous statement.

ric·o·chet (rik′ ə shā′ *n.* the skipping or bouncing of a bullet, a stone, or another object after striking a surface at an angle.

rid·i·cule (rid′ ə kūl) *v.t.* to make someone or something appear foolish; to make fun of.

rit·u·al (rich′ o͞o əl) *n.* a religious or other ceremony observed in accordance with a set procedure; a traditional ceremony.—*adj.* relating to such a ceremony: *ritual mourning.*

riv·u·let (riv′ yə lət) *n.* a tiny stream; a small brook.

ro·bust·ly (rō bust′ lē, rō′ bust lē) *adv.* strongly; with healthy energy.

rum·mage (rum′ ij) *v.i.* to search at random, usually by handling and disarranging things.

ruth·less (ro͞oth′ lis) *adj.* without mercy or pity; cruel and scheming.

S

saw (sô) *n.* a traditional or familiar saying, especially one that is overused.

scoun·drel (skoun′ drəl) *n.* a villain; a dishonest person.

scrub (skrub) *n.* a small tree or shrub.

scru·ple (skro͞o′ pəl) *n.* a feeling of doubt or uncertainty arising from difficulty in deciding what is right or proper; a misgiving; an objection.

scru·ti·ny (skro͞ot′ ən ē) *n.* a close, critical study; a careful examination.

scud·ding (skud′ ing) *adj.* moving swiftly: *scudding clouds.*

sear (sēr) *v.t.* to burn into; to scorch.

se·cre·tion (si krē′ shən) *n.* a substance produced by special cell or gland activity in the body.

ser·mon (sur′ mən) *n.* a speech delivered in public by the clergy for religious or moral instruction.

share·crop·per (shār′ krop′ ər) *n.* a tenant farmer who farms land for the owner in return for a share of the crops.

PRONUNCIATION KEY
at; āpe; cär; end; me; it; īce; hot; ōld; fôrk; wood; fo͞ol; oil; out; up; turn; sing; thin; this, hw in white; zh in treasure; ə stands for a in ago, e in taken, i in pencil, o in lemon, u in circus.

sheaf (shēf) *n.* a bundle of like things put or tied together: *a sheaf of papers.*

short·com·ing (shôrt′ kum′ ing) *n.* a lack of something essential; a missing quality; a fault.

short-lived (shôrt′ līvd′, shôrt′ livd′) *adj.* lasting only a short time; brief.

side·light (sīd′ līt′) *n.* a bit of incidental information.

side·show (sīd′ shō′) *n.* a smaller show connected to or forming part of a circus, a carnival, or another larger entertainment.

sim·u·late (sim′ yə lāt′) *v.t.* to take on the appearance or form of; to imitate: *To test the tires, one can simulate actual road conditions in the factory.*

si·mul·ta·ne·ous·ly (sī′ məl tā′ nē əs lē, sim′ əl tā′ nē əs lē) *adv.* at the same time.

sky·rock·et (skī′ rok′ it) *v.i.* to rise suddenly, rapidly, and greatly: *Apartment rents have skyrocketed.*

slog·ging (slog′ ing) *n.* moving with great effort; plodding.

sloop (slo͞op) *n.* a sailboat with a single mast.

slough (slou) *n.* an area full of soft, deep mud.—*adj.* growing in such an area: *slough grass.*

smirk (smurk) *v.i.* to smile in an affected or a self-satisfied manner.

smol·der (smōl′ dər) *v.i.* to burn and smoke with little or no flame.

smudge (smuj) *n.* a smoky fire built to drive away insects or protect from frost.

sol·ace (sol′ is) *n.* relief from sorrow or disappointment; comfort; consola-tion: *After his wife died, he found solace in the companionship of his friends.*

so·lid·i·fied (sə lid′ ə fīd′) *adj.* made (a gas or a liquid) into a solid; having a definite shape and volume; firm and concrete.

sol·i·tar·y (sol′ ə ter′ ē) *adj.* living or being alone: *a solitary traveler.*

sol·u·ble (sol′ yə bəl) *adj.* capable of being dissolved into another substance: *Salt is soluble in water.*

sol·vent (sol′ vənt) *n.* a substance that dissolves into other substances: *Nail-polish remover is a solvent.*—*adj.* relating to such a substance: *solvent fumes.*

sooth·say·er (so͞oth′ sā′ ər) *n.* a person who claims to be able to predict future events.

sparse·ly (spärs′ lē) *adv.* with few items; thinly; sparingly: *The room was sparsely furnished.*

spec·u·lat·ing (spek′ yə lā′ ting) *adj.* examining carefully and seriously in order to make an accurate guess or draw a reasonable conclusion.

spig·ot (spig′ ət) *n.* a faucet; a waterspout.

spin·dly (spind′ lē) *adj.* having a long, thin shape.

spunk (spungk) *n. Informal English.* courage and spirit; pluck.

sta·bil·i·ty (stə bil′ ə tē) *n.* the state of being well-adjusted to one's surroundings and not given to sudden changes in personality or circumstances.

stanch (stônch, stänch) *v.t.* to stop or check the flow of blood or another fluid.

stark (stärk) *adj.* plain; harsh; severe.

strat·i·fied (strat′ ə fīd′) *adj.* arranged in layers.

stream·lined (strēm′ līnd′) *adj.* positioned or designed so as to offer the least possible resistance to air or water; neat, trim, and having few curves.

stul·ti·fy (stul′ tə fī′) *v.t.* to make worthless, foolish or illogical.

sub·tle (sut′ əl) *adj.* deceitfully cunning; crafty; clever: *a subtle crime.*

suc·cu·lent (suk′ yə lənt) *adj.* juicy; delicious.

suf·fice (sə·fīs′) *v.i.* to be sufficient; to be enough.

suf·frage (suf′ rij) *n.* the right to vote: *Susan B. Anthony helped in the fight for woman's suffrage.—adj.* relating to the right to vote: *Anthony appeared at many suffrage meetings.*

sum·mit (sum′ it) *n.* the highest point; the top of a hill or a mountain.

su·pe·ri·or·i·ty (sə pēr′ ē ôr′ ə tē, sə pēr′ ē or′ ə tē) *n.* the state of being better than others.

sur·ly (sur′ lē) *adj.* bad-tempered, rude, or hostile: *The surly waiter did not receive a tip.*

sur·plus (sur′ plus′, sur′ pləs) *adj.* over and above what is used or needed: *surplus army goods.*

swain (swān) *n.* a male who courts or woos a female in an effort to win her affections; a suitor; a boyfriend.

syc·a·more (sik′ ə môr′) *n.* an American plane tree, common in eastern North America.—*adj.* of or relating to this tree: *sycamore leaves.*

symp·tom (simp′ təm, sim′ təm) *n.* a change in normal body conditions that indicates or accompanies an illness: *A sneeze may be a symptom of a cold.*

T

tac·tic (tak′ tik) *n.* a plan of action used to achieve a goal; a strategy.

tan·ta·liz·ing (tant′ əl īz′ ing) *adj.* tempting.

tap·es·try (tap′ is trē) *n.* a heavy cloth woven with designs and pictures and often used as a wall hanging.—*adj.* relating to this cloth: *a tapestry factory.*

tar·di·ness (tär′ dē nis) *n.* failure to arrive on time; lateness.

tem·pest (tem′ pist) *n.* a violent storm.

tend·en·cy (ten′ dən sē) *n.* likelihood to move or act in a particular way; natural inclination. *She has a tendency to talk when she is nervous.*

ten·don (ten′ dən) *n.* a strong elastic cord or band of tissue that attaches a muscle to a bone or another part of the body.

ter·mi·nal (tur′ mən əl) *adj.* forming or occurring at the end; final; also, in the final stage of a disease that results in death; fatal: *a terminal illness.—n.* a

---

PRONUNCIATION KEY

at; āpe; cär; end; mē; it; īce; hot; ōld; fôrk; wood; fool; oil; out; up; turn; sing; thin; <u>th</u>is, hw in white; zh in treasure; ə stands for a in ago, e in taken, i in pencil, o in lemon, u in circus.

device that is used to put information into and get information from a computer and that usually consists of a keyboard and a viewing screen.

the·o·ret·i·cal (thē' ə ret' i kəl) *adj.* limited to theory instead of being based on experience or put into practice: *theoretical physics.*

ther·a·py (ther' ə pē) *n.* medical treatment for a disease or another physical or mental problem.

thread·bare (thred' bâr') *adj.* worn out; shabby; also, wearing shabby clothes; seedy; poor.

thrice (thrīs) *adv.* three times.

tol·er·ate (tol' ə rāt') *v.t.* to allow to be done without interference; to put up with; to endure.

tou·sled (tou' zəld) *adj.* untidy; messy: *tousled hair.*

trait (trāt) *n.* a basic aspect or quality of a person or a thing.

trance (trans) *n.* a dazed or shocked state.

trans·at·lan·tic (trans' ət lan' tik, tranz' ət lan' tik) *adj.* crossing or extending across the Atlantic Ocean.

trans·fixed (trans' fikst') *adj.* motionless, especially from awe, fear, or another strong feeling: *On seeing the deadly snake, he stood transfixed.*

trans·gres·sion (trans gresh' ən, tranz gresh' ən) *n.* the breaking of a law, a commandment, or a code of behavior; a sin.

tran·si·tion (tran zish' ən) *n.* passage from one position, condition or state to another; change.

trans·lu·cent (trans loo' sənt, tranz loo sənt) *adj.* allowing light to pass through but distorting it so that ob-

jects on the other side cannot be seen clearly: *Frosted glass is translucent.*

trans·mit (trans mit', tranz mit') *v.t.* to send out signals, a radio program, a television program, etc.; to send from one place or person to another.

treach·er·y (trech' ər ē) *n.* betrayal of a trust; traitorous or disloyal behavior.

tread·mill (tred' mil') *n.* a device rotated by walking on a continuously moving belt and used to test physical fitness.

treas·ur·er (trezh' ər ər) *n.* a person in charge of the finances of a business, an organization, or a government.

trea·ty (trē' tē) *n.* a formal agreement between groups or nations that each signs and approves it: *a peace treaty.*

trek·king (trek' ing) *n.* traveling; journeying.

trep·i·da·tion (trep' ə dā' shən) *n.* nervous or fearful anticipation; anxiety: *The thought of tomorrow's test fills her with trepidation.*

triv·i·al (triv' ē əl) *adj.* having little or no importance; minor; insignificant: *trivial details.*

trod·den (trod' ən) *v.i.* stepped on; trampled. (The word is a past participle of *tread.*)

trun·cheon (trun' chən) *n.* a long, slender, sturdy club: *a police officer's truncheon.*

tu·mult (too' məlt, tū' məlt) *n.* noisy confusion; commotion; uproar.

tu·reen (too rēn') *n.* a deep covered dish used for serving soup or other food.

tu·tor (too' tər, tū' tər) *n.* a teacher or another instructor who gives individual or private instruction to a student.

tyr·an·ny (tir′ ə nē) *n.* cruel and unjust use of power; harshness.

U

ul·ti·mate·ly (ul′ tə mit lē) *adv.* in the end; finally.

un·ac·count·a·ble (un′ ə koun′ tə bəl) *adj.* not able to be explained.

u·nan·i·mous (ū nan′ ə məs) *adj.* in complete agreement; agreed upon by all.

un·daunt·ed (un dôn′ tid, un dän′ tid) *adj.* not discouraged; not dismayed; still hopeful of achieving one's goals.

un·earth·li·ness (un urth′ lē nis) *n.* the state of being not of this world; a frightening strangeness; weirdness.

un·fath·om·a·ble (un fa<u>th</u>′ əm ə bəl) *adj.* not able to be measured or understood fully; vast and mysterious.

un·flinch·ing·ly (un flin′ ching lē) *adv.* without drawing back or away from danger, pain, or another unpleasantness.

u·ni·son (ū′ nə sən, ū′ nə zən) *n.* perfect or exact agreement. —**in unison.** at the same time; together.

u·ni·ver·sal (ū′ nə vur′ səl) *adj.* shared by all; occurring in all places; widespread.

un·pre·dict·a·bil·i·ty (un′ pri dik′ tə bil′ ə tē) *n.* behavior that cannot be determined in advance; illogical or changeable behavior.

un·re·al·i·ty (un′ rē al′ ə tē) *n.* a state or a condition that does not actually exist or that seems not to be real.

un·rec·on·ciled (un rek′ ən sīld′) *adj.* not won over to a friendly attitude; unaccepting; hostile.

un·set·tling (un set′ əl ing, un set′ ling) *adj.* making tense or uneasy; disturbing; *an unsettling remark.*

un·sta·ble (un stā′ bəl) *adj.* not settled or steady; emotionally troubled.

un·wit·ting·ly (un wit′ ing lē) *adv.* without knowing; without being aware; without intending.

urn (urn) *n.* a vase or a vaselike flowerpot, usually having a foot or a base and standing on the floor or ground.

u·surp·er (ū surp′ ər, ū zurp′ ər) *n.* a person who seizes power without the legal right to do so; a person who takes possession by using force.

u·til·i·ty (ū til′ ə tē) *n.* a company that provides an essential service to the public, such as an electric company or a water company. —*adj.* relating to such a company: *to pay a utility bill.*

u·ti·lize (ū tə līz′) *v.t.* to take advantage of; to use for some purpose.

V

val·iant (val′ yənt) *adj.* brave.

ve·loc·i·ty (vi los′ ə tē) *n.* the rate of motion in relation to time; speed.

ven·er·a·ble (ven′ ər ə bəl) *adj.* deserving respect because of age, character, or position.

PRONUNCIATION KEY
at; āpe; cär; end; mē; it; īce; hot; ōld; fôrk; wood; fool; oil; out; up; turn; sing; thin; <u>th</u>is, hw in white; zh in treasure; ə stands for a in ago, e in taken, i in pencil, o in lemon, u in circus.

venge·ance (ven′ jəns) *n.* the desire to inflict injury in return for an injury or insult received; the desire to take revenge.

ven·ti·la·tor (vent′ əl ā′ tər) *n.* a device that provides or circulates fresh air or removes foul or stagnant air.

ver·bal (vur′ bəl) *adj.* relating to or consisting of words: *verbal communication.*

verge (vurj) *v.i.* to be on the border or brink.

ver·i·fy (ver′ ə fī′) *v.t.* to prove something to be true; to confirm: *verify the facts.*

vet·er·an (vet′ ər ən, vet′ rən) *n.* a person who has served his or her country in a time of war.

vi·cin·i·ty (vi sin′ ə tē) *n.* the area near a particular place; neighborhood; surroundings.

vine·yard (vin′ yərd) *n.* an area used for grape growing.

vi·o·late (vi′ ə lāt′) *v.t.* to break a law, a rule, an agreement, etc.

vir·tu·al·ly (vur′ choo ə lē) *adv.* for all practical purposes; in effect though not in fact.

vis·age (viz′ ij) *n.* face or facial expression.

vi·tal·i·ty (vī tal′ ə tē) *n.* mental or physical energy.

vit·ri·ol (vit′ rē əl) *n.* harshness, sharpness, or bitterness of feeling: *Her writing was full of vitriol.*

void (void) *n.* space that contains no gas, vapor, living things, or other matter; empty space.

vul·ner·a·ble (vul′ nər ə bəl) *adj.* capable of being wounded or damaged; sensitive.

W

waist·coat (wes′ kət, wāst′ kōt) *n.* a vest. —*adj.* relating to a vest.

wake (wāk) *n.* the trail left by an object moving through water or air.

way·side (wā′ sīd) *n.* the land bordering a road or a path.

whim (hwim, wim) *n.* a sudden or unexpected notion; a fanciful idea.

whole·some (hōl′ səm) *adj.* promoting good health; healthful.

whop·per (hwop′ ər, wop′ ər) *n. Informal English.* something very large; a very big example of something.

with·drawn (with drôn′, with drôn′) *adj.* having retreated from society or reality; shy. —*v.i.* pulled back or away; retreated. (*Withdrawn* is the past participle of *withdraw*.)

wrath (rath) *n.* extreme or violent anger; rage; fury.

writhe (rīth) *v.i.* to move with a turning or twisting motion; to squirm.

wrought (rôt) *v.i.* worked. —*adj.* worked; carved: *wrought iron.* (The word is a past tense and past participle of *work*.)

Z

zeal (zēl) *n.* intense devotion or enthusiasm: *She pursues her interests with zeal.*

ze·nith (zē′ nith) *n.* in the sky, the point that is directly above the observer; the highest point.

zo·ol·o·gist (zō ol′ ə jist) *n.* a scientist trained in *zoology* (zō ol′ ə jē), the branch of biology that deals with the study of animals.

HANDBOOK
OF STUDY AND REFERENCE SKILLS

How to Use This Handbook

This guide contains some of the important study and reference skills that you have learned in school. The skills are presented in three main parts:

PART ONE: Reading and Studying Your Textbooks
PART TWO: Finding What You Want in the Library
PART THREE: Using Reference Books

When should you use the Handbook? The questions and answers below will help you identify those situations in which the Handbook of Study and Reference Skills will be especially useful.

QUESTION	ANSWER
Are you looking for a good book to read?	See the entries in Part Two under "Locating Fiction and Biography," and "Locating Nonfiction."
Are you looking for material for a report?	See the entry in Part Two under "Locating General Reference Books." See also the entries in Part Three for "Almanacs" and "Encyclopedias."
Do you have difficulty keeping up with your study assignments?	See the entries in Part One for "PQRST," "Reading Rate," and "Taking Notes."
Are you unsure of yourself when you take a test?	See the entries in Part One under "Taking a Test."

PART ONE: READING AND STUDYING YOUR TEXTBOOKS

USING BUILT-IN STUDY AIDS

Table of Contents   A table of contents appears at the beginning of most textbooks. It lists the topics in the book by unit or chapter. It also indicates the page number on which each topic begins. The example below is part of a table of contents in a reading textbook.

UNIT I: It's How You Play the Game

The table of contents in your textbook is a survey of the book's contents. Suppose, for example, you are given an assignment in American history on the Revolutionary War. Turn to the table of contents in your American history textbook, find the heading A Republic Is Formed, then look below it for the subtopic, Revolutionary War. Note the page on which the material begins.

Index   The index, usually at the end of the book, provides more detailed information than the table of contents. The index lists people, places, and topics in alphabetical order and the page numbers where information on each appears. The index helps you find the information you want quickly. The sample index below would be useful if you wanted specific information on pronouns.

Pronouns
    agreement with antecedents, 122–124, 126,
       146, 379, 393, 418
    compound, 316, 383
    in compound subject, 158, 318, 383
    indefinite, 124, 127, 147, 395
    personal, 118, 128

Visual Aids Most textbooks include a variety of visual aids. The visual aids are designed to help you better understand the material or to provide additional information. Therefore, it is essential that you know how to use them.

1. *Maps:* In social studies textbooks, maps are usually listed in a special section of the table of contents. In a geography book, maps bring meaning to every place name mentioned. In a history book, maps help you relate the geography of an area to its history, or they help clarify information.

To use the maps in your textbook as effective study tools, you must first learn how to use the scale and the map key, or legend. The scale (Figure 1) shows the relationship of distances on a map to the same distances on earth. The legend (Figure 2) tells you what the colors and other symbols on a particular map stand for.

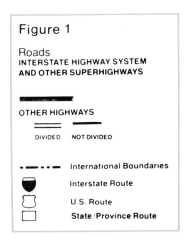

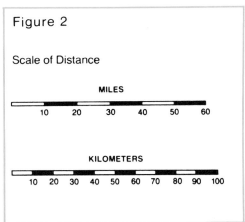

2. *Diagrams, Charts, and Graphs:* Although these three terms are often used as synonyms, there are differences among them. A diagram is a drawing that uses lines and other symbols, but does not use pictures (see Figure 3) to show information. A chart, on the other hand, uses pictures, words, or other symbols to express information (Figure 4). A graph uses dots, lines, and sometimes pictures to present information (Figure 5). Unlike diagrams and

Figure 3

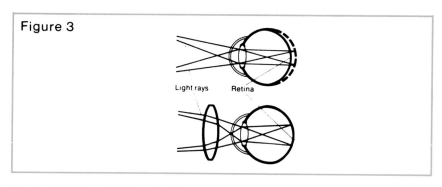

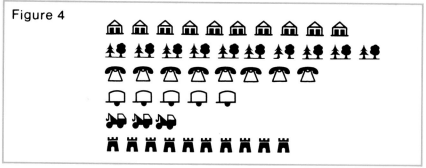

Figure 4

charts, graphs have a mathematical base. There are many different kinds of graphs. In your textbooks you will most likely find line graphs, bar graphs, or pie graphs. Figure 5 is an example of how the same information can be seen on both a line graph and a bar graph.

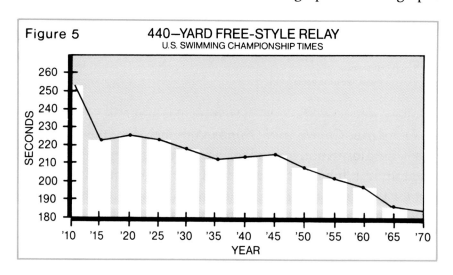

Figure 5   440—YARD FREE-STYLE RELAY
U.S. SWIMMING CHAMPIONSHIP TIMES

3. *Timelines:* A timeline is a line that shows events in chronological order (in correct time sequence), as shown (Figure 6).

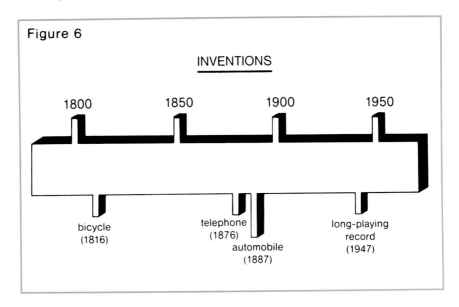

Figure 6

INVENTIONS

1800   1850   1900   1950

bicycle (1816)

telephone (1876)

automobile (1887)

long-playing record (1947)

Footnotes   Footnotes are used in some textbooks. This textbook uses footnotes to provide explanations that might otherwise interrupt the text. Sometimes footnotes are used to help you pronounce or to define unfamiliar words. When you are reading, be on the alert for a small numeral or asterisk above or next to a word that signals a footnote. Footnotes are usually found at the bottom of a page.

Bibliography   Many textbooks include a bibliography, a list of books related to the subject matter in the text. A bibliography provides information that will help you find a particular book in the library. Most bibliographies contain the author, the publisher, and copyright date of a book.

A bibliography can be used to help you identify books that may add to your understanding of a topic. Some bibliographies give a summary of a book; these are called annotated bibliographies.

PQRST   PQRST is a method of reading that can help you study more efficiently. There are five steps in the PQRST method.

STEP 1 — Preview: Look at the material you are going to study before you begin to read. Read the title and the introduction (if there is one). Then preview the section of the book you are using, paying special attention to the headings. If your textbook includes questions related to your assignment, read them, too. Note key words. Look at the pictures and read the captions. Try to associate this assignment with previous assignments.

STEP 2 — Question: Ask yourself, "What are the important facts and ideas in this assignment?" Then try to turn each heading and key word into a question. For example, if a heading in your Earth Science text reads *Families of Igneous Rocks*, ask yourself, "Into which families are igneous rocks divided?" Divide a piece of paper into three columns and record your questions as shown.

HEADING OR KEY WORD	QUESTION	ANSWER
Families of Igneous Rocks	Into which families are igneous rocks divided?	

STEP 3 — Read: You are now ready to read. Keep in mind that you will be reading to find the answers to the questions you prepared for step 2. Look for important ideas that were not included in headings or key words. Add questions about these words to your list.

STEP 4 — Study: Study the material by answering the questions you prepared for steps 2 and 3. With your book closed, write the answers in column 3 on your list. Then check your text to be sure that your answers are correct and complete.

STEP 5 — Test: When you have written all the answers in column 3, you are ready to test yourself. Fold back the answer column on your paper and ask yourself each question. Each time you answer a question, refer to the answer on your list to make certain that you remembered the important facts and ideas.

Reading Rate   Reading rate refers to the number of words read per minute. The reading rate should vary according to the kind of material being read and the reason for reading it. Try to adjust your reading rate so that it is appropriate for your reading purposes. You should read slower if the material is difficult or technical and when it is important to remember details. You should speed up your reading rate when skimming or scanning material.

1. *Skimming:* You skim when you want to get a general idea of content. Keep these suggestions in mind when skimming:
   a. Read the title of the unit or chapter and the paragraphs that introduce that section of the text.
   b. Read the main headings and subheadings, making note of key words in italic or boldface type.
   c. Under each main heading, read the first and last sentence of every paragraph.
   d. Look at all visual aids for additional information.

2. *Scanning:* You scan when you want to locate specific information. Keep these suggestions in mind when scanning:
   a. Identify key words related to information you want.
   b. Look up key words in the index and cite page references.
   c. Scan cited pages looking for key words.
   d. Read the sentence in which the key word appears and the surrounding sentences, if necessary, to get your information.

Taking Notes   When reading, try to select the main ideas and important details and write them down in outline form in a notebook. This study strategy greatly increases your chances of remembering what you have read. Next make a summary of your outline. Summarizing is another valuable device when taking notes. Here are pointers on these two important skills:

1. Outlining: Use lettering, numbering, and indentation to show the relationship between topics, subtopics, and details. You may devise your own pattern, but a common form looks like this:

I.
   A.
      1.
      2.
   B.
      1.
      2.
II.
   A.
      1.
      2.
   B.
      1.
      2.

2. Summarizing: When you summarize, you make a brief statement of the main idea in a paragraph or a series of paragraphs. Do not add anything new and always omit details. Be sure to use your own words and write legibly when summarizing.

TAKING A TEST

Final Review   When you review for a test, carefully study your textbook outlines and notes. Go over key words.

Objective Questions   The tests you take in school usually include objective questions, questions that have only one answer. Such questions are designed to test how well you remember certain facts and ideas. Objective questions may be multiple-choice, true-false, or matching.

Keep the following suggestions in mind when you are answering objective questions:

1. Preview the test before answering any questions. Get an idea of how quickly you will have to work.

2. Read the directions carefully. Pay special attention to *where* (on the test paper or on a separate sheet) and *how* (by crossing out, underlining, circling, etc.) the questions are to be answered.

3. Read all the choices in a multiple-choice question before you choose an answer.

4. Read both sets of information in a matching question before you write an answer.

5. In a true-false question, pay special attention to the words that tell under what conditions a statement may be true or false. Such qualifying words include: *all, some, usually, never, good, bad.*

6. Answer the questions you know and come back to those on which you may have to spend extra time.

Essay Questions   In addition to testing how well you recall what you have learned, essay questions require you to organize that information logically and to express your ideas clearly. Essay questions include short-answer questions (one paragraph) and discussion questions (several paragraphs). Keep the following suggestions in mind when answering essay questions:

1. Read the directions carefully. If you are given a choice of questions, read them all before you make your choice.

2. Carefully divide the time available for the test. Allot more time to a 25-point question than to one worth 10 points.

3. Read the first question you are going to answer and, on a scrap of paper, jot down the facts and ideas required in the answer. Pay special attention to the key words and the qualifying words. Arrange your notes to make certain that you have everything included in logical order.

4. Make your answers complete, but do not add unrelated details.

5. Before you turn your test paper in, check it for clarity and for any mistakes in spelling, grammar, or punctuation.

6. Go over your corrected test paper after it has been returned. Check your answers against your textbook and your notes to see what you may have omitted that your teacher considered important. If you did not interpret a question correctly, take another look at key words and qualifying words and ask for help in understanding them.

PART TWO: FINDING WHAT YOU WANT IN THE LIBRARY

LOCATING FICTION AND BIOGRAPHY

Fiction   Fiction books are kept in a special section of the library. They are arranged on the shelves in alphabetical order by the author's last name. If a library has two or more books by the same author, these books are arranged alphabetically by title. For example:

BEVERLY CLEARY	JOSEPH CONRAD	JOSEPH CONRAD
RIBSY	LORD JIM	TYPHOON

GILLIAN CROSS
THE IRON WAY

If you are looking for a particular book, first check the card catalog to determine if the library has that book. Fiction books are arranged in the catalog alphabetically by author and title and sometimes by subject.

If you do not have a particular book in mind, but are looking for fiction with a theme that interests you, ask your librarian for help. Libraries often have lists that are arranged according to theme (mystery, adventure, etc.) which may include a brief description of the book. If a description captures your interest, copy down the author and title and check the catalog.

Biography and Autobiography   A biography is a story of a real person's life written by someone else. In an autobiography, the person writes about himself or herself. In most libraries, biographies and autobiographies are kept in a separate section and are arranged alphabetically by the last name of the person written about. Collections of biographies are alphabetized by the last name of the author or editor and appear on the shelves after individual biographies.

LOCATING NONFICTION

The Dewey Decimal Classification System   Every library has a classification system, a way of organizing its nonfiction books. Most schools and public libraries use the Dewey Decimal System. This numerical system enables librarians to arrange books on the shelves first by number and then alphabetically by the author's last name. The purpose of this system is to keep books on the same subject together.

    The Dewey Decimal System divides all nonfiction into nine categories, numbering them 100 through 999 and putting all general reference books into the category 000. Many libraries use signs such as "520–529- -Astronomy" to identify those sections in which certain books can be found.

100 PHILOSOPHY
    People's mind and thoughts

200 RELIGION
    Bible stories and mythology

300 SOCIOLOGY
    Brotherhood, government, careers, customs, holidays, folklore and fairy tales

400 LANGUAGE
    Grammar, spelling and foreign languages

500 SCIENCE
    Stars, flowers, birds, seashells, rocks, insects and animals

600 APPLIED SCIENCE
    Invention, engineering, medicine, ships, cars, airplanes, pets, manufacturing and food

700 ARTS AND RECREATION
    Painting, music, sports, hobbies, theater, dance, parties

800 LITERATURE
Poetry, plays

900, 930-990 HISTORY
Europe, Asia, Africa, North and South America

910 TRAVEL
Geography, travels

92, 920 BIOGRAPHY
Individual and collective biographies

000 GENERAL WORKS
Reference books such as encyclopedias

FICTION
Novels, romances

The Library Catalog   All the books in a library are entered in a catalog. In some libraries, the catalog consists of cards kept in drawers in a cabinet. In other libraries, the catalog is entered in books with computer-printed listings or is on microfilm or microfiche, which is read with a special viewer. The newest way to find a book is by using a computer. Whatever method, the arrangement of the entries and the information they give is much the same.

1. Arrangement: All library catalogs are arranged in alphabetical order. In many libraries the author, subject, and title are interfiled. In some libraries, authors are separated in a section of their own. Become familiar with how your library arranges its catalog.

2. The Entries: Although there are at least three entries for each item in the catalog, there is usually only one main entry — the author's last name. This entry gives the most information about a book. The entries below are from a card catalog. Note the different kinds of information that the entries provide.

Figure 7

If you know the author, look for the **author entry.**

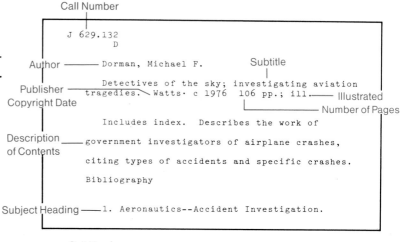

Call Number

J 629.132
    D

Author ——— Dorman, Michael F.   Subtitle

Publisher ———   Detectives of the sky; investigating aviation
Copyright Date   tragedies. Watts· c 1976   106 pp.; ill.——— Illustrated
                                                     ——— Number of Pages

              Includes index. Describes the work of

Description ——— government investigators of airplane crashes,
of Contents
              citing types of accidents and specific crashes.

              Bibliography

Subject Heading ——— 1. Aeronautics--Accident Investigation.

Figure 8

If you know the title, look for the **title entry.**

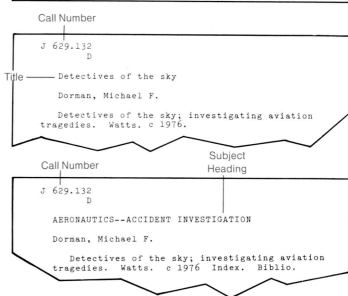

Call Number

J 629.132
    D

Title ——— Detectives of the sky

        Dorman, Michael F.

        Detectives of the sky; investigating aviation
        tragedies. Watts. c 1976.

Figure 9

If you are looking for an unknown book on a particular subject, look for the **subject entry.**

                                    Subject
Call Number   Heading

J 629.132
    D

    AERONAUTICS--ACCIDENT INVESTIGATION

    Dorman, Michael F.

        Detectives of the sky; investigating aviation
    tragedies. Watts.   c 1976 Index. Biblio.

The catalog also includes *see* and *see also* entries. A *see* entry tells you to go to a particular subject. A *see also* entry refers you to other, related subjects.

3. *The Call Number:* The number that appears in the upper left-hand corner of the sample entries is the call number. The call number includes the Dewey Decimal classification plus the initials of the author's last name. The call number on all three sample entries is the same, and also appears on the spine of the book.

LOCATING GENERAL REFERENCE BOOKS

General reference books such as encyclopedias are meant to be consulted for specific information. They are not circulated so they may always be available.

LOCATING MAGAZINE ARTICLES AND PAMPHLETS

Readers' Guide to Periodical Literature Articles in magazines or periodicals can be found by consulting the *Readers' Guide to Periodical Literature*. It lists magazine articles alphabetically by subject and author, and gives you the name of the magazine, the date, and page number. Check with your librarian on the use of this guide.

Some libraries file their magazines on microfilm. A librarian will help you find the article you want and will show you how to use the viewer.

The Vertical File The vertical file is a collection of pamphlets, clippings, pictures, and other nonbook material. It usually consists of current material that will eventually be discarded. Material in the vertical file is arranged alphabetically by subject in clearly marked folders that are kept in a special cabinet or in labeled boxes. The index for the vertical file tells you what topics you will find there.

PART THREE: USING REFERENCE BOOKS

Almanacs Almanacs are published yearly and are an excellent source for the most current statistics on sports, government, famous people, etc. Almanacs also give a chronology of events that occurred the previous year.

An almanac is especially useful when you are looking for a short, quick answer to a specific question or for current information related to a report. Two of the best known almanacs are *World Almanac and Book of Facts* and *Information Please Almanac*.

Atlases   An atlas is a collection of maps. It offers a variety of information about places by including maps that show land and water forms, boundaries, roads, annual rainfall, etc. There are also specialized atlases with historical or religious maps.

The index in an atlas, usually at the back, lists each place name along with a page reference and a code to help you pinpoint the location of a particular place. One well-known atlas is the *National Geographic Atlas of the World.*

Dictionaries   A dictionary is an alphabetical list of words. An abridged, or desk, dictionary includes the most commonly used words in the language. An unabridged dictionary includes almost all of the words in a language.

Many libraries also have dictionaries on specialized topics such as mathematics, music, and foreign languages. There are also dictionaries of synonyms, slang, and rhyming words. The information that follows will help you use an English language dictionary more efficiently.

Finding a Word: The words in a dictionary are listed alphabetically. Guide words at the top of a dictionary page indicate the alphabetical range of the words on that page. The first guide word is the first word listed on the page; the second guide word is the last word on the page.

Written Syllables: Most dictionaries use centered dots or spaces to show where a word is divided in writing (gla • cier).

Part-of-Speech Labels: Dictionaries use part-of-speech labels to show how a word is used in a sentence. Some dictionaries spell out the name of the part of speech (*noun, verb,* etc.). Others use abbreviations (*n., v.,* etc.). If a word may be used as more than one part of speech, each use is labeled.

Phonetic Respelling: A dictionary respells words using special phonetic symbols. A pronunciation key at the beginning of the dictionary explains the symbols. An abbreviated key usually appears on every left- or right-hand page. The dictionary also tells you which syllable to stress when you say a word. Primary, or strong, stress is usually shown with a heavy dark mark. Secondary, or weak, stress is shown with a lighter mark.

Definitions: When a word has two or more meanings, a dictionary lists them by number. Make sure the meaning you choose is the right one for your purpose.

Inflected Forms: Dictionaries give different inflected forms of words. (Examples: s, ed, ing, er, est)

Prefixes and Suffixes: They are included in most dictionaries.

Etymologies: Most dictionaries give etymologies, or word histories, for selected words.

Miscellaneous Information: Many dictionaries include biographical and geographical information, commonly heard foreign words and expressions, and a variety of other information.

Thesauruses   A thesaurus is a book of words grouped by ideas. You use it when you have an idea and you want just the right word to express it.

Encyclopedias   An encyclopedia is a set of general reference books that contain articles on a large variety of topics. Yearbooks help keep encyclopedias up to date by giving current information.

The topics in an encyclopedia are arranged in alphabetical order. Letters on the spine tell you in which volume a topic beginning with a specific letter of the alphabet may be found. The last volume of most encyclopedias is an index of all the places in the set where a topic is discussed. Using the index helps you find the information you want on a specific subject.

Specialized Reference Books   These books are a source of many kinds of information, such as quotations, literary characters, and historical information.

(Acknowledgments continued)

"The Circuit" by Francisco Jiménez appeared originally in *The Arizona Quarterly* (Autumn 1973) and is Copyright by *The Arizona Quarterly*. Reprinted by permission of the author.

"A Contest of Wills" from THE MIRACLE WORKER by William Gibson. Copyright © 1956, 1957 William Gibson; copyright © 1959, 1960 Tamarack Productions, Ltd. & George S. Klein & Leo Garel as trustees under three separate deeds of trust. Reprinted with the permission of Atheneum Publishers, Inc., and Flora Roberts.

"Cut Down to Size" is abridged and adapted from pp. 23-31 from ONE FAT SUMMER by Robert M. Lipsyte. Copyright © 1977 by Robert M. Lipsyte. Reprinted by permission of Harper & Row, Publishers, Inc. and International Creative Management.

"The Delight Song of Tsoai-Talee" from ANGLE OF GEESE by M. Scott Momaday. Copyright by M. Scott Momaday. Reprinted by permission of David R. Godine, Publisher, Boston.

"The Doubtful Guest" by Edward Gorey. Copyright © 1972 by Edward Gorey. Reprinted by permission of Candida Donadio & Associates, Inc.

"The Fire Lizards" adapted from DRAGONSONG by Anne McCaffrey. Copyright © 1976 Anne McCaffrey. Reprinted with the permission of Atheneum Publishers. By permission also of Virginia Kidd.

"The Flying Machine" by Ray Bradbury. Copyright 1953 by Ray Bradbury, renewed in 1981 by Ray Bradbury. Reprinted by permission of Don Congdon Associates, Inc.

"Football vs. Judo" from THE TWO WORLDS OF JIM YOSHIDA by Jim Yoshida with Bill Hosokawa. Reprinted by permission of John Hawkins and Associates.

"From Star Gazing to Star Trekking" from SPACE TRAVEL IN FACT AND FICTION by Keith Deutsch. Copyright © 1980 by Keith Deutsch. Used by permission of Franklin Watts, Inc.

"Growing Up with Gumption" from GROWING UP by Russell Baker. Copyright © 1982 by Russell Baker. Reprinted by permission of Don Congdon Associates, Inc.

"The Great Experimenter" is the abridged and adapted text from Chapter 6 (pp. 43-58) in CHEAPER BY THE DOZEN by Frank Gilbreth, Jr. and Ernestine Gilbreth Carey (Thomas Y. Crowell Company). Copyright 1948, 1963 by Frank B. Gilbreth, Jr. Reprinted by permission of Harper & Row, Publishers, Inc. and McIntosh & Otis, Inc.

"Harriet Tubman" from FAMOUS AMERICAN NEGROES by Langston Hughes. Copyright 1954 by Langston Hughes. Copyright renewed 1982 by George Houston Bass. Reprinted by permission of Dodd, Mead & Company, Inc. By permission also of Harold Ober Associates Incorporated.

"Hunting Monkeys" is an excerpt from SUMMER OF THE MONKEYS by W. Wilson Rawls. Copyright © 1976 by Woodrow Wilson Rawls. Reprinted by Permission of Doubleday & Company, Inc.

"Icarus and Daedalus" is adapted from "The Story of Daedalus and Icarus" in OVID, METAMORPHOSES, translated by Rolfe Humphries. © 1955 by Indiana University Press. © 1983. By permission of the publisher.

"The Indian Cinderella" from CANADIAN WONDER TALES by Cyrus Macmillan. Reprinted by permission of The Bodley Head.

"Into the Tunnel" from M. C. HIGGINS, THE GREAT by Virginia Hamilton. Copyright © 1967 by Virginia Hamilton. Reprinted with permission of Macmillan Publishing Company and McIntosh & Otis, Inc.

"The Invaders" by Jack Ritchie originally appeared in *Boys' Life*, March 1978. © 1978 by Boy Scouts of America. Reprinted by permission of Larry Sternig Literary Agency.

"Katherine Stinston" by Mary Beth Rogers and Janelle D. Scott from WE CAN FLY: STORIES OF KATHERINE STINSON AND OTHER GUTSY TEXAS WOMEN by Mary Beth Rogers, Sherry A. Smith, and Janelle D. Scott. Copyright 1983. By permission of the Texas Foundation for Womens Resources and Ellen C. Temple—Publisher.

"Kilroy's New Act" is abridged and adapted from pages 37-63 (Chapter IV, text only) from KILROY AND THE GULL by Nathaniel Benchley. Copyright © 1977 by Nathaniel Benchley. Reprinted by permission of Harper & Row, Publishers, Inc. and Roberta Pryor, Inc.

"Landscape with the Fall of Icarus" from PICTURES FROM BRUEGHEL by William Carlos Williams. Copyright © 1960 by William Carlos Williams. Reprinted by permission of New Directions Publishing Corporation.

INDEX OF AUTHORS AND TITLES